Mineral processing website

on Sylabus
www.mpri

M000087916

OPTIMIZATION
FOR
ENGINEERING
SYSTEMS

OPTIMIZATION FOR ENGINEERING SYSTEMS

Ralph W. Pike
Professor of Chemical Engineering and Systems Science
Louisiana State University

VNR VAN NOSTRAND REINHOLD COMPANY
———————————————————— New York

Library of Congress Catalog Card Number 85-29466

ISBN 0-442-27581-1

Printed in the United States of America

Van Nostrand Reinhold Company Inc.
115 Fifth Avenue
New York, New York 10003

Van Nostrand Reinhold Company Limited
Molly Millars Lane
Wokingham, Berkshire RG11 2PY, England

Van Nostrand Reinhold
480 La Trobe Street
Melbourne, Victoria 3000, Australia

Macmillan of Canada
Division of Canada Publishing Corporation
164 Commander Boulevard
Agincourt, Ontario M1S 3C7, Canada

16 15 14 13 12 11 10 9 8 7 6 5 4 3 2

Library of Congress Cataloging-in-Publication Data

Pike, Ralph W., 1935–
  Optimization for engineering systems.

  Includes bibliographies and indexes.
  1. Engineering—Mathematical-models.   2. Mathematical
optimization.   I. Title.
TA342.P55   1986   620'.00724   85-29466
ISBN 0-442-27581-1

To

Douglass J. Wilde
who introduced me to optimization,

Patricia J. Pike
who taught me the optimum of a part was not the optimum of the whole,

Jesse Coates
who made it possible for me to teach optimization,

the students in my courses over the years
who gave me their thoughts on the optimal way to learn optimization

PREFACE

Optimization is a many-faceted subject ranging from pure mathematics to automated manufacturing. Over time, there has been a flow of optimization concepts and algorithms from mathematics to applications in engineering design and the operation of manufacturing plants. A classic example is the Simplex Algorithm of linear programming that is used in a wide variety of industrial and other applications.

The mathematics of optimization capitalizes on the structure of the problems to obtain formal proofs of global and local optimality and to develop efficient algorithms for locating best values of the economic model while still satisfying constraints. The Simplex Algorithm and its extensions also illustrate this approach of using the mathematical form of linear equations to find the global optimum. Other examples are geometric programming, in which the economic model and constraints are polynomials; convex programming, with a concave economic model and convex constraints; and dynamic programming, in which the stage structure is exploited by a series of partial optimizations.

This book stands at the interface of mathematics and industrial applications of optimization. The topics were selected for their breadth of application to the optimization of engineering systems, especially continuous ones. Moreover, the mathematics of optimization has been presented to provide a foundation for those methods that have proven successful in industrial applications.

An informal style of writing has been adopted as that best suited for most students by helping to eliminate mathematical tedium. In addition, a large number of simple examples have been included to reinforce the basics.

The material is structured to build on the students' knowledge of calculus and differential equations by beginning with the classical theory of maxima and minima to establish a base for the modern methods. The progression of topics was designed to add depth and breadth to the concepts and applications. Upon completion of the material the reader should have the necessary background for further reading of texts, monographs, and current research literature on the subject.

The text is a product of the author's experience in teaching and research in optimization, which includes developing and teaching a graduate course on optimization for the past 20 plus years to students in engineering, system science, and business administration. Some of the material, however, was developed for continuing education courses taught to practicing engineers.

This book is intended to serve as a text for a first year graduate course in engineering optimization. It is primarily aimed at engineers, but it could serve for a comparable course on operations research in business schools or a mathematical programming course in computer science that emphasizes applications.

The introductory chapter gives a brief historical perspective, the relation of this to other subjects, and an overview of the rationale for the order of presentation of the optimization methods. The second chapter covers analytical methods for constrained and unconstrained problems and serves as a foundation for the subjects that follow. The third chapter, which investigates geometric programming, is presented as an extension of analytical methods that introduces the concept of a dual problem. The fourth chapter covers the most widely used optimization technique, linear programming, and includes an illustration of the application of a commercial code to an industrial plant. In the fifth chapter, single-variable search methods based on the minimax concept are given along with a FORTRAN program for Fibonacci search. These techniques are used in conjunction with the multivariable search methods described in the sixth chapter, where constrained direct methods are emphasized. In the seventh chapter, the sequential partial optimization procedure of dynamic programming is developed, as are the concepts of resource allocation and optimization through time. The text concludes with a chapter on variational methods that gives the important results for obtaining an optimum function rather than an optimum point.

The material provided here is more than adequate for a one-semester course; in addition, references are given to other books and journals on each chapter topic for further research. The idea was to include subjects that have proved to be valuable for industrial applications rather than to approach the text as a handbook. Moreover, the material was prepared with the idea that users of optimization procedures would often be employing packaged computer programs such as the relatively sophisticated linear and nonlinear programming codes that are available on large computers, e.g., MPSX and MINOS V. References to available standard computer codes are also provided.

The author wishes to express his appreciation to Louisiana State University, Professor Lautaro Guerra of the Universidad Tecnica Federico Santa Maria, Valparaiso, Chile, and the LSU Mining and Mineral Resources Research Institute for assistance in preparing the manuscript. Mr. Paul R. Lanoux prepared the MPSX solution to the refinery linear programming example with the assistance of Mr. Daniel Brignac, and Mr. Perry Bando of the Exxon Refinery in Baton Rouge provided some of the economic data for the linear programming model. Mr. Miguelangel R. Giammattei and Mr. Daniel M. Wu prepared the FORTRAN programs for the single and multivariable search methods. Also, Mr. Daniel M. Wu assisted in preparing the solutions to the problems and examples. The patient and careful preparation of the manuscript by Ms. Ana Elizabeth Lobos and Ms. Clara Marisol Lobos was invaluable in converting the draft of this book into a manuscript. Also, thanks are due to students, colleagues, and reviewers for their suggestions, including Mr. George P. Burdell of the Georgia Institute of Technology.

RALPH W. PIKE

Baton Rouge, Louisiana

CONTENTS

1
INTRODUCTION

PERSPECTIVE

The objective of optimization is to select the best possible decision for a given set of circumstances without having to enumerate all the possibilities. From experience, designers learn to recognize good proportions and critical restrictions, so their preliminary work will not require significant modification and improvement. The subject that formulates and explains this talent is a branch of applied mathematics known as *optimization theory,* a science that studies the best (1). In recent years the subject of optimization has matured and is widely used in numerous applications, e.g., petroleum refining operations, routes for commercial aircraft, livestock feed blending, and missile trajectories. Optimization methods take advantage of the mathematical structure of the problem to find the best values efficiently; and the size of the problems being solved has followed the growth in computer capability, especially in the case of linear programming.

Scientists, especially mathematicians, have always been occupied with questions of optimization, i.e., finding extreme points (maxima and minima). Euclid in 300 B.C. was associated with the problem of finding the shortest distance that could be drawn from a point to a line, and Heron of Alexandria in 100 B.C. studied the optimization problem of light traveling between two points by the shortest path. It was Fermat in 1657 who developed the more general principle that light travels between two points in a minimum time. In 1875 Gibbs developed the law that states that a system is in chemical equilibrium if the free energy is a minimum (2). This result is routinely used today to compute the equilibrium composition of a multicomponent mixture of gases, liquids, and solids.

The development of mathematical theory for optimization followed closely the development of calculus, as pointed out by Hancock (3). In fact, Hancock wrote the first modern book on the subject, entitled *Theory of Maxima and Minima,* which was published in 1917. This definitive work serves even today as an authoritative source.

In the late 1930s there was a spurt of interest in the calculus of variations, but the real impetus to optimization came with World War II and the development of the digital computer. In the 1940s Dantzig (4) recognized the mathematical structure of some military logistics problems and developed the Sim-

1

plex Method of linear programming. Linear programming has moved from an interesting mathematical topic to probably the most important and widely applied optimization procedure. Its development followed closely the continually increasing capabilities of the digital computer. The ability to solve large sets of linear equations with the computer has permitted linear programming to be applied to industrial problems, such as the optimization of a large petroleum refinery.

Again in the 1950s optimization received another boost with the advent of the space age. The optimal trajectory for a missile was one of a number of problems for which the methods of dynamic programming and the maximum principle were developed in this country and the U.S.S.R. These methods are now being used in areas that are not space-related.

FORMULATION OF OPTIMIZATION PROBLEMS

Three basic components are required to optimize an industrial process. First, the process or a mathematical model of the process must be available, and the process variables that can be manipulated and controlled must be known. Often, obtaining a satisfactory process model with known control variables is the most difficult task. Secondly, an economic model of the process is required. This is an equation that represents the profit made from the sale of products and costs associated with their production, such as raw materials, operating costs, fixed costs, taxes, etc. Finally, the optimization procedure selected must locate the values of the independent variables of the process to produce the maximum profit or minimum cost as measured by the economic model. Also, the constraints in materials, process equipment, manpower, etc., must be satisfied as specified in the process model.

Figure 1-1 is a diagram that helps place industrial practice in perspective by relating process and economic models and the two levels of optimization. Plant optimization finds the best operating conditions for a plant made up of process units manufacturing specified amounts of various products to maximize the company's profits within the constraints set by the available raw materials and how these raw materials can be transformed in the plant. Plant optimization usually approximates the individual process units in a relatively simple manner to obtain a satisfactory answer in a reasonable time. This requires that the optimal operating conditions of the individual process unit be known, and that these results be used in the plant optimization to have the plant operating with the maximum profit. Also, due to the complexity of large industrial plants, individual process models are usually simplified by using simulation equations to keep the computer programming efforts and computer costs within reason. However, with individual process units it is feasible to use more detailed models to determine more precisely the

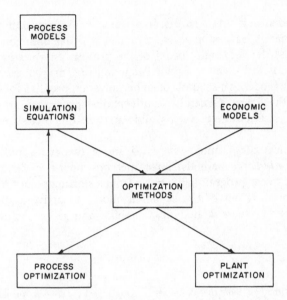

Figure 1-1. Simplified diagram of industrial practice for process and plant optimization.

optimal operating conditions, e.g., temperatures, pressures, recycle rates, etc., to have minimum operating cost known as a function of these variables.

As shown in Figure 1-1, simulation equations are obtained from process models. The procedure is to develop precise process models based on the fundamentals of thermodynamics, kinetics, and transport phenomena. This usually leads to process models that accurately represent the physical and chemical changes taking place over a wide range of conditions. However, these models usually are more complicated in mathematical form and may require the solution of differential equations. Consequently, these process models are usually exercised over the range of operation of the process, and simulation (regression) equations of a simplified mathematical form are developed, which are then used with the optimization method for the plant optimization. However, it may not be necessary to go through the simulation equations step if the equations that describe the key variables, i.e., the ones that effect the economic performance of the process or plant, are not complicated.

TOPICS IN OPTIMIZATION

The two areas of optimization theory are mathematical programming and variational methods, as shown in Figure 1-2. Also, a number of techniques are listed under each of these areas. In mathematical programming, the objective is to locate a best point $\mathbf{x}$ $(x_1, x_2, \ldots x_n)$ that optimizes (maximizes or minimizes) the economic model of the process. In variational methods, the objective is to locate the optimal function that maximizes or minimizes the economic model. An example of an optimization problem for each division is given in the figure. Generally, mathematical programming methods are applicable to steady-state problems, and variational methods are for dynamic problems.

Mathematical programming methods are of two types and are referred to as *direct* or *indirect* methods. Direct methods, such as multivariable search methods and linear programming, move from a starting point through consistently improved values of the economic model to arrive at the optimum. Indirect methods, such as analytical methods and geometric programming,

Optimization

Mathematical Programming

Objective: Find the *best point* that optimizes the economic model.

Example: Optimum operating conditions for a petroleum refinery.

Mathematical Formulation:

Optimize: $y(\mathbf{x})$
Subject to: $f_i(\mathbf{x}) \geq 0$
$\quad\quad\quad i = 1, 2, \ldots m$
where $\mathbf{x} = (x_1, x_2 \ldots x_n)$

Methods

Analytical Methods
Geometric Programming
Linear Programming
Quadratic Programming
Convex Programming
Dynamic Programming (Discrete)
Nonlinear Programming or Multivariable
  Search Methods
Integer Programming
Separable Programming
Goal Programming or Multicriterion Optimization
Combinatorial Programming
Maximum Principle (Discrete)
Heuristic Programming

Variational Methods

Objective: Find the *best function* that optimizes the economic model.

Example: Best temperature profile that maximizes the conversion in a tubular chemical reactor.

Mathematical Formulation:

Optimize: $I[y(x)] = \int F[y(x), y'(x)]dx$
Subject to: Algebraic, integral or differential equation constraints.

Methods

Calculus of Variations
Dynamic Programming (Continuous)
Maximum Principle (Continuous)

Figure 1-2   Areas and Topics in Optimization

solve a set of algebraic equations, and the solution to the set of equations may be the optimum of the economic model. For example, in analytical methods the algebraic equation set is obtained by differentiating the economic model with respect to each independent variable and setting the resulting equations equal to zero.

In this book, the first seven mathematical programming methods listed in Figure 1-2 will be discussed, as will the topic of the calculus of variations under variational methods. These were selected because they are the more widely used in industrial practice. A bibliography of texts on each of these subjects is given at the end of each chapter.

To briefly describe the topics given in Figure 1-2, analytical methods are also called the classical theory of maxima and minima, which is concerned with finding the extreme points of a function. This topic is discussed in Chapter 2 for both unconstrained and constrained optimization problems. Geometric programming may be considered an extension of analytical methods where the economic model and constraints are polynomials, and a dual problem is constructed that may be significantly easier to optimize than the original, or primal, problem, as described in Chapter 3. Linear programming requires that both the economic model and the set of constraint equations be linear, and the Simplex Method is the algorithm that locates the optimum by beginning at a feasible starting point (initially feasible basis), as discussed in Chapter 4. In quadratic programming, the economic model is a quadratic equation, and the constraint equations are linear. Using analytical methods we can convert this problem to a linear programming problem and solve it by the Simplex Method, as shown in Chapter 6. For convex programming, the economic model is a concave function, and the constraint equations are convex functions. The details on this procedure are given in Chapter 2 as part of general analytical methods and show that a global optimum will be located. Dynamic programming uses a series of partial optimizations by taking advantage of the stage structure in the problem and is effective for resource allocation and optimization through time, as discussed in Chapter 7. Nonlinear programming or multivariable search methods, as the theory and algorithms are called, must begin at a feasible starting point and move toward the optimum in steps of improved values of the economic model. The algorithms described in Chapter 6 have been effective for optimization of industrial processes, and they are based on the theory of Chapter 2.

Integer programming is an extension of linear programming where the variables must take on discrete values, and a text on this topic by Taha (5) is available. Separable programming is an extension of linear programming where a small number of nonlinear constraints are approximated by piecewise linear functions. However, the nonlinear functions must have the form such that they can be separated into sums and differences of nonlinear functions of one variable, and the IBM MPSX code (6) is capable of solving these problems. Goal programming is an extension of linear programming also where multiple, conflicting objectives, or goals, are optimized using weights or rankings, for example, and this technique is described by Ignizio (7). Combinatorial programming has been described by Papadimitriou and Steiglitz (8) as a body of mathematical programming knowledge including linear and integer programming, graph and network flows, dynamic programming, and related topics. The maximum principle is comparable to dynamic programming in using the stage structure of the system, but it uses constrained derivatives that require piecewise, continuously differentiable functions and successive approximations (2). Finally, the term *heuristic programming* has been used to describe rules of thumb that can be used for approximations to optimization.

In discussing the various topics in optimization, the economic model has been given several different names. These names arose in the literature as the optimization procedures were being developed. Regardless of the name, the economic model is the equation that expresses the economic return from the process for specified values of the control (manipulative, decision, or independent) variables. The two most common names are the *profit function* or *cost function*. However, in linear programming the term *objective function* is used, and in dynamic programming the term *return function* is employed. Other synonymous names are: *benefit function, criterion, measure of effectiveness,* and *response surface.*

METHOD OF ATTACK

In solving an optimization problem, the structure and complexity of the equations for the economic model and process or plant constraints are very important, for most mathematical programming procedures take advantage of the mathematical form of these models. Examples are linear programming, where all the equations must be linear, and geometric programming where all the equations must be polynomials. Consequently, it is extremely important to have the capabilities of the various optimization techniques in mind when the economic and process models are being formulated. For example, if a satisfactory representation of the economics and process performance can be obtained using all linear equations, the powerful techniques of linear programming can be applied, and this method guarantees that a global optimum will be found. However, if one has to resort to nonlinear equations to represent the economics and process performance, it may be necessary to use a multivariable search method to locate the optimum. Unfortunately, these search techniques find only points that are better than the starting point, and they do not carry any guarantee that a global or a local maximum or minimum has been found.

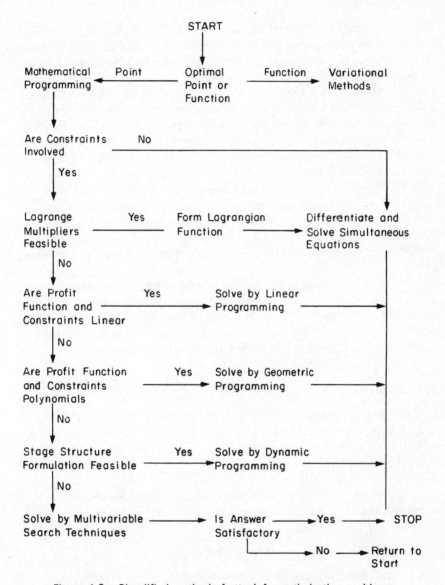

Figure 1-3. Simplified method of attack for optimization problems.

Figure 1-3 shows a *simplified* approach to attacking an optimization problem, and it incorporates some thoughts that should be remembered as the particular optimization techniques are studied. Also, it will give some reasons for the order in which the techniques are presented. At the start, it is necessary to determine if the problem requires an optimal point or function. If it is a point, mathematical programming is applicable; and if an optimal function, variational methods. Let us follow through with mathematical programming. If the equation for the economic model is relatively simple and there are no applicable constraints (process model), it is possible to locate the optimum by differentiating the economic model with respect to the independent variables, setting these equations equal to zero, and solving for the optimum. However, if there are constraints, and there usually are, but the equations are relatively simple, the method of Lagrange multipliers may be used. This converts the constrained problem to an unconstrained problem, and the previous procedure for unconstrained problems is used.

Now, if the problem has a large number of independent variables and the precision needed for the economic and process models can be obtained with linear equations, then linear programming may be used. However, if nonlinear equations are required and polynomial will suffice, it may be possible to determine the optimum rapidly and easily using geometric programming (1).

Not having been successful to this point, it may be feasible to take advantage of the stage structure of the problem and apply dynamic programming with a series of partial optimizations. However, if this is not successful it will be necessary to resort to multivariable search techniques and seek best values without having a guarantee of finding the global optimum.

SUMMARY

This chapter presented a brief discussion of the historical background of optimization. Then the relation of process and plant optimization was described in terms of using simulation equations and problem size. The topics in mathematical programming and variational methods were diagrammed, and a simplified method of attack was described to give some perspective about the different methods as they are studied. The next chapter reviews analytical methods and sets the stage for more modern techniques.

REFERENCES

1. Wilde, D. J., *Globally Optimal Design,* John Wiley & Sons, Inc., New York (1978).
2. Wilde, D. J., and C. S. Beightler, *Foundations of Optimization,* Prentice-Hall, Inc., Englewood Cliffs, N.J. (1967).
3. Hancock, Harris, *Theory of Maxima and Minima,* Dover Publications, Inc., New York (1960).
4. Dantzig, G. B., *Linear Programming and Extensions,* Princeton Univeristy Press, Princeton, N.J. (1963).
5. Taha, H. A., *Integer Programming: Theory, Applications and Computations,* Academic Press, New York (1975).

6. *IBM Mathematical Programming Systems Extended/370 (MPSX/370) Program Reference Manual,* 4th Edition, SH19–1095–3, IBM Corp., White Plains, N.Y. (December 1979).
7. Ignizio, J. P., *Linear Programming in Single- and Multiple-Objective Systems,* Prentice-Hall, Inc., Englewood Cliffs, N.J. (1982).
8. Papadimitriou, C. H., and K. Steiglitz, *Combinatorial Optimization: Algorithms and Complexity,* Prentice-Hall, Inc., Englewood Cliffs, N.J. (1982).

2
CLASSICAL THEORY OF MAXIMA
AND MINIMA

INTRODUCTION

The classical theory of maxima and minima (analytical methods) is concerned with finding the maxima or minima, i.e., extreme points of a function. We seek to determine the values of the n independent variables $x_1, x_2, \ldots x_n$ of a function where it reaches maxima and minima points. Before starting with the development of the mathematics to locate these extreme points of a function, let us examine the shape of the surface of a function of two independent variables, $y(x_1, x_2)$, that could represent the economic model of a process. This should help visualize the location of the extreme points. An economic model is illustrated in Figure 2-1a, where the contours of the function are represented by the curved lines. A cross section of the function along line S through the points A and B is shown in Figure 2-1(b), and in Figure 2-1(c) the first derivative of $y(x_1, x_2)$ along line S through points A and B is given.

In this example, point A is the global maximum in the region and is located at the top of a sharp ridge. Here the first derivative is discontinuous. A second but smaller maximum is located at point B (a local maximum). At point B the first partial derivatives of $y(x_1, x_2)$ are zero, and B is called a stationary point. It is not necessary for stationary points to be maxima or minima, as illustrated by stationary point C, a saddle point. In this example, the minima do not occur in the interior of the region, but on the boundary at points D and E (local minima). To determine the global minima, it is necessary to compare the value of the function at these points.

In essence, the problem of determining the maximum profit or minimum cost for a system using the classical theory becomes one of locating all the local maxima or minima and then comparing the individual values, to determine the global maximum or minimum. The example has illustrated the places to look, which are:

1. at stationary points (first derivatives are zero)
2. on the boundaries
3. at discontinuities in the first derivative

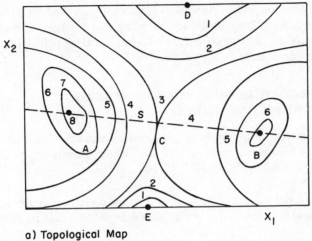

a) Topological Map

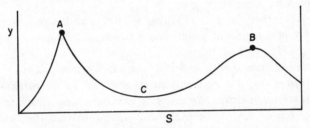

b) Cross Section of $y(x_1, x_2)$ Along Line S
Through Points A and B

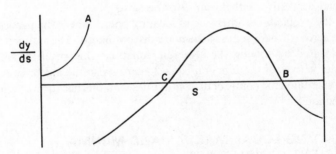

c) First Derivative of y Along Line S
Through Points A and B

Figure 2-1. Geometric interpretation of function yx_1, x_2).

When the function and its derivatives are continuous, the local extreme points will occur at stationary points in the interior of the region. However, it is not necessary that all stationary points be local extreme points, because saddle points can occur also.

LOCATING LOCAL MAXIMA AND MINIMA (NECESSARY CONDITIONS)

Using geometric intuition from the previous example, we can understand the famous Weierstrass theorem (11, 12), which guarantees the existence of maxima and minima. It states:

> *Every function that is continuous in a closed domain possesses a maximum and minimum value either in the interior or on the boundary of the domain.*

The proof is by contradiction.

There is another theorem (13) that tells how to locate extreme points in the interior of a region of a continuous function. It states:

> *A continuous function of n variables attains a maximum or a minimum in the interior of a region only at those values of the variables for which the n partial derivatives either vanish simultaneously (stationary points) or at which one or more of these derivatives cease to exist (i.e., are discontinuous).*

The proof involves examining the Taylor Series expansion at the points where the partial derivatives either vanish or cease to exist.

Thus the problem becomes one of locating points where the partial derivatives are zero or where some of them are discontinuous. The stationary points can be located by solving the algebraic equations that result in setting the partial derivatives of the function equal to zero. Also the algebraic equations must be examined for points of discontinuities, and this has to be accomplished by inspection.

EVALUATING LOCAL MAXIMA AND MINIMA (SUFFICIENT CONDITIONS)

As we have seen, it is not necessary for all stationary points to be local maxima and minima, because there is a possibility of saddle or inflection points. Now we need to develop procedures to determine if stationary points are maxima or minima. These sufficient conditions will be developed for one independent variable first and then extended for two and n independent variables, using the same concepts. Once the local maxima and minima are located, it is necessary to compare the individual points to locate the global maximum and minimum.

SUFFICIENT CONDITIONS FOR ONE INDEPENDENT VARIABLE

To develop criteria establishing whether a stationary point is a local maximum or minimum, we begin by performing a Taylor Series expansion about the stationary point x_0

$$y(x) = y(x_0) + y'(x_0)(x - x_0) + \tfrac{1}{2}y''(x_0)(x - x_0)^2 + \text{higher order terms}$$

Now, select x sufficiently close to x_0 so the higher order terms become negligible compared with the second-order terms. Because the first derivative is zero at the stationary point, the above equation becomes

$$y(x) = y(x_0) + \tfrac{1}{2}y''(x_0)(x - x_0)^2 \qquad (2\text{--}1)$$

We can determine if x_0 is a local maximum or minimum by examining the value of $y''(x_0)$, since $(x - x_0)^2$ is always positive. If $y''(x_0)$ is positive, then the terms $\tfrac{1}{2}y''(x_0)(x - x_0)^2$ will always add to $y(x_0)$ in equation (2--1) for x taking on values that are less than or greater than x_0. For this case $y(x_0)$ is a local minimum. This is summarized in the following:

If $y''(x_0) > 0$ then $y(x_0)$ is a minimum

$y''(x_0) < 0$ $y(x_0)$ is a maximum

$y''(x_0) = 0$ no statement can be made

If the second derivative is zero, it is necessary to examine higher order derivatives. In general if $y''(x_0) = \cdots = y^{(n-1)}(x_0) = 0$, the Taylor Series expansion becomes

$$y(x) = y(x_0) + (1/n!)y^{(n)}(x_0)(x - x_0)^n \qquad (2\text{--}2)$$

If n is even, then $(x - x_0)^n$ is always positive, and the result is:

Even

If $y^{(n)}(x_0) > 0$ then $y(x_0)$ is a minimum

$y^{(n)}(x_0) < 0$ $y(x_0)$ is a maximum

---

odd

If n is odd, then $(x - x_0)^n$ changes sign as x moves from $x < x_0$ to $x > x_0$, and thus there is an inflection point. These results can be summarized in the following theorem (1).

If at a stationary point the first and possibly some of the higher derivatives vanish, then the point is or is not an extreme point, according as the first nonvanishing derivative is of even or odd order. If it is even, there is a maximum or minimum according as the derivative is negative or positive.

The proof of this theorem follows the discussion given above. The following example illustrates the principles discussed.

EXAMPLE 2–1

Locate the extreme points of the following two functions:

$$y(x) = x^4/4 - x^2/2$$

$$y'(x) = x^3 - x = x(x^2 - 1) = x(x - 1)(x + 1) = 0$$

Stationary points are $x = 0, 1, -1$

$$y''(x) = 3x^2 - 1$$

$$y''(0) = -1 \qquad \text{maximum}$$

$$y''(1) = 2 \qquad \text{minimum}$$

$$y''(-1) = 2 \qquad \text{minimum}$$

$$y(x) = x^5$$

$$y'(x) = 5x^4 = 0 \qquad \text{stationary point is } x = 0$$

$$y''(x) = 20x^3 \quad y''(0) = 0$$

$$y'''(x) = 60x^2 \quad y'''(0) = 0 \qquad \text{no statement can be made}$$

$$y^{iv}(x) = 120x \quad y^{iv}(0) = 0$$

$$y^v(x) = 120 \quad y^v(0) = 120 \qquad \begin{array}{l} n \text{ is odd, and the stationary} \\ \text{point is an inflection point} \end{array}$$

SUFFICIENT CONDITIONS FOR TWO INDEPENDENT VARIABLES

2 Vars

To develop the criteria for a local maximum or minimum for a stationary point $x_0(x_{10}, x_{20})$ of a function of two variables, a Taylor's Series expansion is made about this point

$$y(x_1, x_2) = y(x_{10}, x_{20}) + y_{x_1}(x_1 - x_{10}) + y_{x_2}(x_2 - x_{20})$$

$$+ \tfrac{1}{2}[y_{x_1 x_1}(x_1 - x_{10})^2 + 2y_{x_1 x_2}(x_1 - x_{10})(x_2 - x_{20}) \quad (2\text{-}3)$$

$$+ y_{x_2 x_2}(x_2 - x_{20})^2] + \text{higher order terms}$$

where the subscripts x_1 and x_2 indicate partial differentiation with respect to those variables and evaluation at the stationary point.

Again we select $y(x_1, x_2)$ sufficiently close to $y(x_{10}, x_{20})$, so the higher order terms become negligible compared with the second-order terms. Also, the first derivatives are zero at the stationary point. Thus equation (2-3) can be written in matrix form as:

$$y(x_1, x_2) = y(x_{10}, x_{20})$$

$$+ \tfrac{1}{2}[(x_1 - x_{10})(x_2 - x_{20})] \begin{bmatrix} y_{x_1 x_1} & y_{x_1 x_2} \\ y_{x_2 x_1} & y_{x_2 x_2} \end{bmatrix} \begin{bmatrix} (x_1 - x_{10}) \\ (x_2 - x_{20}) \end{bmatrix} \quad (2\text{-}4)$$

In matrix-vector notation, the above equation can be written as

$$y(\mathbf{x}) = y(\mathbf{x}_0) + \tfrac{1}{2}[(\mathbf{x} - \mathbf{x}_0)^T \mathbf{H}^0 (\mathbf{x} - \mathbf{x}_0)] \quad (2\text{-}5)$$

where $\mathbf{H}^0$ is the matrix of second partial derivatives evaluated at the stationary point $\mathbf{x}_0$ and is called the *Hessian matrix*.

The term in the bracket of equation (2-5) is called a *differential quadratic form,* and $y(\mathbf{x}_0)$ will be a minimum or a maximum accordingly if this term is always positive or always negative. Based on this concept, it can be shown (1) that if the following results apply $\mathbf{x}_0$ is a maximum or a minimum. If they do not hold, $\mathbf{x}_0$ could be a saddle point and is not a maximum or a minimum.

Hessian

$y(\mathbf{x}_0)$ is a minimum if $y_{x_1 x_1} > 0$ and $\begin{vmatrix} y_{x_1 x_1} & y_{x_1 x_2} \\ y_{x_2 x_1} & y_{x_2 x_2} \end{vmatrix} > 0$

$y(\mathbf{x}_0)$ is a maximum if $y_{x_1 x_1} < 0$ and $\begin{vmatrix} y_{x_1 x_1} & y_{x_1 x_2} \\ y_{x_2 x_1} & y_{x_2 x_2} \end{vmatrix} > 0$

Pg 43

An illustration of the above results is given in example 2–2. The term in the bracket of equation (2–5) is an example of a quadratic form. It will be necessary to describe a quadratic form briefly before giving the sufficient conditions for maxima and minima for n independent variables.

SIGN OF A QUADRATIC FORM More than 2 Vars

To perform a similar analysis for a function with more than two independent variables, it is necessary to determine what is called the *sign* of the quadratic form. The general quadratic form (1) is written as:

$$Q(A, x) = \sum_{i=1}^{n} \sum_{j=1}^{n} a_{ij} x_i x_j = x^T A x \qquad (2\text{–}6)$$

where a_{ij} are the components of symmetric matrix A, e.g., $a_{ij} = a_{ji}$.

It turns out (1) that we can determine if Q is always positive or negative, for all finite values of x_i and x_j, by evaluating the signs of D_i, the determinants of the principal submatrices of A

$$D_i = \begin{vmatrix} a_{11} & a_{12} & \cdots & a_{1i} \\ a_{21} & a_{22} & \cdots & a_{2i} \\ \vdots & & & \vdots \\ a_{i1} & a_{i2} & \cdots & a_{ii} \end{vmatrix} \qquad (2\text{–}7)$$

The important results that will be used subsequently are:

If $D_i > 0$ for $i = 1, 2, \cdots n$, then: A is positive definite, and $Q(A, x) > 0$

If $D_i < 0$ for $i = 1, 3, \cdots$, and

$D_i > 0$ for $i = 2, 4, \cdots$, then: A is negative definite and $Q(A, x) < 0$

If D_i is neither of these, then $Q(A, x)$ depends on the values of x_i and x_j

---

SUFFICIENT CONDITIONS FOR n INDEPENDENT VARIABLES

The result of the previous two sections can be extended to the case of n independent variables by considering the Taylor Series expansion for n independent variables around stationary point x_0:

$$y(\mathbf{x}) = y(\mathbf{x}_0) + \sum_{i=1}^{n} y_{x_i}(\mathbf{x}_0)(x_i - x_{i\,0})$$

$$+ \frac{1}{2}\left[\sum_{j=1}^{n}\sum_{k=1}^{n} y_{x_j x_k}(\mathbf{x}_0)(x_j - x_{j\,0})(x_k - x_{k\,0})\right] \qquad (2\text{-}8)$$

+ higher order terms

Again select $\mathbf{x}$ sufficiently close to $\mathbf{x}_0$, so the higher order terms become negligible compared with the second-order terms. Also the first derivatives are zero at the stationary point. Thus, equation (2-8) can be written in matrix-vector notation as:

To get sign

$$y(\mathbf{x}) = y(\mathbf{x}_0) + \frac{1}{2}(\mathbf{x} - \mathbf{x}_0)^T \mathbf{H}^0 (\mathbf{x} - \mathbf{x}_0) \qquad (2\text{-}9)$$

where $\mathbf{x}$ is the column vector of independent variables, and $\mathbf{H}^0$, the matrix of second partial derivative evaluated at the stationary point $\mathbf{x}_0$, is the Hessian matrix. This is the same equation as equation (2-5), which was written for two independent variables.

$$\mathbf{H}^0 = \begin{bmatrix} y_{x_1 x_1} & \cdots & y_{x_1 x_n} \\ \vdots & & \vdots \\ y_{x_n x_1} & \cdots & y_{x_n x_n} \end{bmatrix} \qquad (2\text{-}10)$$

The second term on the right-hand side of equation (2-9) is called a *differential quadratic form,* as shown below

$$Q[\mathbf{H}^0, (\mathbf{x} - \mathbf{x}_0)] = (\mathbf{x} - \mathbf{x}_0)^T \mathbf{H}^0 (\mathbf{x} - \mathbf{x}_0) \qquad (2\text{-}11)$$

Equation (2-11) corresponds to equation (2-6) in the previous section, and the determinants of the principal submatrices of $\mathbf{H}_0$ as defined below correspond to equation (2-7)

$$\mathbf{H}_i{}^0 = \begin{bmatrix} y_{x_1 x_1} & y_{x_1 x_2} & \cdots & y_{x_1 x_i} \\ y_{x_2 x_1} & \cdots & & \vdots \\ \vdots & & & \vdots \\ y_{x_i x_1} & \cdots & & y_{x_i x_i} \end{bmatrix} \qquad (2\text{-}12)$$

We can now use the same procedure in evaluating the character of the stationary points for n independent variables. For example, if the term containing the Hessian matrix is always positive for perturbations of the independent variables around the stationary point, then the stationary point is a local minimum. For this differential quadratic form to be positive always, then $|H_i^0| > 0$ for $i = 1, 2, \cdots n$. The same reasoning can be applied for a local maximum, and the results for these two cases are summarized below:

$y(x_0)$ is a minimum if $|H_i^0| > 0$ for $i = 1, 2, \cdots, n$

$y(x_0)$ is a maximum if $|H_i^0| < 0$ for $i = 1, 3, 5, \cdots$ Odd

$\qquad\qquad\qquad\qquad |H_i^0| > 0 \qquad i = 2, 4, 6, \cdots$ Even

---

If zeros occur in the place of some of the positive or negative numbers in the tests above (semidefinite quadratic form), then there is insufficient information to determine the character of the stationary point (1). As discussed in Avriel (10), higher order terms may have to be examined, or local exploration can be performed. If the test is not met (indefinite quadratic form), then the point is neither a maximum or a minimum (1). The following theorem from Cooper (7) summarizes these results. It states:

If $y(x)$ and its first two partial derivatives are continuous, then a sufficient condition for $y(x)$ to have a relative minimum (or maximum) at x_0, when $\partial y(x_0)/\partial x_j = 0$, $j = 1, 2, \cdots n$, is that the Hessian matrix be positive definite (negative definite).

The proof of this theorem employs arguments similar to those given above. The following example illustrates these methods.

EXAMPLE 2–2

The flow diagram of a simple process is shown in Figure 2-2 (2) where the hydrocarbon feed is mixed with recycle and compressed before being passed into a catalytic reactor. The product and unreacted material are separated by distillation, and the unreacted material is recycled. The pressure, P, in psi and recycle ratio, R, must be selected to minimize the total annual cost for the required production rate of 10^7 pounds per year. The feed is brought up to pressure at an annual cost of $1000P$, mixed with the recycle stream, and fed to the reactor at an annual cost of $\$4 \times 10^9/PR$. The product is removed in a separator at a cost of $\$10^5R$ per year, and the unreacted material is recycled in a recirculating compressor that consumes $\$1.5 \times 10^5R$ annually. Determine the optimal operating pressure, recycle ratio, and total annual cost; and show that the cost is a minimum.

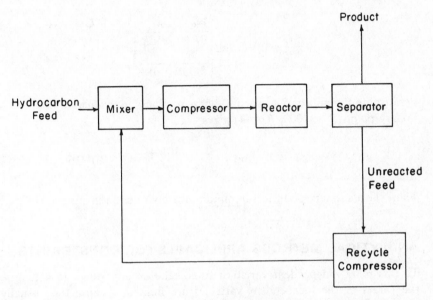

Figure 2-2. Flow diagram of a simple process, after Wilde (2).

$P = Pressure$
$R = Recycle$

Solution: The equation giving the total operating cost is

$$C \ (\$/\text{yr}) = 1000P + 4 \times 10^9/PR + 2.5 \times 10^5R$$

Equating the partial derivatives of C with respect to P and R to zero gives
two algebraic equations to be solved for P and R Take 1st part ders &
set = to zero, solve
for vars

$$\partial C/\partial P = 1000 - 4 \times 10^9/RP^2 = 0$$

$$\partial C/\partial R = 2.5 \times 10^5 - 4 \times 10^9/PR^2 = 0$$

Solving simultaneously gives

$$P = 1000 \text{ psi and } R = 4$$

Substituting to determine the corresponding total operating cost gives

$$C = \$3 \times 10^6 \text{ per year}$$

$C \ (P, R)$ is a minimum if

$$\frac{\partial^2 C}{\partial P^2} > 0 \quad \text{and} \quad \begin{vmatrix} \dfrac{\partial^2 C}{\partial P^2} & \dfrac{\partial^2 C}{\partial P \partial R} \\ \dfrac{\partial^2 C}{\partial R \partial P} & \dfrac{\partial^2 C}{\partial R^2} \end{vmatrix} > 0 \quad \begin{vmatrix} C_{PP} & C_{PR} \\ C_{RP} & C_{RR} \end{vmatrix}$$

Performing the appropriate partial differentiation and evaluation at the stationary point ($P = 1000$, $R = 4$) gives

$$\partial^2 C / \partial P^2 = 2 > 0 \quad \text{and} \quad \begin{vmatrix} 2 & 10^3/4 \\ 10^3/4 & 10^6/8 \end{vmatrix} = 3 \times 10^6/16 > 0$$

Thus, the stationary point is a <u>minimum</u>, for both determinants are positive.

ANALYTICAL METHODS APPLICABLE FOR CONSTRAINTS

To this point independent variables could take on any value. In actuality, the values of the independent variables are limited, because they usually represent physical quantities, such as flow rates, temperatures, pressures, process unit capacities and available resources. Consequently, there are constraints on variables, if nothing more than that they must be nonnegative. In many cases they are bounded within limits as dictated by the process equipment and related by equations such as material balances. The constraints on the variables can be of the form of equalities and inequalities.

Methods to locate the stationary points of functions (economic models) subject to equality constraints (e.g., material and energy balance equations) will be developed, and examples illustrating the techniques will be given. Inequality constraints can be converted to equality constraints, and then these procedures for equality constraints can be applied with some additional considerations.

Let us illustrate the conversion of an inequality constraint to an equality constraint using a simple example to help visualize the concept of slack variables. Figure 2-3 is an example of an equality and an inequality constraint for a distillation column. The material balance that says the feed rate to the column must equal the sum of the overhead and bottom products at steady state is the equality constraint. The upper limit on the capacity of the distillation column, which was set when the equipment was designed, is the inequality constraint. This inequality constraint can be converted to an equality constraint by adding a *slack* variable S as S^2 to ensure that a positive number has been added to the equation

$$F + S^2 = 50,000 \qquad (2\text{--}13)$$

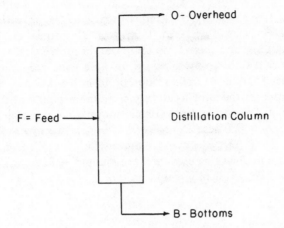

O - Overhead

F = Feed

Distillation Column

B - Bottoms

Material Balance : F - (O + B) = O
(equality constraint)

Upper Limit on the Feed Rate : F≤50,000 barrels per day
(inequality constraint)

Figure 2-3. Illustration of equality and inequality constraints.

The term *slack* is used to represent the difference between the optimal and upper limit on the capacity. It represents the unused, excess, or slack in capacity of the process unit. For example, if $F_{opt} = 30,000$ barrels per day, then $S^2 = 20,000$ barrels per day, a slack of 20,000 barrels per day, and the constraint is said to be *loose,* i.e., the inequality holds. If $F_{opt} = 50,000$ barrels per day, then there is no slack, and the constraint is said to be *tight,* i.e., the equality holds. This will be discussed in more detail later in the chapter. Also, if there was a lower limit on F, e.g., $F \geq 10,000$, the same procedure would apply, except S^2 would be subtracted from F. The equation would be $F - S^2 = 10,000$, and S is called a *surplus* variable.

We can now state a general optimization problem with n independent variables and m equality constraints where the objective is to optimize (maximize or minimize) the economic model $y(\mathbf{x})$ subject to m constraint equations $f_i(\mathbf{x})$

$$\text{optimize: } y(x_1, x_2, \cdots, x_n) \tag{2-14}$$

$$\text{subject to: } f_i(x_1, x_2, \cdots, x_n) = 0 \tag{2-15}$$

$$\text{for } i = 1, 2, \cdots m$$

n - Indeps
m - Constraints

[handwritten: → Have to have more Vars than eqns otherwise there is a unique (1) only Sln per Variable]

There must be fewer equality constraints than independent variables to be able to optimize $y(\mathbf{x})$, i.e., $n > m$. If $m = n$, the values of the x_j's are uniquely determined, and there is no optimization problem. Also if $m > n$, the problem is said to be overdetermined, because there are more equations than unknowns. There is no optimization problem for this case either.

There are three methods of locating the optimum points of the function $y(x_1, x_2, \cdots, x_n)$ of n independent variables subject to m constraint equations $f_i(x_1, x_2, \cdots, x_n) = 0$. These are: *direct substitution, solution by constrained variation,* and *the method of Lagrange multipliers.* We will find that direct substitution cannot always be used, and the method of Lagrange multipliers will be the one most frequently employed.

DIRECT SUBSTITUTION

This simply means to solve the constraint equations for the independent variables and to substitute the constraint equations directly into the function to be optimized. This will give an equation (economic model) with $(n - m)$ unknowns, and the previous techniques for unconstrained optimization are applicable. *[handwritten: ↳ Set 1st der = 0 Solve → Check Curvature @ pt w/ 2nd der]*

Unfortunately, it is not always possible to perform the algebraic manipulations required for these substitutions when the constraint equations are somewhat complicated. Consequently, it is necessary to resort to the following methods.

CONSTRAINED VARIATION

This method (3, 14) is used infrequently, but furnishes a theoretical basis for important multivariable numerical search methods, such as the generalized reduced gradient. It is best illustrated for the case of two independent variables *[handwritten: 2 Inde Vars]* by considering the example shown in Figure 2-4. There is a local minimum of the constrained system at point A and a local maximum at point B. The maximum of the unconstrained system is at C.

At point A the curve $y(x_1, x_2) = 1$ and the curve $f(x_1, x_2) = 0$ are tangent and have the same slope. This means that differential changes, dx_1 and dx_2, produce the same change in the dependent variables $y(x_1, x_2)$ and $f(x_1, x_2)$. This can be expressed as:

$$\left[\frac{dx_1}{dx_2}\right]_y = \left[\frac{dx_1}{dx_2}\right]_f \qquad (2\text{--}16)$$

[handwritten: Slopes of eqns are equal]

We will need the total derivatives of y and f to combine with equation (2–16) to obtain the final result. Using the first terms in a Taylor Series expansion for y and f gives:

Total differentials

$$dy = \frac{\partial y}{\partial x_1}\,dx_1 + \frac{\partial y}{\partial x_2}\,dx_2 = 0$$

$$\text{(2–17)}$$

$$df = \frac{\partial f}{\partial x_1}\,dx_1 + \frac{\partial f}{\partial x_2}\,dx_2 = 0$$

At the minimum, point A, and the maximum, point B, dy is equal to 0; and the constraint is satisfied, i.e., $f = 0$ and $df = 0$.

Combining equations (2–16) and (2–17) gives the following result

Combine prev 2 Eqns

$$\frac{\partial y}{\partial x_1} \cdot \frac{\partial f}{\partial x_2} - \frac{\partial y}{\partial x_2} \cdot \frac{\partial f}{\partial x_1} = 0 \qquad \text{(2–18)}$$

n = 2
m = 1

2–21 → n vars m const

solve this one simult w/ constraint eqn to get stationary pts.

? Plane is created up from $f(x_1, x_2) = 0$ to the surface of $y(x_1, x_2)$

Contour map

Uncanstrained max

min

at ground level

$f(x_1, x_2) = 0$

Result has to be on the $f(x_1, x_2)$ line

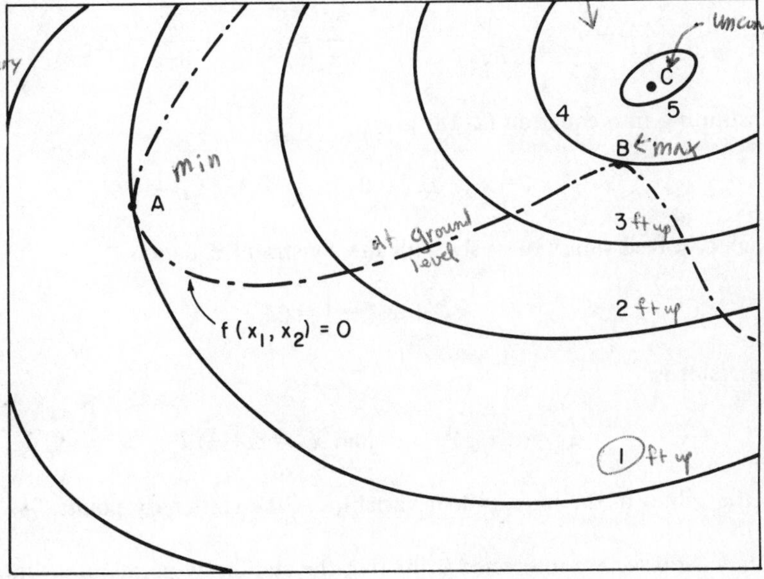

Figure 2-4.   Sketch of a profit function $y(x_1, x_2)$ and a constraint equation $f(x_1, x_2) = 0$.   *2 planes at any 1 pt*

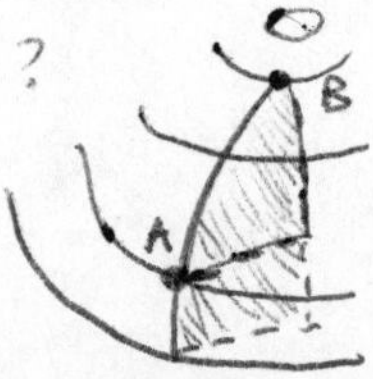

This is an algebraic equation, and it is to be solved in combination with the constraint equation to locate the stationary points. It should be remembered in this case that $\partial y/\partial x_1$ and $\partial y/\partial x_2$ are not necessarily zero. They are zero in the unconstrained case at point C, however.

This technique is illustrated with the following example. Then the extension to the general case for n independent variables will be given.

EXAMPLE 2–3

Find the stationary points of the following function using the method of constrained variation

$$\text{optimize: } y(\mathbf{x}) = x_1 x_2$$

$$\text{subject to: } f(\mathbf{x}) = x_1{}^2 + x_2{}^2 - 1 = 0$$

The first partial derivatives are:

$$\frac{\partial y}{\partial x_1} = x_2 \qquad \frac{\partial y}{\partial x_2} = x_1 \qquad \frac{\partial f}{\partial x_1} = 2x_1 \qquad \frac{\partial f}{\partial x_2} = 2x_2$$

Substituting into equation (2–18) gives

$$x_2 \cdot 2x_2 - x_1 \cdot 2x_1 = 0 \qquad \text{or } x_2{}^2 - x_2{}^1 = 0$$

which is solved simultaneously with the constraint equation

$$x_1{}^2 + x_2{}^2 - 1 = 0$$

The result is:

$$x_1 = \pm (\tfrac{1}{2})^{1/2} \qquad \text{and } x_2 = \pm (\tfrac{1}{2})^{1/2}$$

Plug into here & check maxes & min values of y

for the values of the independent variables at the stationary points.

In general we are interested in finding the stationary points of a function $y(x_1, x_2, \cdots, x_n)$ subject to m constraint equations $f_i(x_1, x_2, \cdots, x_n) = 0$ where $i = 1, \cdots m$, and $n \geq m$. The same reasoning applies in $(n + 1)$ dimensional space as applied to the three-dimensional space above, and this results in the following equations:

# of indep vars has to be greater than eqns (constraints)

$$dy = \frac{\partial y}{\partial x_1} dx_1 + \frac{\partial y}{\partial x_2} dx_2 + \cdots + \frac{\partial y}{\partial x_n} dx_n = 0$$

(handwritten) y Total Differentials

$$df_1 = \frac{\partial f_1}{\partial x_1} dx_1 + \frac{\partial f_1}{\partial x_2} dx_2 + \cdots + \frac{\partial f_1}{\partial x_n} dx_n = 0$$

$$\vdots$$

$$df_m = \frac{\partial f_m}{\partial x_1} dx_1 + \frac{\partial f_m}{\partial x_2} dx_2 + \cdots + \frac{\partial f_m}{\partial x_n} dx_n = 0$$

(2–19)

The set of equations given in equation (2–19) can be solved for $(n - m)$ equations to go with the m constraint equations to locate the stationary points. The $(n - m)$ equations corresponding to equation (2–18) of the two independent variable case can be written in terms of $(n - m)$ Jacobian determinants, which are:

$$J\left[\frac{y, f_1, f_2, \cdots f_m}{x_1, x_2, \cdots x_m, x_{m+1}}\right] = 0$$

$$\vdots \quad \downarrow x_n$$

(2–20)

$$J\left[\frac{y, f_1, f_2, \cdots f_m}{x_1, x_2, \cdots x_m, x_n}\right] = 0$$

The Jacobian determinant for the first equation above is:

(handwritten left margin) Solve Simult w/ (m) Constraint Eqns to get Stationary Pts. Plug Stat. Pts. into Objec. func to check mins & maxs

$$J\left[\frac{y, f_1, f_2, \cdots f_m}{x_1, x_2, \cdots x_{m+1}}\right] = \begin{vmatrix} \frac{\partial y}{\partial x_1} & \frac{\partial y}{\partial x_2} & \cdots & \frac{\partial y}{\partial x_{m+1}} \\ \frac{\partial f_1}{\partial x_1} & \frac{\partial f_1}{\partial x_2} & \cdots & \frac{\partial f_1}{\partial x_{m+1}} \\ \vdots & & & \vdots \\ \frac{\partial f_m}{\partial x_1} & \frac{\partial f_m}{\partial x_2} & \cdots & \frac{\partial f_m}{\partial x_{m+1}} \end{vmatrix}$$

(handwritten right margin) equivalent of 2-18 for many vars (2–21) n vars m constraints Notes 9/18

A total of n equations are solved for the stationary points, i.e., the $(n - m)$ equation generated by (2–20) above and the m constraint equations. A derivation of these results is given by Beveridge and Schechter (6). This involves using Cramer's rule and eliminating the dx_i's. Also similar results are given for this general case in the text by Wilde and Beightler (4). However, a different nomenclature is used, and the results are extended to include Lagrange Multipliers.

To illustrate the use of the Jacobian determinants, consider the following example, which obtains equation (2–18).

EXAMPLE 2–4

$$\text{optimize: } y(x_1, x_2)$$

$$\text{subject to: } f(x_1, x_2) = 0$$

For this problem there are two independent variables ($n = 2$) and one constraint ($m = 1$), so the evaluation of one Jacobian determinant is required.

$$J\left[\frac{y, f}{x_1, x_2}\right] = \begin{vmatrix} \dfrac{\partial y}{\partial x_1} & \dfrac{\partial y}{\partial x_2} \\ \dfrac{\partial f}{\partial x_1} & \dfrac{\partial f}{\partial x_2} \end{vmatrix} = 0$$

Expanding gives the following equation:

$$\frac{\partial y}{\partial x_1}\frac{\partial f}{\partial x_2} - \frac{\partial y}{\partial x_2}\frac{\partial f}{\partial x_1} = 0 \qquad (2\text{-}18)$$

This is the same as equation (2–18), which was solved with the constraint equation for the stationary point values of x_1 and x_2 in Example 2–3.

LAGRANGE MULTIPLIERS   Ratio of partial ders at the max

The most frequently used method for constraints is to employ Lagrange Multipliers. The technique will be presented using two independent variables and one constraint equation to illustrate the concepts. Then the procedure will be extended to the general case of n independent variables and m constraint equations. For the case of two independent variables, we have:

$n = 2$
$m = 1$

$$\text{optimize: } y(x_1, x_2)$$

$$\text{subject to: } f(x_1, x_2) = 0 \qquad (2\text{-}22)$$

We want to show how the Lagrange Multiplier arises and that the constrained problem can be converted into an unconstrained problem. The profit function and the constraint equation are expanded in a Taylor series. Then, using the first-order terms gives:

Total Differentials

$$dy = \frac{\partial y}{\partial x_1} dx_1 + \frac{\partial y}{\partial x_2} dx_2$$

$$0 = \frac{\partial f}{\partial x_1} dx_1 + \frac{\partial f}{\partial x_2} dx_2$$

This form of the constraint equation will be used to eliminate dx_2 in the profit function. Solving for dx_2 gives:

$$dx_2 = -\frac{\frac{\partial f}{\partial x_1}}{\frac{\partial f}{\partial x_2}} dx_1$$

This equation is substituted into the equation for dy to obtain:

$$dy = \frac{\partial y}{\partial x_1} dx_1 - \frac{\partial y}{\partial x_2}\left[\frac{\frac{\partial f}{\partial x_1}}{\frac{\partial f}{\partial x_2}}\right] dx_1$$

and rearranging gives:

Total differentials dy & df Combined

can calc the partial ders at max based on func to maximize

$$dy = \left[\frac{\partial y}{\partial x_1} + \frac{-\frac{\partial y}{\partial x_2}}{\frac{\partial f}{\partial x_2}}\frac{\partial f}{\partial x_1}\right] dx_1$$

Now we can define λ as the value of $[-\partial y/\partial x_2/\partial f/\partial x_2]$ at the stationary point of the constrained function. This ratio of partial derivatives λ is a constant at the stationary point, and the above equation can be written as

See eqn 2-16

$$dy = \left[\frac{\partial y}{\partial x_1} + \lambda\frac{\partial f}{\partial x_1}\right] dx_1$$

w/ respect to x_1

w/ respect to x_2

$$L = y + \lambda f \quad \text{Lagrange func}$$

or

$$dy = \frac{\partial(y + \lambda f)}{\partial x_1} dx_1$$

At the stationary point $dy = 0$, and this leads to:

$$\frac{\partial(y + \lambda f)}{\partial x_1} = 0$$

Now if L is defined as $L = y + \lambda f$, the above gives:

$$\frac{\partial L}{\partial x_1} = 0$$

This is one of the necessary conditions to locate the stationary points of an unconstrainted function L that is constructed from the profit function $y(x_1, x_2)$ and the constraint equation $f(x_1, x_2) = 0$. Now the same manipulations can be repeated to obtain the other necessary conditions:

$$\frac{\partial L}{\partial x_2} = 0 \rightarrow \lambda = \frac{-\frac{\partial y}{\partial x_1}}{\frac{\partial f}{\partial x_1}} \overset{Same}{=} \frac{\frac{\partial y}{\partial x_2}}{\frac{\partial f}{\partial x_2}}$$

Therefore, the constrained problem can be converted to an unconstrained problem by forming the *Lagrangian,* or *augmented,* function and solving this problem by the previously developed methods of setting the first partial derivatives equal to zero. This will give two equations to solve for the three unknowns x_1, x_2, and λ at the stationary point. The third equation to be used is the constraint equation. In fact the Lagrange Multiplier is sometimes treated as another variable, for $\partial L / \partial \lambda = 0$ gives the constraint equation. The example used for the method of constrained variation will be used to illustrate these ideas.

EXAMPLE 2–5

Find the stationary points for the following constrained problem using the method of Lagrange Multipliers

$$\text{optimize: } y(\mathbf{x}) = x_1 x_2$$

$$\text{subject to: } f(\mathbf{x}) = x_1^2 + x_2^2 - 1 = 0$$

$\nearrow L = y + \lambda f$

The Lagrangian, or augmented, function is formed as shown below

Form
Lagrange Eqn

$$L(x_1, x_2, \lambda) = x_1 x_2 + \lambda(x_1^2 + x_2^2 - 1)$$

The following equations are obtained from setting the first partial derivatives equal to zero

Take Partials & Set = to O

$$\partial L/\partial x_1 = x_2 + 2\lambda x_1 = 0$$

$$\partial L/\partial x_2 = x_1 + 2\lambda x_2 = 0$$

$$\partial L/\partial \lambda = x_1^2 + x_2^2 - 1 = 0$$

3 eqns, 3 unks

Solve for stationary Pts & then plug into obj. func to determine by inspection which are maxes & mins

Solving the previous equations simultaneously gives the following stationary points:

$$\text{maxima: } x_1 = (1/2)^{1/2}, \quad x_2 = (1/2)^{1/2}, \quad \lambda = -1/2$$

$$x_1 = -(1/2)^{1/2}, \quad x_2 = -(1/2)^{1/2}, \quad \lambda = -1/2$$

$$\text{minima: } x_1 = (1/2)^{1/2}, \quad x_2 = -(1/2)^{1/2}, \quad \lambda = 1/2$$

$$x_1 = -(1/2)^{1/2}, \quad x_2 = (1/2)^{1/2}, \quad \lambda = 1/2$$

The type of stationary points, i.e., <u>maxima, minima, or saddle, was determined by inspection for this problem</u>. Sufficient conditions for constrained problems will be discussed subsequently in this chapter.

For n Indep Vars & m Constraints

The development of the Lagrangian function of the case of n independent variables and m constraint equations is a direct extension from that of two independent variables and one constraint equation, and Avriel (10) gives a concise derivation of this result (see problem 2–14). The Lagrangian, or augmented, function is formed as previously, and for every constraint equation
✱ there is a Lagrange Multiplier. This is shown below:

m = # of λ

$$\text{optimize: } y(\mathbf{x}) \qquad \mathbf{x} = (x_1, x_2, \cdots, x_n)^T$$

$$\text{subject to: } f_i(\mathbf{x}) = 0 \qquad \text{for } i = 1, 2, \cdots, m \qquad (2\text{–}23)$$

$$\text{where } n > m$$

$$\left(\frac{\partial y}{\partial x_n} + \sum_{i=1}^{m} \lambda_i \frac{\partial f_i}{\partial x_n}\right) dx_n$$

The Lagrangian, or augmented, function is formed from the constrained problem as follows:

$$dy = \frac{\partial y}{\partial x_1} dx_1 + \cdots \frac{\partial y}{\partial x_n} dx_n$$

$$0 = \frac{\partial f_1}{\partial x_1} dx_1 + \cdots \frac{\partial f_1}{\partial x_n} dx_n \quad \lambda_1$$

$$0 = \frac{\partial f_m}{\partial x_1} dx_1 + \cdots \frac{\partial f_m}{\partial x_n} dx_n \quad \lambda_m$$

$$\delta y = \frac{\partial y}{\partial x_1} + \sum_{i=1}^{m} \lambda_i \frac{\partial f_i}{\partial x_1}\bigg) dx_1 + \cdots$$

$$= \frac{\partial}{\partial x_1}\left(y + \sum_{i=1}^{m} \lambda_i f_i\right) dx_1 + \frac{\partial}{\partial x_n}\left(y + \sum_{i=1}^{m} \lambda_i f_i\right)$$

$\dfrac{\delta L}{\delta x_j} = 0$ for $j = 1, 2, n$

$$L(\mathbf{x}, \lambda) = y(\mathbf{x}) + \sum_{i=1}^{m} \lambda_i f_i(\mathbf{x}) \tag{2-24}$$

$\dfrac{\delta L}{\delta \lambda_i} = 0 = f_i(\mathbf{x}) = 0$

To locate the stationary points of the constrained problem, the first partial derivatives of the Lagrangian function with respect to the x_j's and λ_i's are set equal to zero (necessary conditions). There are $(n + m)$ equations to be solved for the $(n + m)$ unknowns: $n - x_j$'s and $m - \lambda_i$'s.

Seems worse than Constrained Variation but It is sometimes said that the method of Lagrange Multipliers requires more work than the method of constrained variation, for an additional m equations have to be solved for the values of the Lagrange Multipliers. However, additional and valuable information is obtained from knowing the values of the Lagrange Multipliers, as will be seen. The following simple example gives a comparison among the three techniques.

Yet to come → Usefulness

EXAMPLE 2–6

For the process in Example 2–1 (2), it is necessary to maintain the product of the pressure and recycle ratio equal to 9000 psi. Determine the optimal values of the pressure and recycle ratio and minimum cost within this constraint by direct substitution, constrained variation, and Lagrange Multipliers.

Again, the problem is to minimize C.

$$C = 1000P + 4 \times 10^9 / PR + 2.5 \times 10^5 R$$

However, C is subject to the following constraint equation

$$PR = 9000$$

Direct Substitution: Solving the constraint above for P and substituting into the objective function gives:

$$C = 9 \times 10^6 / R + (4/9) \times 10^6 + 2.5 \times 10^5 R$$

Setting $dC/dR = 0$ and solving gives:

$$R = 6 \text{ and } P = 1500 \text{ psi}$$

The corresponding cost is:

$$C = 3.44 \times 10^6$$

which is greater than the unconstrained system, as would be expected.

Constrained Variation: The equations to be solved for this case are:

$$\frac{\partial C}{\partial P}\frac{\partial}{\partial R}(PR - 9000) - \frac{\partial C}{\partial R}\frac{\partial}{\partial P}(PR - 9000) = 0$$

$$PR - 9000 = 0$$

The first equation simplifies to:

$$P = 250R$$

which, when solved simultaneously with the second equation, gives the same results as direct substitution.

Lagrange Multipliers: The Lagrangian, or augmented, function is:

$$L = 1000P + 4 \times 10^9/PR + 2.5 \times 10^5 R + \lambda\ (PR - 9000)$$

Setting partial derivatives of L with respect to P, R, and λ equal to zero gives:

$$1000 - 4 \times 10^9/P^2 R + \lambda R = 0$$

$$2.5 \times 10^5 - 4 \times 10^9/PR^2 + \lambda P = 0$$

$$PR - 9000 = 0$$

Solving the above simultaneously gives the same results as the two previous methods and a value for the Lagrange Multiplier

$$P = 1500, \qquad R = 6, \qquad \lambda = -117.3$$

{ Additional Information

METHOD OF STEEPEST ASCENT

A further application of the method of Lagrange Multipliers is developing the method of steepest ascent (descent) for a function to be optimized. This result will be valuable when search methods are discussed.

To illustrate the direction of steepest ascent a geometric representation is shown in Figure 2-5. To obtain the direction of steepest ascent, we wish to

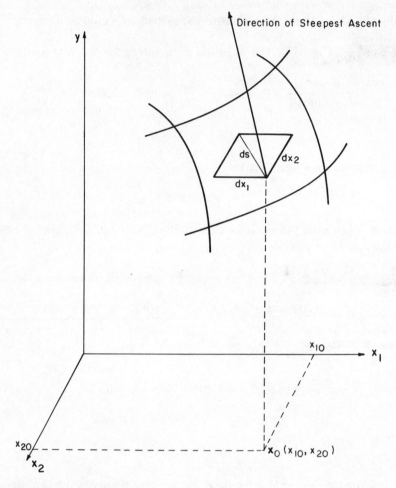

Figure 2-5.   Geometric representation of the direction of steepest ascent.

obtain the maximum value of dy, and $y(x_1, x_2, \cdots x_n)$ is a function of n variables. Also, there is a constraint equation relating $dx_1, dx_2, \cdots dx_n$ and ds, as shown in Figure 2-5 for two independent variables.

The problem is:

$$\text{Maximize:}\quad dy = \sum_{i=1}^{n} \frac{\partial y}{\partial x_i}\, dx_i \tag{2-25}$$

$$\text{Subject to:}\quad (ds)^2 = \sum_{i=1}^{n} (dx_i)^2 \tag{2-26}$$

To obtain the maximum value of dy, the Lagrangian function is formed as follows:

$$L = \sum_{i=1}^{n} \frac{\partial y}{\partial x_i} dx_i + \lambda[(ds)^2 - \sum_{i=1}^{n} (dx_i)^2]$$

Differentiating L with respect to the independent variables dx_j and equating to zero gives:

$$\frac{\partial y}{\partial x_j} - 2\lambda dx_j = 0 \qquad \text{for } j = 1, 2, \cdots n \qquad (2\text{--}27)$$

These n equations are solved simultaneously with the constraint equation for the values of dx_j and λ. Solving for λ gives:

$$\lambda = \pm \frac{1}{2ds} \left[\sum_{i=1}^{n} \left(\frac{\partial y}{\partial x_i} \right)^2 \right]^{1/2} \qquad (2\text{--}28)$$

and solving for dx_j gives:

$$dx_j = \pm ds \left[\sum_{i=1}^{n} \left(\frac{\partial y}{\partial x_i} \right)^2 \right]^{-1/2} \frac{\partial y}{\partial x_j} \qquad \text{for } j = 1, 2, 3, \cdots, n \qquad (2\text{--}29)$$

The term in the brackets is not a function of j, and consequently dx_j is proportional to $\partial y / \partial x_j$. The positive sign indicates the direction of steepest ascent, and the negative sign the direction of steepest descent.

If a constant k is used to represent the term in the brackets in equation (2–29), this equation can be written as:

$$dx_j = \pm k \frac{\partial y}{\partial x_j} \qquad \text{for } j = 1, 2, \cdots, n \qquad (2\text{--}30)$$

If a finite-difference approximation is used for $dx_j = (x_j - x_{j0})$ and $\partial y / \partial x_j$ is evaluated at x_0, then the following equation gives the gradient line

$$x_j = x_{j0} \pm k \frac{\partial y(x_0)}{\partial x_j} \qquad \text{for } j = 1, 2, \cdots, n \qquad (2\text{--}31)$$

This equation can be written in vector notation in terms of the gradient of y evaluated at x_0, $\nabla y(x_0)$, as

$$x = x_0 \pm k \nabla y(x_0) \qquad (2\text{--}32)$$

If the positive sign is used, then movement is along the line in the direction of steepest ascent; if the negative sign is used, then movement is along the line in the direction of steepest descent. The following example illustrates the use of the method of steepest ascent on a simple function.

EXAMPLE 2–7

Find the minimum along the direction of steepest descent for the function given below starting at the point $\mathbf{x_0} = (1, 1)$.

$$y = x_1{}^2 + x_2{}^2$$

Gradient line (steepest descent):

$$\mathbf{x} = \mathbf{x_0} - k\,\nabla y(\mathbf{x_0})$$

or for two independent variables

$$x_1 = x_{10} - k\,\frac{\partial y\,(\mathbf{x_0})}{\partial x_1}$$

$$x_2 = x_{20} - k\,\frac{\partial y\,(\mathbf{x_0})}{\partial x_2}$$

Evaluating the partial derivatives at the starting point $(1, 1)$

$$\frac{\partial y\,(\mathbf{x_0})}{\partial x_1} = 2x_{10} = 2 \qquad \frac{\partial y\,(\mathbf{x_0})}{\partial x_2} = 2x_{20} = 2$$

The gradient line is

$$x_1 = 1 - 2k$$

$$x_2 = 1 - 2k$$

Substituting the gradient line into the function to be minimized gives:

$$y = (1 - 2k)^2 + (1 - 2k)^2 = 2(1 - 2k)^2$$

Computing dy/dk will locate the minimum along the gradient line, i.e.,

$$\frac{dy}{dk} = -8(1 - 2k) = 0$$

and

$$k = \tfrac{1}{2} \text{ is the stationary point}$$

The corresponding values of x_1 and x_2 are

$$x_1 = 1 - 2(\tfrac{1}{2}) = 0 \qquad x_2 = 1 - 2(\tfrac{1}{2}) = 0$$

It turns out that the minimum along the gradient line is also the minimum for the function in this problem, because it is the sum of squares.

The method of steepest ascent is the basis for several search techniques described in Chapter 6, e.g., Steep Ascent Partan. It should be noted that when dealing with physical systems, the direction of steepest ascent (descent) may be only a direction of steep ascent (descent), depending on the scales used to represent the independent variables. This is discussed and illustrated by Wilde (5) and Wilde and Beightler (4).

ECONOMIC INTERPRETATION OF THE LAGRANGE MULTIPLIERS

The values of the Lagrange Multipliers at the optimum provide additional and important information. If the constraint equations are written with parameters b_i on the right-hand side, the Lagrange Multipliers give the change in the profit function with respect to these parameters, i.e., $\partial y / \partial b_i$. Many times, the right-hand sides of the constraint equations represent the availability of raw materials, demand for products, or capacities of process units. Consequently, it is frequently important to know how the optimal solution is affected by changes in availability, demand, and capacities. As we shall see, the Lagrange Multipliers are given the names *shadow prices* and *dual activity* in linear programming where these changes are analyzed by sensitivity analysis.

The following brief derivation obtains the result that $\partial y / \partial b = -\lambda$ for the case of one constraint and two independent variables, and the extension to m constraint equations with n independent variables is comparable

$$\left\{ \begin{array}{l} \text{optimize: } y(x_1, x_2) \\[2ex] \text{subject to: } f(x_1, x_2) = b \end{array} \right. \tag{2-33}$$

First, we can obtain the following equation from the profit function by the chain rule *[handwritten margin top: Shadow prices, dual variable, margin } Lagrange multipliers   b → Capacity of press unit, etc]*

[handwritten left: $\frac{\delta Y}{\delta b_i} = -\lambda_i$ Result]

$$\frac{\partial y}{\partial b} = \frac{\partial y}{\partial x_1}\frac{\partial x_1}{\partial b} + \frac{\partial y}{\partial x_2}\frac{\partial x_2}{\partial b} \qquad (2\text{-}34)$$

Also, we can obtain the next equation from the constraint equation written as $f - b = 0$ by the chain rule

$$\frac{\partial f}{\partial x_1}\frac{\partial x_1}{\partial b} + \frac{\partial f}{\partial x_2}\frac{\partial x_2}{\partial b} - 1 = 0 \qquad (2\text{-}35)$$

Then the equation from the constraint is multiplied by the Lagrange Multiplier and added to the equation from the profit function to give:

$$\frac{\partial y}{\partial b} = \left(\frac{\partial y}{\partial x_1} + \lambda\frac{\partial f}{\partial x_1}\right)\frac{\partial x_1}{\partial b} + \left(\frac{\partial y}{\partial x_2} + \lambda\frac{\partial f}{\partial x_2}\right)\frac{\partial x_2}{\partial b} - \lambda$$

or

$$\frac{\partial y}{\partial b} = \frac{\partial(y + \lambda f)}{\partial x_1}\frac{\partial x_1}{\partial b} + \frac{\partial(y + \lambda f)}{\partial x_2}\frac{\partial x_2}{\partial b} - \lambda$$

or

[handwritten left: $\frac{\frac{\partial Y}{\partial x_2}}{\frac{\partial f}{\partial x_2}} = \frac{\partial y}{\partial x_2}\frac{\partial x_2}{\partial f} \Rightarrow \frac{\partial y}{\partial f}$ kind of]

$$\frac{\partial y}{\partial b} = \frac{\partial L}{\partial x_1}\frac{\partial x_1}{\partial b} + \frac{\partial L}{\partial x_2}\frac{\partial x_2}{\partial b} - \lambda = -\lambda \qquad (2\text{-}36)$$

The values of $\partial L/\partial x_1$ and $\partial L/\partial x_2$ are zero at the stationary point (necessary conditions), and consequently $\partial y/\partial b = -\lambda$. Thus, the change in the profit function y with respect to the right-hand side of the constraint b is equal to the negative of the Lagrange Multiplier. Also, comparable results can be obtained for the case of n independent variables and m constraint equations to obtain the following result using a similar procedure and arguments (7)

[handwritten: How chng in optim Sln is affected by avails, capacity, demand, etc... →]

[handwritten right: Shadow price, dual var, margin]

$$\frac{\partial y}{\partial b_i} = -\lambda_i \quad [\$/\text{unit}] \qquad (2\text{-}37)$$

In the next section, we will see that the Lagrange Multiplier is also a key factor in the analysis of problems with inequality constraints.

INEQUALITY CONSTRAINTS

An additional complication arises when seeking the optimum value of a profit or cost function if inequality constraints are included. Although the same procedures are used, it will be necessary to consider two cases for each inequality constraint equation. One case is when the Lagrange Multiplier is zero, and the other is when the Lagrange Multiplier is not zero. This is best illustrated by the following example, with one inequality constraint equation as shown below

$f(x) + x_s^2 = 0$ Slack var

Optimize: $y(\mathbf{x})$

Subject to: $f(\mathbf{x}) \leq 0$ (2–38)

As described previously, the procedure is to add a slack variable x_s as x_s^2 and form the Lagrangian function:

$$L(\mathbf{x}, \lambda) = y(\mathbf{x}) + \lambda \left[f(\mathbf{x}) + x_s^2 \right] \quad (2\text{–}39)$$

Then the first partial derivatives with respect to the x_i's, x_s, and λ are set equal to zero to have a set of equations to be solved for the stationary points. To illustrate the complication, the equation obtained for the slack variable is:

$\dfrac{\partial L}{\partial x_j} = 0$

$\dfrac{\partial L}{\partial \lambda} = 0$ const Egusback

$$\frac{\partial L}{\partial x_s} = 2\lambda x_s = 0$$

or

$\dfrac{\partial L}{\partial x_s} = 2\lambda x_s$

$\lambda x_s = 0$ (2–40)

The result is two cases, i.e., either $\lambda = 0$ and $x_s \neq 0$, or $\lambda \neq 0$ and $x_s = 0$. If $\lambda = 0$ and $x_s \neq 0$, the inequality holds, and the constraint is said to be *loose*, *passive*, or *inactive*. If $\lambda \neq 0$ and $x_s = 0$, then the equality holds, and the constraint is said to be *tight* or *active*. The following example illustrates this situation using a modification of the previous simple process.

EXAMPLE 2–8

Look @ this Example

For the process the cost function is:

$$C = 1000P + 4 \times 10^9/PR + 2.5 \times 10^5 R$$

However, C is subject to the inequality constraint equation

$$PR \leq 9000$$

Adding the slack variable S, as S^2, and forming the Lagrangian function gives: $L = y + \lambda f$

$$L = 1000P + 4 \times 10^9/PR + 2.5 \times 10^5\, R + \lambda(PR + S^2 - 9000)$$

Setting the first partial derivatives of L with respect to P, R, S, and λ equal to zero gives the following four equations:

$$\frac{\partial L}{\partial P} = 1000 - \frac{4 \times 10^9}{P^2 R} + \lambda R = 0$$

$$\frac{\partial L}{\partial R} = 2.5 \times 10^5 - \frac{4 \times 10^9}{PR^2} + \lambda P = 0$$

$$\frac{\partial L}{\partial S} = 2\lambda S = 0$$

$$\frac{\partial L}{\partial \lambda} = PR + S^2 - 9000 = 0$$

The two cases are $\lambda \neq 0$, $S = 0$ and $\lambda = 0$, $S \neq 0$. For the case of $\lambda \neq 0$, $S = 0$ the equality $PR = 9000$ holds, i.e., the constraint is active. This was the solution obtained in Example 2–6, and the results were:

$$C = \$3.44 \times 10^6 \text{ per year} \qquad P = 1500 \text{ psi} \qquad R = 6 \qquad \lambda = -117.3$$

For the case of $\lambda = 0$, $S \neq 0$, the constraint is an inequality, i.e., inactive. This was the solution obtained in Example 2–2, and the results were:

$$C = \$3.0 \times 10^6 \text{ per year} \qquad P = 1000 \text{ psi} \qquad R = 4 \qquad S = (5000)^{1/2}$$

The example above had only one inequality constraint and two cases to consider. However, with several inequality constraints, locating the stationary points can become time-consuming, for the possibilities must be searched exhaustively. A procedure for this evaluation has been given by Cooper (7) and Walsh (8), as follows:

1. Solve the problem of optimizing: $y(\mathbf{x})$, ignoring the inequality constraints, i.e., having all positive slack variables. Designate this solution $\mathbf{x}_0$. If $\mathbf{x}_0$ satisfies the constraints as inequalities, an optimum has been found.

2. If one or more constraints are not satisfied, select one of the constraints to be an equality, i.e., active (the slack variable for this constraint is zero), and solve the problem. Call this solution x_1. If x_1 satisfies all the constraints, an optimum has been found.
3. If one or more constraints are not satisfied, repeat step 2 until every inequality constraint has been treated as an equality constraint (slack variable being zero) in turn.
4. If step 3 did not yield an optimum, select combinations of two inequality constraints at a time to be equalities, and solve the problem. If one of these solutions satisfies all the constraints, an optimum has been found.
5. If step 4 did not yield an optimum, select combinations of three inequality constraints at a time to be equalities, and solve the problem. If one of these solutions satisfies all the constraints, an optimum has been found. If not, try combinations of four inequality constraints at a time to be equalities, etc.

The above procedure applies, assuming that the stationary point located is a maximum or a minimum of the constrained problem. However, there is a possibility that several stationary points will be located; some could be maxima, some minima, and others saddle points. In Problem 2.6, four stationary points were found; two are maxima, one a minimum, and one a saddle point. Also, from equation (2–40) for each inequality constraint where the strict inequality holds, the slack variable is positive, and the Lagrange Multiplier is zero. For each inequality constraint where the equality holds, the slack variable is zero, and the Lagrange Multiplier is not zero.

In the next section necessary and sufficient conditions for constrained problems are described to determine the character of stationary points. This will be similar to and an extension of the previous discussion for unconstrained problems.

NECESSARY AND SUFFICIENT CONDITIONS FOR CONSTRAINED PROBLEMS

The necessary conditions have been developed by Kuhn and Tucker (14) for a general nonlinear optimization problem with equality and inequality constraints. This optimization problem, written in terms of minimizing $y(\mathbf{x})$, is:

$$x_n = x_1$$

$$\text{Minimize: } y(\mathbf{x}) \tag{2–41}$$

$$\text{Subject to: } f_i(x) \leq 0 \qquad \text{for } i = 1, 2, \cdots, h \tag{2–42}$$

$$f_i(\mathbf{x}) = 0 \qquad \text{for } i = h + 1, \cdots, m \tag{2–43}$$

where $y(\mathbf{x})$ and $f_i(\mathbf{x})$ are twice continuously differentiable real-valued functions.

Any value of $\mathbf{x}$ that satisfies the constraint equations (2–42) and (2–43) is called a feasible solution to the problem in the Kuhn-Tucker theory. Then to locate points that can potentially be local minima of equation (2–41) and satisfy the constraint equations (2–42) and (2–43), the Kuhn-Tucker necessary conditions are used. These conditions are written in terms of the Lagrangian function for the problem, which is: *Surplus Vars*

$$L(\mathbf{x}, \lambda) = y(\mathbf{x}) + \sum_{i=1}^{h} \lambda_i \left[f_i(\mathbf{x}) + x_{n+i}{}^2 \right] + \sum_{i=h+1}^{m} \lambda_i f_i(\mathbf{x}) \qquad (2\text{–}44)$$

where the x_{n+i}'s are the surplus variables used to convert the inequality constraints to equalities.

The necessary conditions for a constrained minimum are given by the following theorem (7, 8, 10, 14).

To minimize $y(\mathbf{x})$ *subject to* $f_i(\mathbf{x}) \leq 0$, $i = 1, 2, \cdots,$ h *and* $f_i(\mathbf{x}) = 0$, i $= h + 1, \cdots,$ m, *the necessary conditions for the existence of a relative minimum at* $\mathbf{x}^*$ *are:*

$\dfrac{\partial L(x^b)}{\partial x_i}$

1. $\dfrac{\partial y(\mathbf{x}^*)}{\partial x_j} + \sum\limits_{i=1}^{h} \lambda_i \dfrac{\partial f_i(\mathbf{x}^*)}{\partial x_j} + \sum\limits_{i=h+1}^{m} \lambda_i \dfrac{\partial f_i(\mathbf{x}^*)}{\partial x_j} = 0 \quad$ for $j = 1, 2, \cdots, n$ *set 1st part dev of Lagrang func = 0*

2. $f_i(\mathbf{x}^*) \leq 0 \quad$ for $i = 1, 2, \cdots, h$ $\dfrac{\partial L(x^b)}{\partial x_j} = \dfrac{\partial y(x^b)}{\partial x_j} + \sum\limits_i^n \lambda_i \dfrac{\partial f}{\partial x_1} x^*$

3. $f_i(\mathbf{x}^*) = 0 \quad$ for $i = h+1, \cdots, m$

Complementary Slackness Conds (2–45)

4. $\lambda_i f_i(\mathbf{x}^*) = 0 \quad$ for $i = 1, 2, \cdots, h$ — *for* $\lambda_i \, x_{ni} = 0$ / *either* $\lambda_i = 0 \quad x_{n+i} \neq 0$ (*Inactive Constraint*) / *or* $\lambda_i \neq 0 \quad x_{n+i} = 0$ (*Active Constraint*)

→ *For min*

$f_i(x) \leq 0$ *necessary for this*

5. $\lambda_i \geq 0 \quad$ for $i = 1, 2, \cdots, h$ *Inequality Constraints*

6. λ_i *is unrestricted in sign for* $i = h+1, \cdots, m$ *Gives necessary conds, now need sufficient conds*

Examining these conditions, the first one is setting the first partial derivatives of the Lagrangian function with respect to the independent variables $x_1, x_2, \cdots, x_n$ equal to zero to locate the Kuhn-Tucker point, ($\mathbf{x}^*$.) The second and third conditions are repeating the inequality and equality constraint equations that must be satisfied at the minimum of the constrained problem. The fourth condition is another way of expressing $\lambda_i x_{n+i} = 0$, $i = 1, 2, \cdots,$ h from setting the partial derivatives of the Lagrangian function with respect to the surplus variables equal to zero. Either $\lambda_i \neq 0$ and $x_{n+i} = 0$ (constraint is active) or $\lambda_i = 0$ and $x_{n+i} \neq 0$ (constraint is inactive). Thus, the product of the Lagrange Multiplier and the constraint equation set equal to zero is an equivalent statement, and this is called the _complementary slackness condition_ (15). The fifth condition comes from examining equation (2–37), i.e., $\partial y(\mathbf{x}^*)/\partial b_i = -\lambda_i$. The argument is that as b_i is increased, the constraint region is enlarged; and this cannot result in a higher value for $y(\mathbf{x}^*)$, the minimum in the region. However, it could result in a lower value of $y(\mathbf{x}^*)$; and correspondingly $\partial y(\mathbf{x}^*)/\partial b_i$ would be negative, i.e., as b_i increases, $y(\mathbf{x}^*)$ could decrease. Therefore, if $\partial y(\mathbf{x}^*)/\partial b_i$ is negative, then the Lagrange Multiplier, λ_i, must be positive for equation (2–37) to be satisfied. This condition is called a _constraint qualification,_ as will be discussed subsequently. For the sixth condition, it has been shown by Bazaraa and Shetty (15) that the Lagrange Multipliers associated with the equality constraints are unrestricted in sign, and there is not an argument comparable to the one given above for the Lagrange Multipliers associated with the inequality constraints.

For the problem of maximizing $y(\mathbf{x})$ subject to inequality and equality constraints, the problem is as follows:

$$\text{Maximize: } y(\mathbf{x}) \tag{2–46}$$

$$\text{Subject to: } f_i(\mathbf{x}) \leq 0 \qquad \text{for } i = 1, 2, \cdots, h \tag{2–47}$$

$$f_i(\mathbf{x}) = 0 \qquad \text{for } i = h+1, \cdots, m \tag{2–48}$$

For this problem the Kuhn-Tucker conditions are:

1. $\dfrac{\partial y(\mathbf{x}^*)}{\partial x_j} + \sum\limits_{i=1}^{h} \lambda_i \dfrac{\partial f_i(\mathbf{x}^*)}{\partial x_j} + \sum\limits_{i=h+1}^{m} \lambda_i \dfrac{\partial f_i(\mathbf{x}^*)}{\partial x_j} = 0 \qquad \text{for } j = 1, 2, \cdots, n$

2. $f_i(\mathbf{x}^*) \leq 0 \qquad \text{for } i = 1, 2, \cdots, h$

3. $f_i(\mathbf{x}^*) = 0 \qquad \text{for } i = h+1, \cdots, m$ $\qquad\qquad$ (2–49)

4. $\lambda_i f_i(\mathbf{x}^*) = 0 \qquad \text{for } i = 1, 2, \cdots, h$

5. $\lambda_i \leq 0 \qquad \text{for } i = 1, 2, \cdots, h$
   $\quad \hookrightarrow$ For max

6. λ_i is unrestricted in sign for $i = h+1, \cdots, m$

These conditions are the same as the ones for minimizing given by equation (2–45), except the inequality is reversed for the Lagrange Multipliers in the fifth condition. Also, the inequality constraints are written as less than or equal to zero for convenience in the subsequent discussion on sufficient conditions.

The following example illustrates the Kuhn-Tucker necessary conditions for a simple problem.

EXAMPLE 2–9

Locate the five Kuhn-Tucker points of the following problem, and determine their character, i.e., maximum, minimum, or saddle point.

$$\text{optimize:} \quad y = x_1 x_2$$

$$\text{subject to:} \quad x_1 + x_2 \leq 1$$

$$-x_1 + x_2 \leq 1$$

$$-x_1 - x_2 \leq 1$$

$$x_1 - x_2 \leq 1$$

A diagram of the above equations is given in Figure 2-6. The function being optimized is the classic saddle point function that is constrained by planes. The first step in the procedure is to locate the stationary points by ignoring the inequality constraints, i.e., $\lambda_1 = \lambda_2 = \lambda_3 = \lambda_4 = 0$. If this point satisfies the constraints as inequalities, an optimum may have been found. For this problem:

$$\frac{\partial y}{\partial x_1} = x_2 = 0 \qquad \frac{\partial y}{\partial x_2} = x_1 = 0$$

The Kuhn-Tucker point is x_0 $(0, 0)$, and evaluating its character by the unconstrained sufficiency conditions gives the following result:

$$\frac{\partial^2 y}{\partial x_1^2} = 0 \qquad \frac{\partial^2 y}{\partial x_2^2} = 0 \qquad \frac{\partial^2 y}{\partial x_1 x_2} = 1 \qquad \frac{\partial^2 y}{\partial x_2 x_1} = 1$$
$$\qquad\qquad\qquad\qquad\qquad\qquad y_{x_1 x_2} \qquad\qquad y_{x_2 x_1}$$

and

see pg 15

$$|H_1| = 0 \qquad |H_2| = \begin{vmatrix} 0 & 1 \\ 1 & 0 \end{vmatrix} = -1$$

Conds don't hold So saddle pt

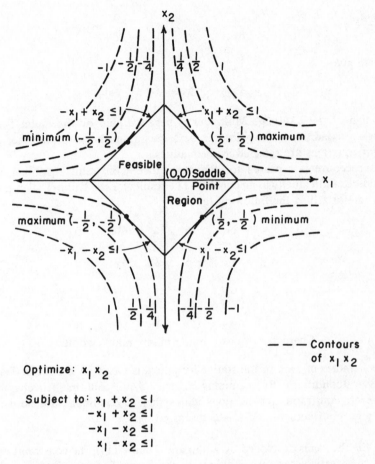

Figure 2-6. Diagram of optimization problem given in Example 2-9.

The point $\mathbf{x}_0$ (0, 0) is a saddle point, and the constraints are satisfied. Proceeding to step 2, one constraint equation at a time is selected, and the character of the Kuhn-Tucker point is determined. Beginning with the first constraint equation as an equality, i.e., $\lambda_1 \neq 0$, and considering the other three as inequalities, i.e., $\lambda_2 = \lambda_3 = \lambda_4 = 0$, gives the following equation for the Lagrangian function: $L = y + \lambda f$

$$L(x_1, x_2, \lambda_1) = x_1 x_2 + \lambda_1(x_1 + x_2 - 1)$$

and

$$\frac{\partial L}{\partial x_1} = x_2 + \lambda_1 = 0 \qquad \frac{\partial L}{\partial x_2} = x_1 + \lambda_1 = 0 \qquad \frac{\partial L}{\partial \lambda} = x_1 + x_2 - 1 = 0$$

Solving gives:

$$x_1 = \frac{1}{2}, \qquad x_2 = \frac{1}{2} \qquad \lambda = -\frac{1}{2} \qquad y(\frac{1}{2}, \frac{1}{2}) = \frac{1}{4}$$

The sign of the Lagrange Multiplier is negative, and by the Kuhn-Tucker necessary conditions, the point can be a maximum, because the other constraint equations are satisfied as inequalities.

The procedure is repeated for the other three constraint equations, each considered individually as an equality. The results for the Kuhn-Tucker points are summarized in the following table:

$y:$	$\frac{1}{4}$	$-\frac{1}{4}$	$\frac{1}{4}$	$-\frac{1}{4}$	0
$x_1:$	$\frac{1}{2}$	$-\frac{1}{2}$	$-\frac{1}{2}$	$\frac{1}{2}$	0
$x_2:$	$\frac{1}{2}$	$\frac{1}{2}$	$-\frac{1}{2}$	$-\frac{1}{2}$	0
$\lambda:$	$-\frac{1}{2}$	$\frac{1}{2}$	$-\frac{1}{2}$	$\frac{1}{2}$	0
Character:	max	min	max	min	saddle

The character of each of the stationary points is based on the Kuhn-Tucker necessary conditions. By examining Figure 2-5, we confirm their character. However, constraint qualifications and sufficient conditions are needed to give a general method, and this is discussed next.

In the theorems developed by Kuhn and Tucker (14), the constraint equations must satisfy certain conditions at the Kuhn-Tucker points, and these conditions are called *constraint qualifications*. As given in Bazaraa and Shetty (15), there are several forms of constraint qualifications, and one, according to Gill et al. (16), is important for nonlinear constraints. This is the condition that the gradients of the constraint equations at the Kuhn-Tucker point are linearly independent. This constraint qualification is required for the necessary conditions given by equations (2–45) and (2–49). As an example, Kuhn and Tucker (14) constructed the constraint equations:

$$f_1 = (1 - x_1)^3 - x_2 \geq 0$$

$$f_2 = x_1 \geq 0$$

$$f_3 = x_2 \geq 0$$

These do not satisfy this condition at point $x_2^* = 1$ and $x_2^* = 0$. At this point $\nabla f_1 = [-3(1 - x_1)^2, -1] = (0, -1)$, $\nabla f_2 = (1, 0)$, and $\nabla f_3 = (0, 1)$ are not linearly independent. At such a point as this one, the necessary condition may fail to hold, and Kuhn and Tucker (14) give arguments that this constraint qualification is required to ensure the existence of the Lagrange multipliers at the optimum point. Verification of the constraint qualifications for a general nonlinear programming problem is almost an impossible task according to Avriel (10). He states that fortunately in practice constraint qualification usually holds, and it is justifiable to use the existence of the Lagrange Multipliers as a basis for having the necessary conditions hold.

The same concepts used for unconstrained problems are followed to develop the sufficient conditions for constrained problems. This involves expanding the Lagrangian function in a Taylor Series about the Kuhn-Tucker point located using the necessary conditions. The Taylor Series is simplified by neglecting third- and higher order terms to give a function that contains only terms involving second partial derivatives evaluated at the Kuhn-Tucker point. This gives a differential quadratic form, and a test similar to the one for the unconstrained problem is obtained to determine if the Kuhn-Tucker point is a maximum, minimum, or saddle. The sufficient conditions for the case of both inequality and equality constraints are more elaborate than if only equality constraints are involved. We have space to give only the appropriate theorems and describe their development and use. Further details are given by Avriel (10), Bazaraa and Shetty (15), and Reklaitis et al. (17).

Considering the case of only equality constraints first, the Lagrangian function for n independent variables and m equality constraint equations is given by the following equation:

$$L(\mathbf{x}, \boldsymbol{\lambda}) = y(\mathbf{x}) + \sum_{i=1}^{m} \lambda_i f_i(\mathbf{x}) \tag{2--50}$$

Expanding the Lagrangian function in a Taylor Series about the Kuhn-Tucker point $\mathbf{x}^*$ gives:

$$L(\mathbf{x}, \boldsymbol{\lambda}) = L(\mathbf{x}^*, \boldsymbol{\lambda}) + \sum_{i=1}^{n} L_{x_i}(\mathbf{x}^*, \boldsymbol{\lambda})(x_i - x_i^*)$$

$$+ \tfrac{1}{2}\left[\sum_{j=1}^{n} \sum_{k=1}^{n} L_{x_j x_k}(\mathbf{x}^*, \boldsymbol{\lambda})(x_j - x_j^*)(x_k - x_k^*) \right] + \begin{array}{l} \text{higher order} \\ \text{terms} \end{array} \tag{2--51}$$

This equation is comparable to equation (2–8), and subscripts x_i, x_j, and x_k indicate partial differentiation with respect to those variables. Again, the first partial derivatives are zero at the Kuhn-Tucker point by the necessary conditions, and x is selected sufficiently close to **x***, such that the higher order terms are negligible when compared with the second-order terms. This gives the following equation, which is comparable to equation (2–9) for the unconstrained case

$$L(\mathbf{x}, \lambda) = L(\mathbf{x}^*, \lambda) + \tfrac{1}{2}\left[\sum_{j=1}^{n} \sum_{k=1}^{n} L_{x_j x_k} (\mathbf{x}^*, \lambda)(x_j - x_j{}^*)(x_k - x_k{}^*) \right] \quad (2\text{–}52)$$

As previously, we need to determine if the term in the brackets remains positive (minimum), remains negative (maximum), or changes sign (saddle point) for small feasible changes in x about **x***. The term in the bracket is a differential quadratic form.

To determine if the quadratic form is always positive or always negative, results comparable to those given by equation (2–7) are required, with the extension that the constraints also be satisfied, i.e., for feasible values of **x**. A theorem given by Avriel (10) establishes these conditions, and this theorem is then applied to the differential quadratic form of the Lagrangian function. The result, after Avriel (10), is the following theorem for the sufficient conditions of the optimization problem with only equality constraints. In this theorem the second partial derivatives of the Lagrangian function evaluated at the Kuhn-Tucker point **x*** are $L_{x_j x_k}$ (**x***, λ^*) and are written as L_{jk}. Also, first partial derivatives of the constraint equations evaluated at the Kuhn-Tucker point **x*** are ∂f_j (**x***)$/\partial x_k$ and are written f_{jk}.

Let $y(\mathbf{x})$ *and* $f_i(\mathbf{x}) = 0$, $i = 1, 2, \cdots, m$, *be twice continuously differentiable real-valued functions. If there exist vectors* **x*** *and* λ^*, *such that:*

$$L_i (\mathbf{x}^*, \lambda^*) = 0, \qquad i = 1, 2, \cdots, n$$

and if:

$$D_p = (-1)^m \begin{vmatrix} L_{11}, & \cdots, & L_{1p}, & f_{11}, & \cdots, & f_{m1} \\ \vdots & & \vdots & \vdots & & \vdots \\ L_{1p}, & \cdots, & L_{pp}, & f_{1p}, & \cdots, & f_{mp} \\ f_{11}, & \cdots, & f_{1p}, & 0, & \cdots, & 0 \\ \vdots & & \vdots & \vdots & & \vdots \\ f_{m1}, & \cdots, & f_{mp}, & 0, & \cdots, & 0 \end{vmatrix}$$

for $p = m + 1, \cdots, n$, *then* $y(\mathbf{x}^*)$ *has a strict local minimum at* **x***, *such that:*

$$f_i(\mathbf{x}^*) = 0, \qquad i = 1, 2, \cdots, m$$

The proof of this theorem is given by Avriel (10) and follows the discussion of the concepts given above. The comparable result for a strict maxima is obtained by changing $(-1)^m$ in the above theorem to $(-1)^p$, according to Avriel (10). The following example illustrates the application of this theorem.

EXAMPLE 2–10

Consider the following problem:

$$\text{Optimize: } x_1^2 + 2x_2^2 + 3x_3^2$$

$$\text{Subject to: } x_1 + 2x_2 + 4x_3 - 12 = 0$$

$$2x_1 + x_2 + 3x_3 - 10 = 0$$

Forming the Lagrangian function and differentiating with respect to x_1, x_2, x_3, λ_1, and λ_2 gives the following set of equations to be solved for the Kuhn-Tucker point:

$$L_{x_1} = 2x_1 + \lambda_1 + 2\lambda_2 = 0$$

$$L_{x_2} = 4x_2 + 2\lambda_1 + \lambda_2 = 0$$

$$L_{x_3} = 6x_3 + 4\lambda_1 + 3\lambda_2 = 0$$

$$L_{\lambda_1} = x_1 + 2x_2 + 4x_3 - 12 = 0$$

$$L_{\lambda_2} = 2x_1 + x_2 + 3x_3 - 10 = 0$$

Solving the above equation set simultaneously gives the following values for the Kuhn-Tucker point.

$$x_1 = 112/81, \qquad x_2 = 118/81, \qquad x_3 = 52/17,$$
$$\lambda_1 = -80/27, \qquad \lambda_2 = 8/81$$

From the necessary conditions of equations (2–45) or (2–49), the Lagrange Multipliers are unrestricted in sign, and the value of the determinants from the theorem on sufficiency conditions is required to determine the character of this point. The partial derivatives needed for this evaluation are:

$$L_{11}=2 \qquad L_{12}=0 \qquad L_{13}=0$$

$$L_{21}=0 \qquad L_{22}=4 \qquad L_{23}=0$$

$$L_{31}=0 \qquad L_{32}=0 \qquad L_{33}=6$$

$$f_{11}=1 \qquad f_{12}=2 \qquad f_{13}=4$$

$$f_{21}=2 \qquad f_{22}=1 \qquad f_{23}=3$$

The determinant is ($m = 2$, $n = 3$, $p = 3$, only one in this case):

$$D_3 = (-1)^2 \begin{vmatrix} 2 & 0 & 0 & 1 & 2 \\ 0 & 4 & 0 & 2 & 1 \\ 0 & 0 & 6 & 4 & 3 \\ 1 & 2 & 4 & 0 & 0 \\ 2 & 1 & 3 & 0 & 0 \end{vmatrix} = 162$$

The value of D_3 is positive, and the Kuhn-Tucker point is a minimum.

The sufficient conditions for problems with equality and inequality constraints, equations (2–41), (2–42), and (2–43), are summarized in the following theorem. There are a number of mathematical concepts and theorems required to obtain this result. These are given in some detail by Avriel (10), Bazaraa and Shetty (15), and Reklaitis et al. (17); it is not feasible to describe them in the space available here.

Let y (x), f_i (x) $\geq$ 0, $i = 1, 2, \cdots$, h, *and* f_i (x) = 0, $i = h + 1, \cdots$, m *be twice continuously differentiable real-valued functions. If there exist vectors* x* *and* λ* *satisfying*

$$\frac{\partial L}{\partial x_j} = \frac{\partial y}{\partial x_j}(\mathbf{x}^*) - \sum_{i=1}^{h} \lambda_i \frac{\partial f_i}{\partial x_j}(\mathbf{x}^*) - \sum_{i=h+1}^{m} \lambda_i \frac{\partial f_i}{\partial x_j}(\mathbf{x}^*) = 0 \, j = 1, 2, \cdots, n$$

$$\lambda_i f_i(\mathbf{x}^*) = 0 \qquad i = 1, 2, \cdots, h$$
$$\lambda_i \geq 0 \qquad i = 1, 2, \cdots, h$$

and for every z $\neq$ 0 *such that:*

$$\sum_{j=1}^{n} z_j \frac{\partial f_i}{\partial x_j}(\mathbf{x}^*) \geq 0 \qquad i = 1, 2, \cdots, h$$

$$\sum_{j=1}^{n} z_j \frac{\partial f_i}{\partial x_j} (\mathbf{x}^*) = 0 \qquad i = h+1, \cdots, m$$

it follows that:

$$\sum_{j=1}^{n} \sum_{k=1}^{n} \frac{\partial^2 L}{\partial x_j \, \partial x_k} (\mathbf{x}^*, \lambda^*) z_j z_k > 0$$

then $\mathbf{x}^*$ *is a strict local minimum.*

The following example illustrates the application of this theorem.

EXAMPLE 2–11

Consider the following problem after Reklaitis et al. (17):

$$\text{Minimize: } (x_1 - 1)^2 + x_2^2$$

$$\text{Subject to: } -x_1 + x_2^2 \geq 0$$

Applying the theorem gives:

$$2(x_1 - 1) + \lambda = 0$$

$$2x_2 - 2x_2\lambda = 0$$

$$\lambda(-x_1 + x_2^2) = 0$$
$$\lambda \geq 0$$

Solving this set of equations gives $x_1 = 0$, $x_2 = 0$, $\lambda = 2$ for the Kuhn-Tucker point. Then applying the sufficient conditions gives the following results at $\mathbf{x}^* = (0, 0)$:

$$2z_1^2 - 2z_2^2 > 0$$

However, for all finite values of $\mathbf{z}$, the above inequalities cannot be satisfied, and the second-order sufficiency conditions show that the point is not a minimum.

In summary, the necessary and sufficient conditions for nonlinear programming problems have been described and illustrated with examples. References have been given for more details for this theory.

An important special case is when the economic model is concave, and all the constraint equations are convex and are inequalities. This is known as *convex programming.* "A function is concave if linear interpolation between its values at any two points of definition yields a value not greater than its actual value at the point of interpolation; such a function is the negative of a convex function" according to Kuhn and Tucker (14). Thus, the convex programming problem can be stated as follows:

$$\text{maximize: } y(\mathbf{x}) \tag{2-53}$$

$$\text{subject to: } f_i(\mathbf{x}) \le 0 \qquad \text{for } i = 1, 2, \cdots, m \tag{2-54}$$

The necessary and sufficient conditions for the maximum of concave function $y(\mathbf{x})$ subject to convex constraints $f_i(\mathbf{x}) \le 0$, $i = 1, 2, \cdots, m$ are the Kuhn-Tucker conditions given below as:

$$1. \ \frac{\partial L}{\partial x_j}(\mathbf{x}^*, \boldsymbol{\lambda}^*) = 0 \qquad j = 1, 2, \cdots, n$$

$$2. \ \lambda_i f_i(\mathbf{x}^*) = 0 \qquad i = 1, 2, \cdots, m \tag{2-55}$$

$$3. \ \lambda_i \le 0 \qquad i = 1, 2, \cdots, m$$

$$4. \ f_i(\mathbf{x}^*) \le 0 \qquad i = 1, 2, \cdots, m$$

The theorem from from Cooper (7) that establishes the above result is:

If $y(\mathbf{x})$ *is a strictly concave function and* $f_i(\mathbf{x})$, $i = 1, 2, \cdots$, m, *are convex functions that are continuous and differentiable, then the Kuhn-Tucker conditions (2-49) are sufficient as well as necessary for a global maximum.*

The proof of this theorem uses the definition of convex and concave functions and the fact that the Lagrangian function can be formulated as the sum of concave functions, which is concave.

These concepts and results for the Kuhn-Tucker conditions and those given previously will be valuable in our discussion of modern optimization procedures in the following chapters. Those interested in further theoretical results are referred to the references at the end of this chapter and Chapter 6. Also, in industrial practice we will see that the concepts from the Kuhn-Tucker conditions are used in computer programs for advanced multivariable search methods to optimize economic and process models that are too elaborate for the algebraic manipulations required to use these theories directly.

CLOSURE

In the chapter we have discussed the necessary and sufficient conditions to evaluate the character of stationary points for unconstrained and constrained optimization problems. It was necessary to confine the illustration of these procedures to simple algebraic models. Even though we are not able to apply these procedures directly to the optimization of industrial processes, the concepts developed in this chapter are used many times over in the following chapters.

It is worthwhile to attempt to solve the following unconstrained economic model from the design of horizontal vapor condensers in evaporators used in water desalination plants to see one of the major limitations of the classical theory of maxima and minima. The problem is to minimize the cost given by the following equation:

$$C = aN^{-7/6} D^{-1} L^{-4/3} + b N^{-0.2} D^{0.8} L^{-1} + c NDL$$
$$+ d N^{-1.8} D^{-4.8} L \qquad (2\text{--}56)$$

In this equation the cost is in dollars per year; N is the number of tubes in the condenser; D is the nominal diameter of the tubes in inches; L is the tube length in feet; and a, b, c, and d are coefficients that vary with the fluids involved and the construction costs. Avriel and Wilde (18) give further details about the significance of each term. This equation is typical of the form that is obtained from assembling correlations of equipment costs and related process operating conditions for preliminary cost estimates.

Differentiating this equation with respect to the three independent variables N, D, and L, and setting the results equal to zero, gives the following three equations to be solved for the values of N, D, and L that would give the minimum cost:

$$(-7a/6) N^{-13/6} D^{-1} L^{-4/3} + (-0.2b) N^{-1.2} D^{0.8} L^{-1} + cDL$$
$$+ (-1.8d) N^{-2.8} D^{-4.8} L = 0$$

$$-aN^{-7/6} D^{-2} L^{-4/3} + 0.8bN^{-0.2} D^{-0.2} L^{-1} + cNL$$
$$+ (-4.8d) N^{-1.8}D^{-5.8} L = 0 \qquad (2\text{--}57)$$

$$(-4a/3)N^{-7/6} D^{-2} L^{-7/5} - N^{-0.2} D^{0.8} L^{-2} + cND$$
$$+ dN^{-1.8} D^{-4.8} = 0$$

There is no straightforward way to solve this relatively complicated set of three nonlinear algebraic equations other than numerically with a root-finding procedure at this point. This then illustrates one of the major limitations with classical methods, i.e., if the variables in the economic model have fractional exponents, then a set of nonlinear algebraic equations are obtained that will probably require an iterative solution using a computer. However, as will be seen in the next chapter on geometric programming, we will be able to obtain the optimal solution for this economic model by solving a set of linear algebraic equations. We will take advantage of the mathematical structure of the problems to be able to find the optimum readily. In fact, this will be true of most of the modern methods; they take advantage of the mathematical structure of the optimization problem to quickly find the best values of the independent variables and the maximum profit or minimum cost.

REFERENCES

1. Hancock, H., *Theory of Maxima and Minima,* Dover Publications, Inc., New York (1960).
2. Wilde, D. J., *Ind. Eng. Chem.,* 57(8):18 (1965).
3. Smith, C. L., R. W. Pike, and P. W. Murrill, *Formulation and Optimization of Mathematical Models,* International Textbook Co., Scranton, Pa. (1970).
4. Wilde, D. J., and C. S. Beightler, *Foundations of Optimization,* Prentice-Hall, Inc., Englewood Cliffs, N. J. (1967).
5. Wilde, D. J., *Optimum Seeking Methods,* Prentice-Hall Inc., Englewood Cliffs, N. J. (1965).
6. Beveridge, G. S. G., and R. S. Schechter, *Optimization Theory and Practice,* McGraw-Hill Book Co., New York (1970).
7. Cooper, L., *Mathematical Programming for Operations Researchers and Computer Scientists,* Ed. A. G. Holtzman, Marcel Dekker, Inc., New York (1981).
8. Walsh, G. R., *Methods of Optimization,* John Wiley & Sons, Inc., New York (1979).
9. Sivazlian, B. D., and L. E. Stanfel, *Optimization Techniques in Operations Research,* Prentice-Hall, Inc., Englewood Cliffs, N. J. (1975).
10. Avriel, M. *Nonlinear Programming, Analysis and Methods,* Prentice-Hall, Inc., Englewood Cliffs, N. J. (1976).
11. Courant, R., and D. Hilbert, *Methods of Mathematical Physics,* vol. I, p. 164, Interscience Publishers, Inc., New York (1953).
12. Burley, D. M., *Studies in Optimization,* John Wiley & Sons, Inc., New York (1974).
13. Sokolnikoff, I. S., and R. M. Redheffer, *Mathematics of Physics and Modern Engineering,* 2nd Edition, McGraw-Hill Book Co., New York (1966).
14. Kuhn, H. W., and A. W. Tucker, "Nonlinear Programming," *Proceedings of the Second Berkeley Symposium on Mathematical Statistics and Probability,* Ed. Jerzy Neyman, University of California Press, Berkeley, pp. 481–92 (1951).
15. Bazaraa, M. S., and C. M. Shetty, *Nonlinear Programming—Theory and Algorithms,* John Wiley & Sons, Inc., New York (1979).
16. Gill, P. E., W. Murray, and M. H. Wright, *Practical Optimization,* Academic Press, New York (1981).
17. Reklaitis, G. V., A. Ravindran, and K. M. Ragsdell, *Engineering Optimization: Methods and Applications,* John Wiley & Sons, Inc., New York (1983).

18. Avriel, M., and D. J. Wilde, "Optimal Condenser Design by Geometric Programming," *Ind. Eng. Chem. Process Design and Development*, 6(2):256 (1967).

PROBLEMS

2-1 Locate the stationary points of the following functions and determine their character.

a. $y = x^4/2 - x^2/2$

b. $y = x^7$

c. $y = x_1^2 + x_1x_2 + x_2^2$

d. $y = 2x_1^2 + 3x_2^2 + 4x_3^2 - 8x_1 - 12x_2 - 24x_3 + 110$

2-2. Find the global maximum of the function

$$y(x_1, x_2) = 5(x_1 - 3)^2 - 12(x_2 + 5)^2 + 6x_1x_2$$

in the region

$$0 \le x_1 \le 10$$

$$0 \le x_2 \le 5$$

2-3. Use the Jacobian determinants and obtain the two equations to be solved with the constraint equation for the following problem

$$\text{Optimize: } y(x_1, x_2, x_3)$$

$$\text{Subject to: } f(x_1, x_2, x_3) = 0$$

2-4. Solve the following problem by the method of constrained variation and the method of Lagrange Multipliers, evaluating x_1, x_2, and the Lagrange Multiplier λ at the optimum:

$$\text{Maximize: } x_1 + x_2$$

$$\text{Subject to: } x_1^2 + x_2^2 = 1$$

2-5. Solve the following problem by the method of Lagrange Multipliers and give the character of the stationary point:

$$\text{Minimize: } y = 2x_1^2 - 4x_1x_2 + 4x_2^2 + x_1 - 3x_2$$

$$\text{Subject to: } 10x_1 + 5x_2 \le 3$$

2–6. Consider the following problem

$$\text{Optimize: } -x_1^2 - 2x_1 + x_2^2$$

$$\text{Subject to: } x_1^2 + x_2^2 - 1 \leq 0$$

a. Obtain the equation set to be solved to locate the stationary points of the above problem using the method of Lagrange Multipliers. Convert the inequality constraint to an equality constraint with the slack variable x_3 as x_3^2; *why?*

b. Show that the following are solutions to the algebraic equations obtained in (a).

Stationary Points

	A	B	C	D
x_1	$-\frac{1}{2}$	$-\frac{1}{2}$	-1	1
x_2	$\sqrt{3}/2$	$-\sqrt{3}/2$	0	0
x_3	0	0	0	0
λ	-1	-1	0	2

c. Based on the value of the function being optimized, state whether stationary points A through D are maximum, minimum, or saddle.

2–7. The cost of operation of a continuous, stirred-tank reactor is given by the following equation:

$$C_T = C_f c_{Ao} q + C_m V$$

The total operating cost C_T ($/hr) is the sum of the cost of the feed, $C_f c_{Ao} q$, and the cost of mixing, $C_m V$. The following gives the values for the reactor.

C_f = $5.00/lb-mole of A, cost of feed
c_{Ao} = 0.04 lb-mole/ft³, initial concentration of A
q = volumetric flow rate of feed to the reactor in ft³/hr
C_m = $0.30/hr-ft³, cost of mixing
V = volume of reactor in ft³

We are interested in obtaining the minimum operating cost and the optimal values of the feed rate, q; reactor volume, V; and concentration in the reactor, c_A. The following first-order reaction takes place in the reactor:

$$A \rightarrow B$$

where the rate of formation of B, r_B, is given by

$$r_B = kc_A$$

where $k = 0.1 \text{ hr}^{-1}$.

a. If 10 lb-moles per hour of B are to be produced, give the two material balance constraint equations that restrict the values of the independent variables. (There is no B in the feed stream.)

b. Form the Lagrangian function and perform the appropriate differentiation to obtain the set of equations that would be solved for the optimal values of the independent variables. How many equations and variables are obtained?

c. Solve for the optimal values of the reactor volume, V; feed rate, q; and concentration of A in the product, c_A.

2–8. Solve the following problem by the method of Lagrange Multipliers and determine the character of the stationary point:

$$\text{Optimize: } y = 2x_1^2 + 2x_1x_2 + x_2^2 - 20x_1 - 14x_2$$

$$\text{Subject to: } x_1 + 3x_2 \le 5$$

$$2x_1 - x_2 \le 4$$

2–9.[9] Solve the following problem by the method of Lagrange Multipliers and determine the character of the stationary point:

$$\text{Optimize: } (1/3)x_1 + x_2$$

$$\text{Subject to: } -x_1 + x_2 \le 0$$

$$x_1 + x_2 \le 3$$

2–10. The total feed rate to three chemical reactors in parallel is 1100 pounds per hour. Each reactor is operating with a different catalyst and conditions of temperature and pressure. The profit function for each reactor has the feed rate as the independent variable, and the parameters in the equation are determined by the catalyst and operating conditions. The profit functions for each reactor are given below:

$$P_1 = 0.2F_1 - 2(F_1/100)^2$$

$$P_2 = 0.2F_2 - 4(F_2/100)^2$$

$$P_3 = 0.2F_3 - 6(F_3/100)^2$$

Determine the maximum profit and the optimal feed rate to each reactor.

2–11. Solve the following problem by the method of Lagrange Multipliers and determine the character of the stationary points:

$$\text{Maximize: } 3x_1^2 + 2x_2^2$$

$$\text{Subject to: } x_1^2 + x_2^2 \le 25$$

$$9x_1 - x_2^2 \le 27$$

2–12. Find the stationary points of the following problem, and determine their character, i.e., maximum, minimum or saddle point:

$$\text{Optimize: } 2x_1^2 + x_2^2 - 5x_1 - 4x_2$$

$$\text{Subject to: } x_1 + 3x_2 \le 5$$

$$2x_1 - x_2 \le 4$$

2–13. The rate of return (ROR) is defined as the interest rate where the net present value (NPV) is zero for a specified number of years n and initial cash flow CF_0. This can be formulated as an optimization problem, as follows:

$$\text{minimize: } (NPV)^2$$

For the case of constant cash flows $CF_j = A$, develop the equation to determine the rate of return. The net present value is given by the following equation.

$$NPV = -|CF_0| + A[1 - (i + 1)^{-n}]/i$$

2–14. Derive the Lagrangian function for n independent variables and m constraint equations, equation (2–24). Begin by multiplying the constraint equations given in equation (2–19) by Lagrange multipliers $\lambda_1, \lambda_2, \cdots, \lambda_m$. Then add all the equations, rearrange terms, and obtain the result as equation (2–24).

2–15.[7] For sufficient conditions of the equality constraint problem to determine if the quadratic form is positive or negative definite, the signs of the roots of a polynomial can be evaluated. This characteristic polynomial is obtained by evaluating the following determinant, which includes the second partial derivatives of the Lagrangian function evaluated at the Kuhn-Tucker points, $L_{x_j x_k}$ $(\mathbf{x}^*, \lambda)$ written as L_{jk} for simplicity, and the first partial derivative of the constraint equations evaluated at the Kuhn-Tucker point, ∂f_j $(\mathbf{x}^*)/\partial x_k$ written as f_{jk} for simplicity.

$$
P(a) = \begin{vmatrix}
L_{11} - a & L_{12} & \cdots L_{1n} & f_{11} \cdots f_{m1} \\
L_{21} & L_{22} - a & \cdots L_{2n} & f_{12} \cdots f_{m2} \\
\vdots & \vdots & \vdots & \vdots \\
L_{n1} & L_{n2} & \cdots L_{nn} - a & f_{1n} \cdots f_{mn} \\
f_{11} & f_{12} & f_{1n} & 0 \cdots 0 \\
\vdots & \vdots & \vdots & \vdots \\
f_{m1} & f_{m2} & f_{mn} & 0 \cdots 0
\end{vmatrix}
$$

The following results are used to evaluate the type of stationary points. First, evaluate the roots of $P(a)$ using the above equation. If each root of $P(a)$ is positive, then $\mathbf{x}^*$ is a minimum. If each root of $P(a)$ is negative, then $\mathbf{x}^*$ is a maximum. Finally, if the roots are of mixed sign, then $\mathbf{x}^*$ is a saddle point.

Use the results given in Example 2–10 in the above determinant, and confirm the character of the Kuhn-Tucker point by this method. (There is a comparable sufficient condition test for the unconstrained problem that is described by Sivazlian and Stanfel (9).)

3
GEOMETRIC PROGRAMMING

INTRODUCTION

In 1961 Clarence M. Zener, Director of Science at Westinghouse, published the first of several papers on a new optimization technique he had discovered while working on the optimal design of transformers (1). These papers attracted the attention of Professor D. J. Wilde of Stanford University, and in 1963 he described them to the author of this textbook who obtained copies from Dr. Zener. In this work, Dr. Zener used the mathematical result called Cauchy's arithmetic-geometric inequality, which showed that the arithmetic mean of a group of terms always was greater than or equal to the geometric mean of the group, and he was able to convert the optimization of the nonlinear economic model for transformer design to one of solving a set of linear algebraic equations to obtain the optimum. The use of Cauchy's arithmetic-geometric inequality led to the name of geometric programming for the technique.

Two relatively parallel and somewhat independent efforts began to expand and extend the ideas about geometric programming. These were by Zener and colleagues and by Wilde and his students. A professor of mathematics at Carnegie Mellon University, Richard Duffin, began collaborating with Zener to extend the procedure. They were joined by Elmor Peterson, a Ph.D. student of Duffin. In 1967 Duffin, Peterson, and Zener published a text on their work, entitled *Geometric Programming* (2). In this work the economic model was limited to minimizing the cost of the sum of positive terms.

Wilde and his student Ury Passey developed the theory for negative coefficients and inequality constraints using Lagrange methods (3). This research went directly into the text *Foundations of Optimization,* which was published in 1967, and the result is that geometric programming is now applicable to a polynomial economic model with polynomial constraints as equalities and inequalities.

Four other books have followed the publication of those mentioned above. Zener followed with a book entitled *Engineering Design by Geometric Programming* in 1971 (4). Nijhamp wrote a book on the subject, entitled *Planning of Industrial Complexes by Means of Geometric Programming,* in 1972. The third and fourth volumes, completely covering the theory and application of the subject, were *Applied Geometric Programming* by Beightler and Phillips

(6), published in 1976, and *Globally Optimal Design* by Wilde (14), published in 1978.

The more important results for this optimization procedure will be described in this book, which will take us through unconstrained polynomial optimization. This will show the advantages and disadvantages of the techniques and how the method capitalizes on the mathematical structure of the optimization problem. Also, this will give those who are interested the ability to proceed with additional material on the topic given in the previously mentioned books without significant difficulty. Beginning with posynomial optimization, we will then proceed to polynomial optimization. We will find that the global minimum is obtained with posynomials, but only local stationary points are obtained when the economic model is a polynomial. Our approach will follow that of Wilde and Passey (3). On seeing Zener's work, they were able to obtain the same results from the classical theory of maxima and minima and extend this to polynomials. Consequently, we will use the classical theory to develop geometric programming, although this will not describe Zener's original development using the geometric-arithmetic inequality. However, it will require less effort to obtain the final result, for the background and arguments associated with the geometric-arithmetic inequality will not be required, and the results for polynomial optimization will follow directly from posynomial optimization.

OPTIMIZATION OF POSYNOMIALS

It is typical to find cost equations for preliminary equipment design to be *posynomials,* a polynomial whose terms are all positive. The cost equation in Example 2–2 of the previous chapter is an example of a posynomial. In general form, a posynomial can be written as:

$$y(\mathbf{x}) = \sum_{t=1}^{T} c_t \prod_{n=1}^{N} x_n{}^{a_{tn}} \qquad (3\text{–}1)$$

where the c_t's are the positive cost coefficients, the x_n's are the independent variables, the a_{tn}'s are the exponents on the independent variables, N is the total number of independent variables, and T is the total number of terms in the cost equation.

The cost equation from the simple process from Example 2–2 is given below as an illustration of equation (3–1):

$$y = 1000x_1 + 4 \times 10^9 x_1{}^{-1} x_2{}^{-1} + 2.5 \times 10^5 x_2 \qquad (3\text{–}2)$$

In this case $T = 3$, and $N = 2$, with the values of the c_t's and a_{tn}'s given below:

$$c_1 = 1000 \qquad a_{11} = 1 \qquad a_{21} = -1 \qquad a_{31} = 0$$

$$c_2 = 4 \times 10^9 \qquad a_{12} = 0 \qquad a_{22} = -1 \qquad a_{32} = 1$$

$$c_3 = 2.5 \times 10^5$$

The classical theory of Chapter 2 will be used to develop the geometric programming method of optimizing posynomials. Also some counterintuitive manipulations will be required to obtain the orthogonality and normality conditions of geometric programming. The result will be another problem to be solved that arises from the original problem. This will be encountered in other methods also, where the original or primal optimization problem is converted into another related or dual optimization problem. This dual problem should be easier to solve for the optimum for the procedure to be successful, and there will be a one-to-one correspondence between the optimal solution of the primal and dual problems.

To begin, the first partial derivatives of equation (3–1), with respect to each of the n independent variables, are set equal to zero according to the necessary conditions given in Chapter 2. This gives the following set of equations

$$\frac{\partial y}{\partial x_i} = \sum_{t=1}^{T} c_t a_{ti} x_i^{a_{ti}-1} \prod_{\substack{n=1 \\ n \neq i}}^{N} x_n^{a_{tn}} = 0 \tag{3–3}$$

for $i = 1, 2, \cdots, N$, which after multiplying by x_i can be rewritten as:

$$\sum_{t=1}^{T} c_t a_{ti} \prod_{n=1}^{N} x_n^{a_{tn}} = 0 \tag{3–4}$$

for $i = 1, 2, \cdots, N$. This is a set of N nonlinear algebraic equations, and, if solved by the classical theory, there will be all the problems associated with attempting to optimize equation (2–56) as described at the end of Chapter 2.

Another procedure was suggested (2) where a dual problem is developed using equations (3–1) and (3–4). We will say that equation (3–4) has been solved for the optimal values of the x_i's and the minimum cost has been computed using equation (3–1). This is the counterintuitive part of the development where the optimal values of the x_i's and y are used in principle, but their numerical values are not known specifically.

First, both sides of equation (3–1) are divided by the optimal value of y to give:

$$1 = \sum_{t=1}^{T} \left[c_t \prod_{n=1}^{N} x_n{}^{a_{tn}}/y \right] \tag{3–5}$$

Then the terms in the brackets of equation (3–5) are defined as optimal weights w_t, and equation (3–5) becomes

$$\sum_{t=1}^{T} w_t = 1 \tag{3–6}$$

where

$$w_t \equiv c_t \prod_{n=1}^{N} x_n{}^{a_{tn}}/y \tag{3–7}$$

Now the equation set from the necessary conditions, equation (3–4), can be divided by the optimal value of y and written as:

$$\sum_{t=1}^{T} a_{ti} \left[c_t \prod_{n=1}^{N} x_n{}^{a_{tn}}/y \right] = 0 \tag{3–8}$$

for $i = 1, 2, \cdots, N$, and in terms of the optimal weights this equation becomes:

$$\sum_{t=1}^{T} a_{tn} w_t = 0 \tag{3–9}$$

for $n = 1, 2, \cdots, N$, where the subscript n has been used in the place of i for convenience.

At this point there is a set of $N + 1$ linear algebraic equations that have been obtained from the original problem. These equations are referred to as the *normality* and *orthogonality conditions* of geometric programming:

$$\text{Normality condition: } \sum_{t=1}^{T} w_t = 1 \tag{3–6}$$

$$\text{Orthogonality condition: } \sum_{t=1}^{T} a_{tn} w_t = 0 \tag{3–9}$$

for $n = 1, 2, \cdots, N$. And the definition of the optimal weights:

$$w_t = c_t \prod_{n=1}^{N} x_n^{a_{tn}} / y \tag{3-7}$$

It will be necessary to pursue some additional algebraic manipulations to obtain an equation that relates the optimal value of y with the optimal weights w_t and the cost coefficients c_t. We begin using equation (3–6) as an exponent on y as:

$$y = y^1 = y^{\sum_{t=1}^{T} w_t} = \prod_{t=1}^{T} y^{w_t} \tag{3-10}$$

Equation (3–7) is now used to eliminate y from the right-hand side of equation (3–10), and introduce c_t and w_t as:

$$y = \prod_{t=1}^{T} \left[c_t \prod_{n=1}^{N} x_n^{a_{tn}} / w_t \right]^{w_t} \tag{3-11}$$

which can be written as:

$$y = \prod_{t=1}^{T} (c_t / w_t)^{w_t} \prod_{t=1}^{T} \prod_{n=1}^{N} x_n^{a_{tn} w_t} \tag{3-12}$$

The double-product term can be simplified using equation (3–9) as:

$$\prod_{t=1}^{T} \prod_{n=1}^{N} x_n^{a_{tn} w_t} = \prod_{n=1}^{N} x_n^{\sum_{t=1}^{T} a_{tn} w_t} = \prod_{n=1}^{N} x_n^{0} = 1 \tag{3-13}$$

and equation (3–12) simplifies to the following:

$$y = \prod_{t=1}^{T} (c_t / w_t)^{w_t} \tag{3-14}$$

which is the equation needed to relate the optimal value of y with the optimal weights w_t and the cost coefficients c_t.

The following example will illustrate the use of equations (3–6), (3–7), (3–9), and (3–14) to find the minimum cost of the simple process given in Example 2–2. This will give the geometric programming solution for posynomials, and this computational procedure is different from other methods. First, the values of the optimal weights are computed using equations

(3–6) and (3–9). Then the minimum cost is evaluated using equation
(3–14). Finally the optimal values of the independent variables are calculated
using the definition of the optimal weights, equation (3–7).

EXAMPLE 3–1 (3)

Find the minimum cost of the simple process of Example 2–2 by geometric
programming. The cost function is:

$$y = 1000x_1 + 4 \times 10^9 x_1^{-1} x_2^{-1} + 2.5 \times 10^5 x_2$$

Normality and orthogonality conditions from equations (3–6) and (3–9) are:

$$w_1 + w_2 + w_3 = 1$$
$$w_1 - w_2 \qquad = 0$$
$$- w_2 + w_3 = 0$$

Solving simultaneously gives

$$w_1 = w_2 = w_3 = \tfrac{1}{3}$$

Solving for the minimum cost using equation (3–14) gives:

$$y = [1000/(\tfrac{1}{3})]^{1/3} [4 \times 10^9/(\tfrac{1}{3})]^{1/3} [2.5 \times 10^5/(\tfrac{1}{3})]^{1/3} = 3 \times 10^6$$

which is the same result as obtained previously. To calculate the optimal
values of the independent variables using equation (3–7), there is a choice,
i.e., three equations for the w_t's and two x_i's:

$$w_1 = 1000x_1/3 \times 10^6 = \tfrac{1}{3} \rightarrow x_1 = 1000$$

$$w_2 = 4 \times 10^9 x_1^{-1} x_2^{-1}/3 \times 10^6 = \tfrac{1}{3}$$

$$w_3 = 2.5 \times 10^5 x_2/3 \times 10^6 = \tfrac{1}{3} \rightarrow x_2 = 4$$

The equations that most readily permit the evaluation of the optimal values of the independent variables are selected. In this case they were w_1
and w_3.

In Example 3–1 it turned out that the number of terms in the cost function,
T, was one more than the number of independent variables N. Consequently,
there were the same number of optimal weights as there were equations

from the normality and orthogonality conditions, and the values of the optimal weights could be determined uniquely. Then these optimal weights were used to compute the minimum cost and the optimal values of the independent variables. However, if the number of terms T is greater than the number of independent variables plus one, then the method of geometric programming becomes a constrained optimization as stated below:

$$\text{Maximize: } y(w) = \prod_{t-1}^{T} (c_t/w_t)^{w_t} \qquad (3\text{-}14)$$

$$\text{Subject to: } \sum_{t=1}^{T} w_t = 1 \qquad (3\text{-}6)$$

$$\sum_{t=1}^{T} a_{tn} w_t = 0 \qquad (3\text{-}9)$$

for $n = 1, 2, \cdots, N, w_t > 0$.

The above is a statement of the dual problem of geometric programming obtained from the primal problem, which is to minimize equation (3–1). The significance of this dual problem will be discussed further, but first, let us examine the following example, which is a modification of Example 3–1. It illustrates the effect of having an additional term in the cost function.

EXAMPLE 3–2 (3)

Find the minimum cost of the simple process where an additional annual cost of $9000x_1 x_2$ for a purifying device must be added. The cost function becomes:

$$y = 1000x_1 + 4 \times 10^9 x_1^{-1} x_1^{-1} + 2.5 \times 10^5 x_2 + 9000x_1 x_2$$

Normality and orthogonality conditions from equations (3–6) and (3–9) are

$$w_1 + w_2 + w_3 + w_4 = 1$$

$$w_1 - w_2 + w_4 = 0$$

$$- w_2 + w_3 + w_4 = 0$$

which must be solved along with dual function of equation (3–14), i.e.:

$$y = (c_1/w_1)^{w_1}(c_2/w_2)^{w_2}(c_3/w_3)^{w_3}(c_4/w_4)^{w_4}$$

The methods of Chapter 2 for constrained optimization are required. All those methods would require differentiating the dual function with respect to the w_i's. The direct substitution approach (3) gives:

$$w_1 = (1 - 2w_4)/3$$

$$w_2 = (1 + w_4)/3$$

$$w_3 = (1 - 2w_4)/3$$

and the function to differentiate with respect to w_4 to locate the minimum cost is:

$$y = [3000/(1 - 2w_4)]^{(1-2w_4)/3}[12 \times 10^9/(1 + w_4)]^{(1+w_4)/3} \cdot$$
$$[7.5 \times 10^5/(1 - 2w_4)]^{(1-2w_4)/3}[9000/w_4]^{w_4}$$

At this point it is only reasonable to return to the primal problem, which is unconstrained, and solve it for the minimum cost, rather than continuing with the dual problem, which is significantly more complicated algebraically. (See Reference 3 for the solution.) It is said that this problem has a degree of difficulty of 1, i.e.:

$$T - (N + 1) = 4 - (2 + 1) = 1$$

and the problem of Example 3–1 had a degree of difficulty of 0:

$$T - (N + 1) = 3 - (2 + 1) = 0$$

Geometric programming problems can be classified by their degree of difficulty, which can be determined prior to attempting to solve the optimization problem by this method. We will summarize the results obtained in terms of the degrees of difficulty as measured by $T - (N + 1)$, having seen that if the degree of difficulty is zero, only a set of linear algebraic equations need be solved for the minimum cost. However, if the degree of difficulty is greater than zero a constrained optimization problem has to be solved.

The primal problem is:

$$\text{Minimize:} \quad y(\mathbf{x}) = \sum_{t=1}^{T} c_t \prod_{n=1}^{N} x_n^{a_{tn}} \qquad (3\text{--}15)$$

$$\text{subject to: } c_t > 0$$

$$x_n > 0$$

The dual problem is:

$$\text{Maximize: } y(\mathbf{w}) = \prod_{t=1}^{T} (c_t/w_t)^{w_t} \tag{3-16}$$

$$\text{subject to: } \sum_{t=1}^{T} w_t = 1$$

$$\sum_{t=1}^{T} a_{tn} w_t = 0$$

for $n = 1, 2, 3, \cdots, N$, $w_t > 0$, where:

$$w_t = c_t \prod_{n=1}^{N} x_n{}^{a_{tn}}/y \tag{3-7}$$

There is a direct correspondence between the primal and dual problems, i.e., the dual problem is constructed from the primal problem. It has been shown (3) that the primal problem, a posynomial, has a global minimum and the dual problem has a global maximum. The numerical value of the minimum of the primal problem is the same as the maximum of the dual problem.

As has been seen if $T - (N + 1)$ is zero, the posynomial optimization problem is solved without difficulty; and if $T - (N + 1)$ is greater than zero, it may be easier to attempt the solution of the primal problem by a method other than geometric programming. Also, it is necessary to consider the case where $T - (N + 1)$ is less than zero, i.e., the number of terms is fewer than the number of variables plus one. In this situation the algebraic equation set from the normality and orthogonality conditions has more equations than variables, i.e., the equation set is overdetermined. Consequently, the primal problem cannot be solved by geometric programming, and the dual problem is said not to be consistent with the primal problem, i.e., the primal problem does not give a dual problem with at least zero degrees of difficulty. However, it has been suggested (3) that a subset of the orthogonality equations could be selected to give several zero degree of difficulty problems to be solved. It was proposed that this would give some information about the optimization problem. This is equivalent to setting some of the independent variables in the primal problem equal to one, and, depending on the problem, this might yield some useful information.

Before we move to optimization of polynomials by geometric programming, let us examine the solution of the economic model for the vapor condenser given at the end of Chapter 2. This will demonstrate the facility of the technique when fractional exponents are part of the economic model.

EXAMPLE 3–3 (7)

The following cost equation was developed for the optimal design of a vapor condenser with a fixed heat load for use in a desalination plant and includes the cost of steam, fixed charges, and pumping costs:

$$C = aN^{-7/6}D^{-1}L^{-4/4} + bN^{-0.2}D^{0.8}L^{-1} + cNDL + dN^{-1.8}D^{-4.8}L$$

where C is the cost in dollars per year; N is the number of tubes in the condenser; D is the nominal diameter of the tubes in inches; L is the tube length in feet, and a, b, and c are coefficients that vary with the fluids involved and the construction costs. For a seawater desalination plant using low-pressure steam for heating, these values are $a = 3318.8$, $b = 1.1991$, $c = 3.4014 \times 10^{-4}$, and $d = 11.624$.

The orthogonality and normality conditions are given below:

$$w_1 + w_2 + w_3 + w_4 = 1$$

$$-(7/6)w_1 - 0.2w_2 + w_3 - 1.8w_4 = 0$$

$$-w_1 + 0.8w_2 + w_3 - 4.8w_4 = 0$$

$$-(4/3)w_1 - w_2 + w_3 + w_4 = 0$$

The degree of difficulty for this problem is zero, and a unique solution for the optimal weights is obtained:

$$w_1 = 2/5 \qquad w_2 = 1/30 \qquad w_3 = 8/15 \qquad w_4 = 1/30$$

The minimum cost is computed using equation (3–16)

$$y = [1.724 \times 10^5 \times 5/2]^{2/5}[9.779 \times 10^4 \times 30]^{1/30} \cdot$$
$$[1.57 \times 15/8]^{8/15}[3.82 \times 10^{-2} \times 30]^{1/30} = \$526.50/\text{yr}.$$

The optimal values of N, D, and L can be obtained by solving three of the following four equations:

$$(3318.8)\, N^{-7/6}D^{-1}L^{-4/3}/526.5 = 2/5$$

$$(1.199)\, N^{-0.2}D^{0.8}L^{-1}/526.5 = 1/30$$

$$(3.4014 \times 10^{-4})\, NDL/526.5 = 8/15$$

$$(11.624)\, N^{-1.8}D^{-4.8}L/526.5 = 1/30$$

The solution of the above equations gives $N = 112$, $D = 1.0$ inch, and $L = 14.0$ feet. An extension to a more detailed design is given by Avriel and Wilde (7).

OPTIMIZATION OF POLYNOMIALS

For this case either the cost or profit can be represented by a polynomial. The same procedure employing classical methods (8) will be used to obtain the dual problem, and the techniques will be essentially the same to find the optimum. However, the main difference is that stationary points will be found, and there will be no guarantee that either a maximum or a minimum has been located. It will be necessary to use the methods of Chapter 2 or local exploration to determine their character.

It is convenient to group the positive terms and the negative terms together to represent a general polynomial. This is written as:

$$y(\mathbf{x}) = \sum_{t=1}^{k} c_t \prod_{n=1}^{N} x_n{}^{a_{tn}} - \sum_{t=k+1}^{T} c_t \prod_{n=1}^{N} x_n{}^{a_{tn}} \qquad (3\text{-}17)$$

An example of this equation, given below, will be used to illustrate the solution technique for polynomials:

$$y = 3x_1{}^{0.25} - 3x_1{}^{1.1}x_2{}^{0.6} - 115x_2{}^{-1}x_3{}^{-1} - 2x_3 \qquad (3\text{-}18)$$

And comparing equations (3-17) and (3-18) gives:

$$c_1 = 3 \qquad c_2 = 3 \qquad c_3 = 115 \quad c_4 = 2$$

$$a_{11} = 0.25 \qquad a_{21} = 1.1 \qquad a_{31} = 0 \qquad a_{41} = 0$$

$$a_{12} = 0 \qquad a_{22} = 0.6 \qquad a_{32} = -1 \quad a_{42} = 0$$

$$a_{13} = 0 \qquad a_{23} = 0 \qquad a_{33} = -1 \quad a_{43} = 1$$

As done previously, the first partial derivatives of equation (3-17) with respect to the n independent variables are set equal to zero according to the necessary conditions. This gives the following set of equations:

$$\frac{\partial y}{\partial x_i} = \sum_{t=1}^{k} c_t a_{ti} x_i{}^{a_{ti}-1} \prod_{\substack{n=1 \\ n \neq i}}^{N} x_n{}^{a_{tn}} - \sum_{t=k+1}^{T} c_t a_{ti} x_i{}^{a_{ti}-1} \prod_{\substack{n=1 \\ n \neq i}}^{N} x_n{}^{a_{tn}} = 0 \qquad (3\text{-}19)$$

for $i = 1, 2, 3, \cdots, N$, which, after multiplying by x_i/y, can be written as:

$$\sum_{t=1}^{k} a_{ti} \left[c_t \prod_{n=1}^{N} x_n{}^{a_{tn}}/y \right] - \sum_{t=k+1}^{T} a_{ti} \left[c_t \prod_{n=1}^{N} x_n{}^{a_{tn}}/y \right] = 0 \quad (3.20)$$

for $i = 1, 2, \cdots, N$.

The definition of the optimal weights (equation 3–7) can now be used to give the orthogonality conditions for polynomial optimization, i.e.:

$$\sum_{t=1}^{k} a_{tn} w_t - \sum_{t=k+1}^{T} a_{tn} w_t = 0 \quad (3–21)$$

for $n = 1, 2, \cdots, N$, where the subscript n has been used in place of i for convenience.

Also the normality condition is obtained the same way as equation (3–6) by dividing equation (3–17) by the optimal value of y, which is known in principle from the solution of the set of equations given by equation (3–20). The result is:

$$\sum_{t=1}^{k} w_t - \sum_{t=k+1}^{T} w_t = 1 \quad (3–22)$$

The only algebraic manipulations that remain are to obtain the equation comparable to equation (3–14) for a polynomial profit or cost function. The procedure is the same and uses equation (3–22) as follows:

$$y = y^1 = y^{\sum_{1}^{k} w_t - \sum_{k+1}^{T} w_t} = y^{\sum_{1}^{k} w_t}/y^{\sum_{1}^{T} w_t}_{k+1} = \prod_{t=1}^{k} y^{w_t} / \prod_{t=k+1}^{T} y^{w_t} \quad (3–23)$$

Again the definition of the optimal weights, equation (3–7), is used to eliminate y from the right-hand side of equation (3–23) and introduce c_t and w_t as:

$$y = \prod_{t=1}^{k} (c_t/w_t)^{w_t} \prod_{n=1}^{N} x_n{}^{a_{tn} w_t} \Big/ \prod_{t=k+1}^{T} (c_t/w_t)^{w_t} \prod_{n=1}^{N} x_n{}^{a_{tn} w_t} \quad (3–24)$$

and the above can be written as

$$y = \left[\prod_{t=1}^{k} (c_t/w_t)^{w_t} \Big/ \prod_{t=k+1}^{T} (c_t/w_t)^{w_t} \right] \left[\prod_{n=1}^{N} x_n{}^{\sum_{1}^{k} a_{tn} w_t} \Big/ \prod_{n=1}^{n} x_n{}^{\sum_{k+1}^{T} a_{tn} w_t} \right]$$

$$(3–25)$$

The term in the second brackets can be written as

$$\prod_{n=1}^{N} x_n^{\sum_{1}^{k} a_{tn}w_t - \sum_{k+1}^{T} a_{tn}w_t} = \prod_{n=1}^{N} x_n^{0} = 1 \qquad (3\text{--}26)$$

Using equation (3–21) and performing the manipulations done to obtain equation (3–13), the result is comparable to equation (3–14) and is:

$$y = \prod_{t=1}^{k} (c_t/w_t)^{w_t} \Big/ \prod_{t=k+1}^{T} (c_t/w_t)^{w_t} \qquad (3\text{--}27)$$

The primal and dual problems for the method of geometric programming for polynomials can be stated as:

Primal problem:

$$\text{optimize: } y(\mathbf{x}) = \sum_{t=1}^{k} c_t \prod_{n=1}^{N} x_n^{a_{tn}} - \sum_{t=k+1}^{T} c_t \prod_{n=1}^{N} x_n^{a_{tn}} \qquad (3\text{--}17)$$

$$\text{subject to: } c_t > 0$$

$$x_n > 0$$

Dual problem:

$$\text{optimize: } y(\mathbf{w}) = \prod_{t=1}^{k} (c_t/w_t)^{w_t} \Big/ \prod_{t=k+1}^{T} (c_t/w_t)^{w_t} \qquad (3\text{--}27)$$

$$\text{subject to: } \sum_{t=1}^{k} w_t - \sum_{t=k+1}^{T} w_t = 1 \qquad (3\text{--}22)$$

$$\sum_{t=1}^{k} a_{tn}w_t - \sum_{t=k+1}^{T} a_{tn}w_t = 0 \qquad (3\text{--}21)$$

for $n = 1, 2, \cdots, N$, $w_t > 0$.

The term *optimize* is used for both the primal and dual problems. A polynomial can represent a cost to be minimized or a profit to be maximized, for terms of both signs are used. The results obtained from the dual problem could be a maximum, a minimum, or a saddle point, because stationary points are computed. Consequently, tests from Chapter 2 or local exploration would be required to determine the character of these stationary points. Before this is discussed further, let us examine the geometric programming solution of equation (3–18) to illustrate the procedure.

EXAMPLE 3–4

Obtain the geometric programming solution for equation (3–18).

$$y = 3x_1^{0.25} - 3x_1^{1.1}x_2^{0.6} - 115x_2^{-1}x_3^{-1} - 2x_3$$

$$c_1 = 3 \qquad c_2 = 3 \qquad c_3 = 115 \qquad c_4 = 2$$

$$a_{11} = 0.25 \qquad a_{21} = 1.1 \qquad a_{31} = 0 \qquad a_{41} = 0$$

$$a_{12} = 0 \qquad a_{22} = 0.6 \qquad a_{32} = -1 \qquad a_{42} = 0$$

$$a_{13} = 0 \qquad a_{23} = 0 \qquad a_{33} = -1 \qquad a_{43} = 1$$

The normality and orthogonality conditions are:

$$w_1 - w_2 \quad - w_3 - w_4 = 1$$

$$0.25w_1 - 1.1w_2 \qquad\qquad = 0$$

$$- 0.6w_2 + w_3 \qquad = 0$$

$$w_3 - w_4 = 0$$

Solving simultaneously gives:

$$w_1 = 2, \qquad w_2 = 5/11, \qquad w_3 = 3/11, \qquad w_4 = 3/11$$

The optimal value of y, in this case, is a maximum:

$$y = (3/2)^2/[(3 \times 11/5)^{5/11} (115 \times 11/3)^{3/11} (2 \times 11/3)^{3/11}] = 0.1067$$

and the optimal value of x_1, x_2, and x_3 can be computed from the definitions of the optimal weights by selecting the most convenient form from among the following:

$$3x_1^{0.25}/0.1067 = 2$$

$$3x_1^{1.1}x_2^{0.6}/0.1067 = 5/11$$

$$115x_2^{-1}x_3^{-1}/0.1067 = 3/11$$

$$2x_3/0.1067 = 3/11$$

Using the first, third, and fourth gives:

$$x_1 = 2.560 \times 10^{-5}, \qquad x_2 = 2.716 \times 10^5, \qquad x_3 = 1.455 \times 10^{-2}$$

A problem can be encountered from the formulation of a geometric programming problem where the result will be negative values for the optimal weights (3, 6). The dual problem requires that the optimum value of y be positive. If the economic model is formulated in such a way that the optimal value is negative when calculated from the primal problem, the result will be negative weights computed in the dual problem, and it will not be possible to compute the optimum value of the function using equation (3–27). However, the value of the weights will be correct in numerical value but incorrect in sign. The previous example will be used to illustrate this difficulty, and the proof and further discussion is given by Beightler and Phillips (6).

In Example 3–4 a maximum was found, and the value of the profit function was 0.1067. Had the example been to find the minimum cost, i.e., $-y$, the result would have been -0.1067. However, this value could not have been calculated using equation (3–27). Reformulating the problem of $-y$ with the positive terms first as:

$$y = 3x_1^{1.1}x_2^{0.6} + 115x_2^{-1}x_3^{-1} + 2x_3 - 3x_1^{0.25}$$

The normality and orthogonality conditions are:

$$w_1 + w_2 + w_3 - \quad w_4 = 1$$

$$1.1w_1 + \quad\quad - 0.25w_4 = 0$$

$$0.6w_1 - w_2 \quad\quad\quad = 0$$

$$- w_2 + w_3 \quad\quad = 0$$

The solution to the equation set is:

$$w_1 = -5/11, \qquad w_2 = -3/11, \qquad w_3 = -3/11, \qquad w_4 = -2$$

and unacceptable negative values of the optimal weights are obtained. Although not obvious, the cause of this is that the value of the function is negative at the stationary point, i.e., -0.1067. Reformulating the problem to find the stationary point of the negative of the function will give positive optimal weights and a positive value of the function, as was illustrated in Example 3–4.

In the illustration, Example 3–4, the degree of difficulty, $T - (N + 1)$, was 0. As in posynomial optimization, the degree of difficulty must be 0 or greater to be able to solve the problem by geometric programming. Also if the degree of difficulty is 1 or more, then the dual problem is a constrained optimization problem, which has to be solved by the procedures of Chapter 2 or other methods. However, Agognio (18) has proposed a primal-dual, normed space (PDNS) algorithm that uses the primal problem and the dual problem together to locate the optimum. This algorithm consists of operations within the primal and dual programs and two sets of mappings between them that depend on a least-squares solution minimizing the two-norm of the overdetermined set of linear equations. The PDNS algorithm was tested on a number of standard problems and performed essentially equally with other methods. Also, the dissertation of Agogino (18) describes multiobjective optimization applications of the algorithm.

CLOSURE

In this chapter we have covered the geometric programming optimization of unconstrained posynomials and polynomials. Posynomials represented the cost function of a process, and the procedure located the global minimum by solving the dual problem for the global maximum. Polynomials represented the cost or profit function of a process, and the procedure of solving the dual problem located stationary points that could be maxima, minima, or stationary points. Their character had to be determined by the methods of Chapter 2 or by local exploration. Also, for polynomials if the numerical value of the function being optimized was negative at the stationary point, this caused the optimal weights of the dual problem to be negative. It was then necessary to seek the optimum of the negative of the function to have a positive value at the stationary point. This gave positive optimal weights, and then the numerical value of the function at the stationary point was computed using equation (3–27).

A complete discussion of geometric programming, given by Beightler and Phillips (6), includes extensions to equality and inequality constraints. These extensions have the same complications as associated with the degrees of difficulty that occur with the unconstrained problems presented here. Because of these limitations the lengthy details for constraints will not be summarized here, and those who are interested in exploring this subject further are referred to the texts by Beightler and Phillips (6) and Reklaitis et al. (17).

The dual problem is solved when it is less complicated than the primal problem. An exponential transformation procedure for the dual problem has been described by Reklaitis et al. (17) to make the computational problem easier when the degree of difficulty is greater than zero and also if constraints are involved. In addition, Reklaitis et al. (17) reported on comparisons of computer codes for geometric programming optimization based on their research and that of others, including Dembo and Sarma. The testing showed that the best results were obtained with the quotient form of the generalized geometric programming problem, and second was the generalized reduced gradient solution of the exponential form of the primal problem. Also, results by Knopf, Okos, and Reklaitis (9) for batch and semicontinuous process optimization showed that the dual problem can be solved more readily than the primal problem using the generalized reduced gradient multidimensional search technique. Moreover, Phillips (10) has reported other successful applications with nonzero degrees of difficulty requiring multidimensional search methods, which are the topic of Chapter 6. In summary, if the economic model and constraints can be formulated as polynomials, there are many advantages of extensions of geometric programming that can be used for optimization.

REFERENCES

1. Zener, C. M., "A Mathematical Aid in Optimizing Engineering Designs," *Proceedings of the National Academy of Science,* 47(4):537–9 (1961).
2. Duffin, R. J., E. L. Peterson, and C. M. Zener, *Geometric Programming,* John Wiley & Sons, Inc., New York (1967).
3. Wilde, D. J., and C. S. Beightler, *Foundations of Optimization,* Prentice-Hall, Inc., Englewood Cliffs, N. J. (1967).
4. Zener, C. M., *Engineering Design by Geometric Programming,* John Wiley & Sons, Inc., New York (1971).
5. Nijhamp, P., *Planning of Industrial Complexes by Means of Geometric Programming,* Rotterdam Univ. Press, Rotterdam, Netherlands (1972).
6. Beightler, C. S., and D. T. Phillips, *Applied Geometric Programming,* John Wiley & Sons, Inc., New York (1976).
7. Avriel, M., and D. J. Wilde, "Optimal Condenser Design by Geometric Programming," *Ind. Eng. Chem., Process Design and Development,* 6(2):256 (1967).
8. Chen, N. H., "A Simplified Approach to Optimization by Geometric Programming," Preprint 12b, 65th National Meeting, American Institute of Chemical Engineers, Cleveland, Ohio (May 4–7, 1969).
9. Knopf, C. F., M. R. Okos, and G. V. Reklaitis, "Optimal Design of Batch/Semicontinuous Processes," *Ind. Eng. Chem. Process Design and Development,* 21(1):79 (1982).
10. Phillips, D. T., *Mathematical Programming for Operations Researchers and Computer Scientists,* Ed. A. G. Holtzman, Marcel Dekker, Inc., New York (1981).
11. Stocker, W. F., *Design of Thermal Systems,* McGraw-Hill Book Co., New York (1971).
12. Sherwood, T. K., *A Course in Process Design,* MIT Press, Cambridge, Mass. (1963).

13. Beightler, C. S., D. T. Phillips, and D. J. Wilde, *Foundations of Optimization,* 2nd Ed., Prentice-Hall, Inc., Englewood Cliffs, N. J. (1979).
14. Wilde, D. J., *Globally Optimal Design,* John Wiley & Sons, Inc., New York, (1978).
15. Ray, W. H., and J. Szekely, *Process Optimization with Applications in Metallurgy and Chemical Engineering,* John Wiley & Sons, Inc., New York (1973).
16. Beveridge, G. S. G., and R. S. Schechter, *Optimization: Theory and Practice,* McGraw-Hill Book Co., New York (1970).
17. Reklaitis, G. V., A. Ravindran, and K. M. Ragsdell, *Engineering Optimization: Methods and Applications,* John Wiley & Sons, Inc., New York (1983).
18. Agogino, A. M., "A Primal-Dual Algorithm for Constrained Generalized Polynomial Programming: Application to Engineering Design and Multiobjective Optimization," Ph.D. dissertation, Stanford University, Stanford, California (1984).

PROBLEMS

3–1. Solve the following problem by geometric programming:

$$\text{minimize: } y = x_1^2 + 2x_2^2 + 3/x_1x_2 + 2x_1x_2$$

3–2.[10] Solve the following problem by geometric programming:

$$\text{minimize: } y = 5x_1^{-1}x_2^{-3} + 2x_1^2x_2x_3^{-2} + 10x_1x_2^4x_3^{-1} + 20x_3^2$$

3–3.[13] Solve the following problem by geometric programming:

$$\text{minimize: } y = 60x_1^{-3}x_2^{-2} + 50x_1^3x_2 + 20x_1^{-3}x_2^3$$

3–4. a. Solve the following problem by geometric programming:

$$\text{minimize: } y = 4x_1 + x_1/x_2^2 + 4x_2/x_1$$

b. If an additional term, $2x_2$, is added to the function being minimized, set up the necessary equations and discuss the procedure to find the optimum.

3–5. Solve the following problem by geometric programming:

$$\text{minimize: } y = 4x_1^{-1}x_2^{-1}x_3^{-1} + 8x_1x_2 + 4x_2x_3 + 4x_1x_3$$

3–6.[16] Consider the following geometric programming problem:

$$\text{minimize: } y = x_1^2 + x_2 + 3/x_1x_2 + 2x_1x_2$$

a. Show that the following is the dual problem:

$$\text{maximize: } y = \left(\frac{1}{w_1}\right)^{w_1} \left(\frac{1}{w_2}\right)^{w_2} \left(\frac{3}{w_3}\right)^{w_3} \left(\frac{2}{w_4}\right)^{w_4}$$

$$\text{subject to: } w_1 + w_2 + w_3 + w_4 = 1$$

$$2w_1 \qquad - w_3 + w_4 = 0$$

$$2w_2 - w_3 + w_4 = 0$$

Discuss the method of solution to obtain the optimal value of y and x_1 and x_2. It is not necessary to carry out the calculations.

b. Two sets of values of the weights that satisfy the constraints $\mathbf{w_1} = (1/15, 2/15, 7/15, 1/3)$ and $\mathbf{w_2} = (1/10, 1/5, 9/20, 1/4)$. Calculate the optimal value of y for $\mathbf{w_1}$ and $\mathbf{w_2}$. What is your conclusion?

3–7.[11] Treatment of a waste is accomplished by chemical treatment and dilution to meet effluent code requirements. The total cost is the sum of the treatment plant, pumping power requirements, and piping cost. This cost is given by the following equation:

$$C = 150\,D + \frac{972{,}000\ Q^2}{D^5} + \frac{432}{Q}$$

where C is in dollars, D in inches, and Q in cfs. Find the minimum cost and best values of D and Q by geometric programming.

3–8. The work done by a three-stage compressor is given by the following equation:

$$W = (P_1 V_1 / e)\left[(P_2 / P_1)^e + (P_3 / P_2)^e + (P_4 / P_3)^e - 3\right]$$

where P_1 is the inlet pressure to stage 1, P_2 is the discharge pressure from stage 1 and inlet pressure to stage 2, P_3 is the discharge pressure from stage 2 and inlet pressure to stage 3, P_4 is the discharge pressure from stage 3, and e is equal to $(k - 1)/k$, where k is the ratio of specific heats, a constant.

For specified inlet and exit pressures P_1 and P_4, determine intermediate pressures P_2 and P_3 that minimize the work by geometric programming.

3–9.[11] Determine the optimal pipe diameter for the minimum installed plus operating costs by geometric programming for 100 feet of pipe conveying a given flow rate of water. The installed cost in dollars is 150

D, and the lifetime pumping cost in dollars is $122,500/D^5$. The diameter D is in inches.

3–10. Sherwood (12) considered the optimum design of a gas transmission line and obtained the following expression for annual charges (less fixed expenses):

$$C = 4.55 \times 10^5 \frac{L^{1/2}}{F^{0.387}D^{2/3}} + 3.69 \times 10^4 D$$

$$+ \frac{6.57 \times 10^6}{L} + 7.72 \times 10^8 \frac{F}{L}$$

where L is equal to pipe length between compressors in feet, D is the diameter in inches, $F = r^{0.219} - 1$, where r is the ratio of inlet to outlet pressure. Determine the minimum cost, and the optimal values of L, F, D, and r.

3–11.[15] The economic model for the annual cost is given below for a furnace in which a slag-metal reaction is to be conducted:

$$C = 1 \times 10^{13}/L^3 T^2 + 100L^2 + 5 \times 10^{-11}L^2 T^4$$

In this equation L is the characteristic length of the furnace in feet and T is the temperature in °K.

a. Determine the minimum cost and the corresponding best value of L and T by geometric programming.

b. If an additional term, $1000L^3$, is added to the cost function, give the geometric programming problem to be solved, i.e., dual problem, and indicate how the solution could be obtained.

c. If the cost function contained only the first two terms, deleting the third term, indicate the effect on the solution by geometric programming.

3–12. The profit function for each of three chemical reactors operating in parallel with the same feed is given by the three equations below. Each reactor is operating with a different catalyst and conditions of temperature and pressure. The profit function for each reactor has the feed rates x_1, x_2, and x_3 as the independent variable, and the parameters in the equation are determined by the catalyst and operating conditions:

$$P_1 = 0.2x_1 - 2(x_1/100)^2$$

$$P_2 = 0.2x_2 - 4(x_2/100)^2$$

$$P_3 = 0.2x_3 - 6(x_3/100)^2$$

    a. For the equation for the total profit $(P = P_1 + P_2 + P_3)$ from operating the three reactors, give the geometric programming dual problem with the normality and orthogonality conditions. Compute the optimal weights.

    b. Calculate the maximum profit.

    c. Calculate the values of the three flow rates of feed to the reactors using the definition of the optimal weights.

3–13. A batch process has major equipment components—reactor, heat exchanger, centrifuge, and dryer. The total cost in dollars per batch of feed processed is given by the following equation, and it is the sum of the costs associated with each piece of equipment:

$$C = 315V^{0.57}t_1{}^{-1} + 370V^{-0.22}t_1 + 460V^{0.54}t_2{}^{-1} + 450V^{-0.72}t_2$$

      reactor   heat exchanger   centrifuge   dryer

where V is the volume of feed to be processed per batch in cubic feet, and t_1 and t_2 are residence times in hours for the two sections of the process.

    a. Find the optimum values of the volume of feed to be processed per batch, V, and the residence times, t_1 and t_2, by geometric programming.

    b. If packaging costs are added as $120V^{0.52}$, set up this geometric programming problem, and discuss the procedure for finding the minimum cost.

    c. Obtain the equations to be solved for the minimum cost by analytical methods, and discuss the feasibility of solving the problem by this method (not with the packaging costs).

3–14. [6] A total of 400 cubic yards of gravel must be ferried across a river. The gravel is to be shipped in an open box of length x_1, width x_2, and height x_3. The ends and bottom of the box cost \$20/yd² to build, the sides, \$5/yd². Runners cost \$2.50/yd, and two are required to slide the box. Each round trip on the ferry cost \$0.10. The problem is to find the optimal dimensions of the box that minimize the total costs of construction and transportation. This total cost is given by:

$$y = 40x_1{}^{-1}x_2{}^{-1}x_3{}^{-1} + 20x_1x_2 + 10x_1x_3 + 40x_2x_3 + 5x_1$$

    a. Give the orthogonality and normality equations to solve this problem by geometric programming. Discuss how the problem would be solved and any difficulties that would be encountered. Beightler and Phillips (6) give the following results:

$$w_1 = 0.3858 \quad y^* = \$108.75 \quad x_1^* = 1.542 \text{ yd}$$

$$w_2 = 0.1575 \qquad\qquad\qquad x_2^* = 0.561 \text{ yd}$$

$$w_3 = 0.1575 \qquad\qquad\qquad x_3^* = 1.107 \text{ yd}$$

$$w_4 = 0.2284$$

$$w_5 = 0.0709$$

b. Neglect the runner's cost, $5x_1$, and give the orthogonality and normality equation set. Show that the solution to this equation set is:

$$w_1 = 2/5, \qquad w_2 = 1/5, \qquad w_3 = 1/5, \qquad w_4 = 1/5$$

c. Compute the minimum cost.
d. Compute the values of the independent variables, and compare with the results obtained in part a.

4
LINEAR PROGRAMMING

INTRODUCTION

Linear programming is the most widely applied of all the optimization methods. The technique has been used for optimizing many diverse applications, including refineries and chemical plants, livestock feed blending, routing of aircraft, and scheduling their crews. Many industrial allocation and transportation problems can be optimized with this method. The application of linear programming has been successful, particularly in cases of selecting the best set of values of the variables when a large number of interrelated choices exists. Often such problems involve a small improvement per unit of material flow times large production rates to have as the net result a significant increase in the profit of the plant. A typical example is a large oil refinery where the stream flow rates are very large, and a small improvement per unit of product is multiplied by a very large number to obtain a significant increase in profit for the refinery.

The term *programming* of linear programming does not refer to computer programming but to scheduling. Linear programming was developed about 1947, before the commercial advent of the computer, when George B. Dantzig (1) recognized a generalization in the mathematics of scheduling and planning problems. Developments in linear programming have followed advances in digital computing, and now problems involving several thousand independent variables and constraints equations can be solved.

In this chapter a geometric representation and solution of a simple linear programming problem will be given initially to introduce the subject and illustrate the way to capitalize on the mathematical structure of the problem. This will be followed by a presentation of the simplex algorithm for the solution of linear programming problems. Having established the computational algorithm, we will give the procedure to convert a process flow diagram into a linear programming problem, using a simple petroleum refinery as an illustration. The method of solution, using large linear programming computer codes, then will be described, and the solution of the refinery problem, using the IBM Mathematical Programming System Extended (MPSX), will illustrate the procedure and give typical results obtained from these large codes. Once the optimal solution has been obtained, sensitivity analysis procedures will be detailed that use the optimal solution to determine ranges on the important parameters where the optimal solution remains optimal. Thus, another linear programming solution is not required. This will be illustrated also using results of the refinery problem obtained from the MPSX solution. Finally, a summary will be given of extensions to linear programming and other related topics.

CONCEPTS AND GEOMETRIC INTERPRETATION

As the name indicates, all the equations used in the linear programming must be linear. Although this appears to be a severe restriction, there are many problems that can be cast in this context. In a linear programming formulation, the equation that determines the profit or cost of operation is referred to as the *objective function*. It must have the form of the sum of linear terms. The equations that describe the limitations under which the system must operate are called the *constraints*. The variables must be nonnegative, i.e., positive or zero only.

The best way to introduce the subject is with an example. This will give some geometric intuition about the mathematical structure of the problem and the way this structure can be used to find an optimal solution.

EXAMPLE 4.1

A chemical company makes two types of small, solid-fuel rocket motors for testing; for motor A the profit is $3.00 per motor, and for motor B the profit is $4.00 per motor. A total processing time of 80 hours per week is available to produce both motors. An average of four hours per motor is required for A, but only two hours per motor is required for B. However, due to the hazardous nature of the material in B, a preparation time of five hours is required per motor, and a preparation time of two hours per motor is required for A. The total preparation time of 120 hours per week is available to produce both motors. Determine the number of each motor that should be produced to maximize the profit.

Solution:
The objective function and constraint equations for this case are:

$$\text{Maximize: } 3A + 4B \qquad \text{Profit}$$

$$\text{Subject to: } 4A + 2B \leq 80 \qquad \text{Processing time}$$

$$2A + 5B \leq 120 \qquad \text{Preparation time}$$

$$A, \quad B \geq \quad 0$$

$$A \geq 0$$
$$B \geq 0$$

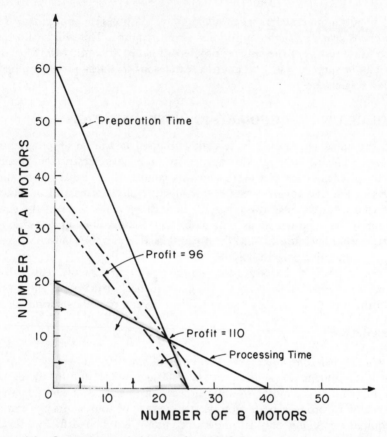

Figure 4-1. Constraints and objective function for maximizing rocket motor profit.

It would be tempting to make all B motors using the preparation time limitation $120/5 = 24$ for a profit of $96. If all A motors were made, there is a processing time limitation $80/4 = 20$ for a profit of $60. However, there is a best solution, and this can be seen from Figure 4-1. The small arrows show the region enclosed by the constraint equations that is feasible for the variables. For the processing time and preparation time, any values of the variables lying above the lines violate the constraint equations. Consequently feasible values must lie on or inside the lines and the A and B axes (because A and B must be nonnegative). This is called the *feasible region*. The objective function is shown in Figure 4-1 for $P = 96$, and this is the one of the family of lines:

$$3A + 4B = P$$

or

$$A = -(4/3) B + P/3$$

where P can increase as long as the values of the variables A and B stay in the feasible region. By increasing P, the profit equation shown above moves up with a constant slope of $-4/3$, and P reaches the maximum value in the feasible region at the vertex $A = 10$, $B = 20$, where $P = \$110$.

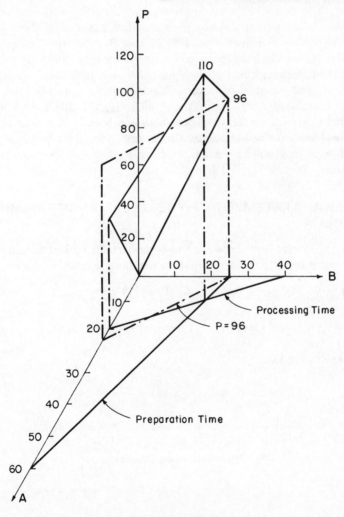

Figure 4-2. Geometric representation of constraints and objective function for maximizing rocket motor profit.

Another geometric representation of the profit function and constraints is shown in Figure 4-2. The profit function is a plane, and the highest point is the vertex $A = 10$, $B = 20$. The intersection of the profit function and planes of P = constant give a line on the profit function plane as shown for $P = 96$. The projection of this line on the response surface (the $A - B$ plane) is the same line shown in Figure 4-1 for $P = 96$. This diagram emphasizes the fact that the profit function is a plane, and the maximum profit will be at the highest point on the plane and located on the boundary at the intersection of constraint equations, a vertex.

This example can be used to illustrate *infeasibility* also, i.e., no feasible solution to linear programming problems. For example, if there were constraints on A and B such that $A \geq 21$ and $B \geq 25$, then there would be no solution, for the processing and preparation time constraints could not be satisfied. Although it is obvious here that A and B could not have these values, it is not unusual in large problems to make a mistake and have the linear programming code return the result INFEASIBLE SOLUTION—the constraints are inconsistent. Almost always a blunder has been made, and the constraints do not represent the process. However, in large problems the blunder may not be obvious, and some effort may be required to find the error.

GENERAL STATEMENT OF THE LINEAR PROGRAMMING PROBLEM

There are several ways to write the general mathematical statement of the linear programming problem. First, in the usual algebraic notation:

Objective function:

$$\text{Optimize: } c_1 x_1 = c_2 x_2 + \cdots + c_n x_n \tag{4-1a}$$

Constraint equations:

$$\text{Subject to: } a_{11}x_1 + a_{12}x_2 + \cdots + a_{1n}x_n \geq b_1$$

$$a_{21}x_1 + a_{22}x_2 + \cdots + a_{2n}x_n \geq b_2$$

$$\vdots \qquad \qquad \vdots \qquad \vdots \tag{4-1b}$$

$$a_{m1}x_1 + a_{m2}x_2 + \cdots + a_{mn}x_n \geq b_m$$

$$x_j \geq 0 \text{ for } j = 1, 2, \cdots n \tag{4-1c}$$

We seek the values of the x_j's that optimize (maximize or minimize) the objective function, equation (4–1a). The coefficients, c_j's, of the x_j's are referred to as *cost coefficients.* These can be positive and negative depending on the problem. Also the values of the x_j's must satisfy the constraint equations, equation (4–1b), and be nonnegative, equation (4–1c).

There are more unknowns than constraint equations after the inequalities have been converted to equalities using slack variables. There will be m positive x_j's that optimize the objective function and the remaining $(n - m)$ x_j's will be zero. In a chemical or refinery process, the independent variables can be flow rates, for example; and the constraint equations can be material and energy balances, availability of raw materials, limits on process unit capacities, demands for products, etc.

The general formulation can also be written as:

$$\text{Optimize: } \sum_{j=1}^{n} c_j x_j \tag{4–2a}$$

$$\text{Subject to: } \sum_{j=1}^{n} a_{ij} x_j \geq b_i \qquad \text{for } i = 1, 2, \cdots, m \tag{4–2b}$$

$$x_j \geq 0 \qquad j = 1, 2, \cdots, n \tag{4–2c}$$

Matrix notation is another convenient method of writing the above:

$$\text{Optimize: } \mathbf{c}^T \mathbf{x} \tag{4–3a}$$

$$\text{Subject to: } \mathbf{A} \mathbf{x} \geq \mathbf{b} \tag{4–3b}$$

$$\mathbf{x} \geq 0 \tag{4–3c}$$

where

$$\mathbf{c}^T = [c_1, c_2, \cdots, c_n]$$

$$\mathbf{x}^T = [x_1, x_2, \cdots, x_n]$$

$$\mathbf{A} = \begin{bmatrix} a_{11} & a_{12} \cdots a_{1n} \\ a_{21} & \cdots & a_{2n} \\ \vdots & & \vdots \\ a_{m1} & a_{m2} \cdots a_{mn} \end{bmatrix} \quad \text{and} \quad \mathbf{b} = \begin{bmatrix} b_1 \\ b_2 \\ \vdots \\ b_m \end{bmatrix}$$

The constraint equations given above have been written as inequalities. However, linear programming requires the constraints be inequalities. In the next section, the use of slack and surplus variables are described to convert the inequalities to equalities.

SLACK AND SURPLUS VARIABLES

In Example 4–1 the constraints equations were inequalities, and the graphical method of locating the optimum was not affected by the constraints being inequalities. However, the computational method to determine the optimum, the Simplex Method, requires equality constraints. As was done in Chapter 2, the inequalities are converted to equalities by introducing slack and surplus variables. This is illustrated by converting the inequality equation (4–4) to an equality, equation (4–5):

$$x_1 + x_2 \leq b \tag{4-4}$$

Here a positive x_3 is being added to the left-hand side of equation (4–4), and x_3 is the slack variable:

$$x_1 + x_2 + x_3 = b \tag{4-5}$$

If the inequality had been of the greater than or equal to type, then a surplus variable would have been subtracted from the left-hand side of the equation to convert it to an equality.

In linear programming it is not necessary to use x_3^2, as in Chapter 2, because the computational method to find the optimum, the Simplex Method, does not allow variables to take on negative values. If the slack variable is zero, as it is in some cases, the largest value of the sum of the other variables $(x_1 + x_2)$ is optimum, and the constraint is tight or active. If the slack variable is positive, then this would represent a difference, or slack, between the optimum values of $(x_1 + x_2)$ and the total value that $(x_1 + x_2)$ could have. In this case the constraint is loose or passive.

BASIC AND BASIC FEASIBLE SOLUTIONS OF THE CONSTRAINT EQUATIONS

Now let us focus on the constraint equation set alone, written as equalities (i.e., slack variables have been added), and discuss the possible solutions that can be obtained. This set can be written as:

$$\mathbf{A}\,\mathbf{x} = \mathbf{b} \tag{4-6}$$

where there are m equations and n unknowns (for convenience using n again, which now would include the slack variables also).

A number of solutions can be generated for this set of linear algebraic equations by selecting $(n - m)$ of the x_j's to be equal to zero. In fact, this number can be computed using the following formula (9):

$$\text{Maximum number of basic solutions} = \frac{n!}{m!\,(n - m)!} \quad (4\text{-}7)$$

[handwritten margin note: Simplex method]
[handwritten: 1) Set (n-m) vars = to zero & solve constraint set for remaining vars. Plug into obj func to get answer]

Thus, a *basic solution* of the constraint equations is a solution obtained by setting $(n - m)$ variables equal to zero and solving the constraint set for the remaining m variables. From this set of basic solutions, the group of solutions is selected where the values of the variables are all nonnegative. This can be estimated by the following formula (18):

$$\text{Approximate number of basic feasible solutions} = 2m \quad (4\text{-}8)$$

[handwritten: 2) If x5 & x6 were zero then choose x4 & x5 or x6 & x1 to be zero. Solve constraints. if answer in step 2 goes the way you want continue if not go other way till min or max is achieved.]

Thus, a *nondegenerate basic feasible solution* is a basic solution where all the m variables are positive. A solution of m variables that are all positive is called a *basis* in the linear programming jargon. *[handwritten: → m = n in this case]*

Let us focus on the objective function, equation (4–1a), now that we have a set of basic feasible solutions from the constraint equations. It turns out that one of the basic feasible solutions is the minimum of the objective function, and another one of these basic feasible solutions is the maximum of the objective function. The Simplex Algorithm begins at a basic feasible solution and moves to the maximum (or minimum) of the objective function stepping from one basic feasible solution to another with ever increasing (or decreasing) values of the objective function until the maximum (or minimum) is reached. The optimum is found in a finite number of steps, usually between m and $2m$ (7).

We will need to know how to obtain the first basic feasible solution and how to apply the Simplex Algorithm. Also, it will be seen that when the maximum (or minimum) is reached, the algorithm has an automatic stopping procedure. Having briefly described the Simplex Method, let us give the procedure, illustrate its use with an example, and present some of the mathematical basis for the methodology in the next section.

OPTIMIZATION WITH THE SIMPLEX METHOD

The Simplex Method is an algorithm that steps from one basic feasible solution (intersection of the constraint equations or vertex) to another basic feasible solution in such a manner that the objective function always increases or decreases. Without attempting to show a model associated with the following linear programming problem (2), let us see how the algorithm operates.

EXAMPLE 4.2

For the following linear programming problem, convert the constraint equations to equality constraints using slack variables:

$$\text{Maximize:} \quad x_1 + 2x_2 \qquad\qquad = P$$

$$\text{Subject to:} \quad 2x_1 + x_2 \le 10 \qquad 2x_1 + x_2 + x_3 = 10$$

$$x_1 + x_2 \le 6 \qquad x_1 + x_2 + x_4 = 6$$

$$-x_1 + x_2 \le 2 \qquad -x_1 + x_2 + x_5 = 2$$

$$-2x_1 + x_2 \le 1 \qquad -2x_1 + x_2 + x_6 = 1$$

$$x_1, \quad x_2 \ge 0$$

n−m
6−4 = 2

When the slack variables are inserted, the constraint equations are converted to equalities, as shown below:

$$\text{Maximize:} \quad x_1 + 2x_2 \qquad\qquad\qquad = p$$

$$\text{Subject to:} \quad 2x_1 + x_2 + x_3 \quad 0 \quad 0 \quad 0 \quad = 10$$

$$x_1 + x_2 \quad 0 + x_4 \quad 0 \quad 0 \quad = 6$$

$$-x_1 + x_2 \quad 0 \quad 0 + x_5 \quad 0 \quad = 2$$

$$-2x_1 + x_2 \quad 0 \quad 0 \quad 0 + x_6 = 1$$

$$x_j \ge 0, j = 1, 2, \cdots, 6.$$

where p represents the value of the objective function.

n−m
6−4 = 2

There are six variables in the set of four constraint equations in Example 4-2. To generate basic solutions, two of the variables are set equal to zero, and the equations are solved for the remaining four variables for the solution. This has been done (2), and all the basic feasible solutions were selected from the basic solutions and listed in Table 4-1. These correspond to the

$x_4 = 0$
$x_5 = 0$ · 2 4 2 1

Table 4-1. Basic feasible solutions of the constraint equations in Example 4-2.

VERTEX	x_1	x_2	x_3	x_4	x_5	x_6	p
A	0	0	10	6	2	1	0
B	0	1	9	5	1	0	2
C	1	3	5	2	0	0	7
D	2	4	2	0	0	1	10
E	4	2	0	0	4	7	8
F	5	0	0	1	7	11	5

vertices of the convex polygon A—B—C—D—E—F, as shown in Figure 4-3. Also shown in Table 4-1 are the values of the objective function evaluated for each basic feasible solution. As can be seen, the maximum of the objective function is at the basic feasible solution, $x_1 = 2$, $x_2 = 4$ (vertex D); and the minimum is at the basic feasible solution, $x_1 = 0$, $x_2 = 0$ (vertex A).

The number of basic solutions is given by equation (4–7). For $n = 6$ and $m = 4$ the number of basic solutions is 15. The approximate number of basic feasible solutions given by equation (4–8) is eight, which is close to the actual number of six. One of the basic solutions of the constraint equations is obtained by setting $x_1 = x_4 = 0$, and the result is:

$$x_1 = 0, \qquad x_2 = 6, \qquad x_3 = 4, \qquad x_4 = 0, \qquad x_5 = -4, \text{ and } x_6 = -5$$

Bad

Here two of the four values of the variables are negative.

Referring to Table 4-1 and Figure 4-3 and comparing the variables in a basis with those in an adjacent basis, it is seen that each has all but one nonzero variable in common. For example, to obtain basis B from basis A it is necessary to remove x_6 from the basis (i.e., set $x_6 = 0$) and bring x_2 into the basis (i.e., solve for $x_2 \neq 0$). The Simplex Method does this and moves from one basic feasible solution to another. Each time it moves in a direction of an improved value of the objective function. This is the key to the Simplex Algorithm. To move in this fashion requires only the use of Gaussian elimination applied to the constraints and then to the objective function to determine its new improved value.

The procedure to solve a linear programming problem using the *Simplex Algorithm to maximize the objective function is:* *→ obj func coeffs must be neg*

1. Place the problem in a linear programming format with linear constraint equations and linear objective function.
2. Introduce slack variables to convert inequalities to equalities, and adjust the constraint equations to have positive right-hand sides.

To minimize: obj func coeffs must be +

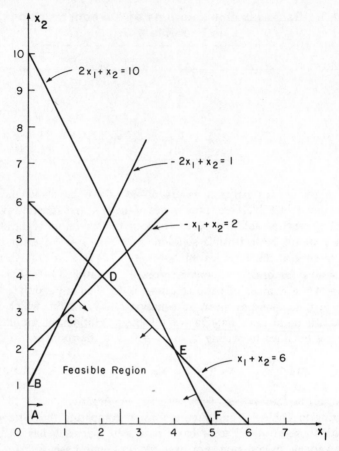

Figure 4-3. Geometric representation of the constraint equations in Example 4-2.

3. Select an initial basic feasible solution. If all the constraint equations were inequalities of the less than or equal to form, the slack variables can be used as the initially feasible basis.
4. Perform algebraic manipulations to express the objective function in terms of variables that are not in the basis, i.e., are equal to zero. This determines the value of the objective function for the variables in the basis. *↗ Enter Basis*
5. Inspect the objective function and select the variable with the largest positive coefficient to bring into the basis, i.e., make nonzero. If there are no positive coefficients, the maximum has been reached (automatic stopping feature of the algorithm).

[handwritten: → Min ratios → Leave basis]

[handwritten margin left: repeat]

6. Inspect the constraint equations to select the one to be used for algebraic manipulations to change the variable in the basis. The selection is made to have positive right-hand sides from the Gaussian elimination. This is necessary to guarantee that all the variables in the new basis will be positive. Use this equation to eliminate the variable selected in step 5 from all the other constraint equations.

7. Use the constraint equation selected in step 6 to eliminate the variable selected in step 5 from the objective function. This moves one of the variables previously in the basis to the objective function, and it is dropped from the basis, i.e., set equal to zero. Also this determines the new value of the objective function.

8. Repeat the procedure of steps 5 through 7 until all coefficients in the objective function are negative, and stop. If the procedure is continued past this point, then the value of the objective function would decrease. This is the automatic stopping feature of the algorithm.

The Simplex Algorithm will be applied to Example 4–2 to illustrate the computational procedure. The first two steps have been completed, and the slack variables will be used as the initial feasible basis (step 3).

EXAMPLE 4–3

Apply the Simplex Method to the linear programming problem of Example 4–2 using the slack variables as the first basic feasible solution.

$$\text{Maximize:} \quad x_1 + 2x_2 \qquad\qquad = p \qquad p = 0$$

$$\text{Subject to:} \quad 2x_1 + x_2 + x_3 \qquad\qquad = 10 \qquad x_3 = 10 \quad \textit{[handwritten: }^{10}\!/_0\textit{]}$$

$$x_1 + x_2 \quad + x_4 \qquad\qquad = 6 \qquad x_4 = 6 \quad \textit{[handwritten: }^6\!/_1\textit{]}$$

$$-x_1 + x_2 \qquad + x_5 \qquad = 2 \qquad x_5 = 2 \quad \textit{[handwritten: }^2\!/_1\textit{]}$$

$$-2x_1 + x_2 \qquad\qquad + x_6 = 1 \qquad x_6 = 1 \quad \textit{[handwritten: }^1\!/_1\textit{] use}$$
[handwritten: Constraint 4]

[handwritten: Eliminate x_2 from everything]

$$x_1 = 0$$

$$x_2 = 0$$

Continuing with the procedure, x_2 is the variable in the objective function with the largest positive coefficient. Thus, increasing x_2 will increase the objective function (step 5). The fourth constraint equation will be used to eliminate x_2 from the objective function (step 6). The variable x_2 is said to enter the basis, and x_6 is to leave.

Proceeding with the Gaussian elimination gives:

Maximize: $5x_1$ $-2x_6 = p - 2$ $p = 2$

Subject to: $4x_1$ $+ x_3$ $- x_6 = 9$ $x_3 = 9$ $9/4$

$3x_1$ $+ x_4$ $- x_6 = 5$ $x_4 = 5$ $5/3$

x_1 $+ x_5 - x_6 = 1$ $x_5 = 1$ $1/1$

$-2x_1 + x_2$ $+ x_6 = 1$ $x_2 = 1$ $-1/2$

$4x_1 - 2x_2$ $-2x_6 = -2$

$x_1 = 0$

$x_6 = 0$

The nonzero variables in the basis are x_2, x_3, x_4, and x_5; and the objective function has increased from $p = 0$ to $p = 2$.

The procedure is repeated (step 8) selecting x_1 to enter the basis. The third constraint equation is used, and x_5 leaves the basis. Performing the manipulations gives:

Maximize: $-5x_5 + 3x_6 = p - 7$ $p = 7$

Subject to: $x_3 - 4x_5 + 3x_6 = 5$ $x_3 = 5$

$x_4 - 3x_5 + 2x_6 = 2$ $x_4 = 2$

x_1 $+ x_5 - x_6 = 1$ $x_1 = 1$

x_2 $+ 2x_5 - x_6 = 3$ $x_2 = 3$

$x_5 = 0$

$x_6 = 0$

The procedure is repeated, and x_6 is selected to enter the basis. The second constraint equation is used, and x_4 leaves the basis. The results of the manipulations are:

Maximize: $\qquad -3/2x_4 - 1/2x_5 \qquad\qquad = p - 10 \quad p = 10$

Subject to: $\qquad x_3 - 3/2x_4 + 1/2x_5 \qquad = 2 \qquad x_3 = 2$

$$1/2x_4 - 3/2x_5 + x_6 \ = 1 \qquad x_6 = 1$$

$$x_1 \qquad + 1/2x_4 - 1/2x_5 \qquad = 2 \qquad x_1 = 2$$

$$x_2 \qquad + 1/2x_4 + 1/2x_5 \qquad = 4 \qquad x_2 = 4$$

$$x_4 = 0$$

$$x_5 = 0$$

All the coefficients in the objective function are negative for the variables that are not in the basis. If x_4 or x_5 were increased from zero to a positive value, the objective function would decrease. Thus, the maximum is reached, and the optimal basic feasible solution has been obtained.

Referring to Table 4-1 and Figure 4-3 for the set of basic feasible solutions, it is seen that the Simplex Method started at vertex A. The first application of the procedure stepped to the adjacent vertex B, with an increase in the objective function to 2. Proceeding, the Simplex Method then moved to vertex C, where the objective function increased to 7. At the next application of the algorithm, the optimum was reached at vertex D with $p = 10$. At this point the application of the Simplex Method stopped because the maximum had been reached.

Let us use this example to demonstrate that the Simplex Method can be used to find the minimum of an objective function by only slightly modifying the logic of the algorithm for maximizing the objective function. If we begin by minimizing the objective function given in the last step of Example 4–3, the largest decrease in the objective function is made by selecting x_4 to enter the basis (step 5), i.e., selecting the variable that is not in the basis and whose coefficient is the largest in absolute value and negative. Then select the second constraint equation for the manipulations to have positive right-hand sides of the constraints. This has x_4 entering the basis, and x_6 leaving the basis. The results are the same as in the next to last step of the example. Proceeding, x_5 is selected to enter the basis, the third constraint equation is used for the manipulations, and x_1 leaves the basis. The results are the same as the second step of the example. Continuing, x_6 is selected to enter the basis, the fourth constraint equation is used for the manipulations, and x_2 leaves the basis. The results are the same as the first step in the example, and all the coefficients of the variables in the objective function are positive for the variables not in the basis. The minimum has been reached, because if either x_1 or x_2 were brought into the basis, i.e., made positive, the objective function would increase.

Thus, the Simplex Algorithm applies for both maximizing or minimizing the objective function. The logic of the algorithm is essentially the same in both cases, and it differs only in the selection of the variable to enter the basis, i.e., largest positive coefficient for maximizing or the largest in absolute value and negative for minimizing.

With this example we have illustrated the computational procedure of the Simplex Algorithm. Also, we have seen that a solution of the constraints gives the maximum of the objective function, and another solution gives the minimum of the objective function. These results can be proven mathematically to be true for the linear programming problem stated as equation (4–1), and the details are given in texts devoted to linear programming. In the following section we will give a standard tabular method for the Simplex Method, and then the key theorems of linear programming will be presented along, with a list of references where more details can be found on mathematical aspects of linear programming.

SIMPLEX TABLEAU

In using the Simplex Method, it is not necessary to write the x_j symbols when doing the Gaussian elimination procedure, and a standard method for hand computations has been developed that uses only the coefficients of the objective function and constraints in a series of tables. This is called the Simplex Tableau, and this procedure will be illustrated using the problem given in Example 4–3.

The Simplex Tableau for the three applications of the Simplex Algorithm of Example 4–3 is shown in Figure 4-4. In this table, dots have been used in places that have to be zero, as opposed to just turning out to be zero. Also, the objective function has been set equal to $-y$, because the tableau procedure minimizes the objective function and is called z, i.e., $z = -y = -x_1 - 2x_2$. Then the objective function is included in the last row of the tableau as $-z - x_1 - 2x_2 = 0$ to have the same form as the constraint equations. Iteration 0 in Table 4-4 is the initial tableau.

The slack variables are the initially feasible basis in this example, and the Simplex Algorithm first locates the smallest coefficient in the objective function of the variables not in the basis. In this case it is x_2 as shown in Figure 4-4 with a coefficient of -2; x_2 will enter the basis, i.e., becomes positive. A pivotal element is located to ensure the next basis is feasible using a minimum ratio test, i.e., selecting the smallest value of (10/1, 6/1,

Iteration	Basis	Value	x_1	x_2	x_3	x_4	x_5	x_6
0	x_3	10	2	1	1	.	.	.
	x_4	6	1	1	.	1	.	.
	x_5	2	-1	1	.	.	1	.
	x_6	1	-2	1*	.	.	.	1
	$-z$	0	-1	-2	.	.	.	.

Initial tableau, x_2 enters basis, x_6 leaves the basis.

Iteration	Basis	Value	x_1	x_2	x_3	x_4	x_5	x_6
1	x_3	9	4	.	1	.	.	-1
	x_4	5	3	.	.	1	.	-1
	x_5	1	1*	.	.	.	1	-1
	x_2	1	-2	1	.	.	.	1
	$-z$	2	-5	.	.	.	.	2

First iteration, x_1 enters the basis, x_5 leaves the basis.

Iteration	Basis	Value	x_1	x_2	x_3	x_4	x_5	x_6
2	x_3	5	.	.	1	.	-4	3
	x_4	2	.	.	.	1	-3	2*
	x_1	1	1	.	.	.	1	-1
	x_2	3	.	1	.	.	2	-1
	$-z$	7	.	.	.	.	5	-3

Second iteration, x_6 enters the basis, x_4 leaves the basis.

Iteration	Basis	Value	x_1	x_2	x_3	x_4	x_5	x_6
3	x_3	2	.	.	1	-3/2	1/2	.
	x_6	1	.	.	.	1/2	-3/2	1
	x_1	2	1	.	.	1/2	-1/2	.
	x_2	4	.	1	.	1/2	1/2	.
	$-z$	10	.	.	.	3/2	1/2	.

Final iteration, coefficients are positive, minimum has been reached

*Pivotal element from the minimum ratio test

Figure 4-4.   Illustration of Simplex Tableau.

2/1, 1/1), and the pivotal element is indicated as an asterisk identifying the pivotal row used for the Gaussian elimination to move to iteration 1, with x_6 leaving the basis.

The above procedure is repeated for two more iterations, as shown in Figure 4-4. The pivotal elements are indicated by an asterisk, having been located by the minimum ratio test. The procedure ends when the values in the objective function row are all positive, for this is a minimizing problem. Also, a comparison of the results in Figure 4-4 with those in Example 4–3 shows the concise nature of the Simplex Tableau. In addition, if a pivotal element cannot be located using the minimum ratio test, this means that the problem has an unbounded solution or a blunder has been made.

The Simplex Tableau procedure can be used effectively for hand calculations when artificial variables are employed to start the solution with an initially feasible basis and to identify problems such as degeneracy. The topics of degeneracy and artificial variables will follow the discussion of the mathematics of linear programming.

MATHEMATICS OF LINEAR PROGRAMMING

The mathematics of convex sets and linear inequalities has to be developed to prove the theorems that establish the previous procedure for locating the optimal solution of the linear programming problem. This is done in many of the standard texts devoted to the subject and is beyond the scope of this brief discussion. However, the appropriate theorems will be given with an explanation, to convey these concepts. Those who are interested in further details are referred to standard works such as Garvin (3) or Gass (7).

A *feasible solution,* is any solution to the constraint equations, equation (4–4) and also is a convex set. A *convex set* is illustrated in Figure 4-5a, for two dimensions and is a collection of points, such that if it contains any two points A and B, it also contains the straight line $\underline{AB}$ between the points. An example of a nonconvex set is shown in Figure 4-5b. Also an *extreme point* or *vertex* of a convex set is a point that does not lie on any segment joining two other points in the set. The important theorem relating convex sets with feasible and basic feasible solutions is:

> *The collection of feasible solutions constitutes a convex set whose extreme points correspond to basic feasible solutions.* (4)

In the proof of the above theorem it is shown that a linear combination of any two feasible solutions is a feasible solution and hence lies on a straight line between the two. Thus, this constitutes a convex set. To prove that a basic feasible solution is an extreme point, it is assumed that a basic feasible

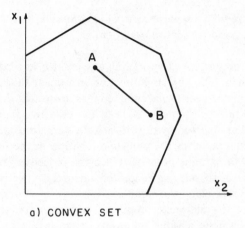

a) CONVEX SET

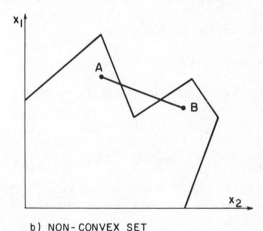

b) NON-CONVEX SET

Figure 4-5. Convex and nonconvex sets.

solution can be expressed as a linear combination of feasible solutions. Then it is shown by contradiction that this is impossible. Thus, it must be an extreme point.

The next important theorem is an existence theorem:

If a feasible solution exists, then a basic feasible solution exists. (5)

This is proved by showing that a basic feasible solution can be constructed from a feasible solution.

The next theorem relates the maximum or minimum of the objective function to the basic feasible solutions of the constraint equations.

If the objective function possesses a finite minimum, then at least one optimal solution is a basic feasible solution. (6)

This theorem can be proved by writing any point P as a convex combination of extreme points. The objective function is a linear function, and it can be written as a sum of linear terms obtained by substituting the convex combination for the point P. Then the value of the objective function evaluated at P is less than that obtained by substituting the minimum value of the objective function for each value of the objective function in the linear combination. Thus, there is an extreme point at which the objective function assumes its minimum value. Also, one can be located where the objective function obtains its maximum value using the same analysis.

To formalize the Simplex computational procedure, consider the set of equations with a basic feasible solution $\mathbf{x} = (x_4, x_5, x_6)$.

$$\text{Maximize: } c_1 x_1 + c_2 x_2 + c_3 x_3 \qquad\qquad = p_0 \qquad (4\text{-}9a)$$

$$\text{Subject to: } a_{11}x_1 + a_{12}x_2 + a_{13}x_3 + x_4 \qquad\quad = b_1$$

$$a_{21}x_1 + a_{22}x_2 + a_{23}x_3 \qquad + x_5 \quad = b_2 \qquad (4\text{-}9b)$$

$$a_{31}x_1 + a_{32}x_2 + a_{33}x_3 \qquad\qquad + x_6 = b_3$$

$$x_j \geq 0 \quad i = 1, 2, \cdots 6$$

If c_1 is the largest positive coefficient and b_1/a_{11} is the smallest positive ratio, then x_1 enters the basis and x_4 leaves the basis. Performing the elimination yields the result:

Maximize:
$$(c_2 - c_1 a_{12}/a_{11})x_2 + (c_3 - c_1 a_{13}/a_{11})x_3 - (c_1 a_{14}/a_{11})x_4 =$$
$$p_0 - c_1 b_1/a_{11} = p_1 \qquad (4\text{-}10a)$$

Subject to:
$$x_1 + a_{12}/a_{11}x_2 + \qquad a_{13}/a_{11}x_3 + \qquad a_{14}/a_{11}x_4 = b_1/a_{11}$$

$$(a_{22} - a_{21}a_{12}/a_{11})x_2 + (a_{23} - a_{21}a_{13}/a_{11})x_3 -$$
$$a_{21}a_{14}/a_{11}x_4 + x_5 = b_2 - a_{21}b_1/a_{11}$$

$$(a_{32} - a_{31}a_{12}/a_{11})x_2 + (a_{33} - a_{31}a_{13}/a_{11})x_3 -$$
$$a_{31}a_{14}/a_{11}x_4 + x_6 = b_3 - a_{31}b_1/a_{11} \qquad (4\text{-}10b)$$

If $p_1 > p_0$, then there is an improvement in the objective function, and the solution is continued. If $p_1 < p_0$, then no improvement in the objective function is obtained, and x is the basic feasible solution that maximizes the objective function. The following theorem given by Gass (7) is:

If for any basic feasible solution $x_k = (x_1, x_2, \cdots, x_m)$ *the condition* $p(x_k) > p(x_j)$ *for all* $j = 1, 2, \cdots, n$ $(j \neq k)$, *then* x_k *is a basic feasible solution that maximizes the objective function.*

The proof of this theorem is similar to that of the previous theorem. Also a corresponding result can be obtained for the basic feasible solution that minimizes the objective function.

Further information is given in the textbooks by Garvin (6), Gass (7), and others in the list of selected texts at the end of the chapter. These books give detailed proofs to the key theorems and other related ones.

DEGENERACY

In the Simplex Method there is an improvement in the objective function in each step as the algorithm converges to the optimum. However, a situation can arise where there is no improvement in the objective function from an application of the algorithm, and this is referred to as *degeneracy*. Also there is a possibility that cycling could occur, and the optimum would not be reached. Degeneracy occurs when the right-hand side of one of the constraint equations is equal to zero, and it is selected for the algebraic manipulation to change variables in the basis and evaluate the objective function. Graphically this occurs when two vertices coalesce into one vertex. It is reported (6) that it is not unusual for degeneracy to occur in the various applications of linear programming. However, there has not been a case of cycling reported. An example of cycling has been constructed, and a procedure to prevent cycling has been developed. However, these are not usually employed. The following example from Garvin (6) illustrates degeneracy, and an optimal solution is found even if it does occur.

EXAMPLE 4–4

Solve the following problem by the Simplex Method:

$$\text{Maximize: } 2x_1 + x_2$$

$$\text{Subject to: } x_1 + 2x_2 \leq 10$$

$$x_1 + x_2 \leq 6$$

$$x_1 - x_2 \leq 2$$

$$x_1 - 2x_2 \leq 1$$

$$2x_1 - 3x_2 \leq 3$$

A graphical representation of the constraint equation is shown in Figure 4-6. It shows that the last three constraint equations all intersect at vertex *C*. Vertex *C* is said to be overdetermined. If the constraint equation $x_1 - 2x_2 \leq 1$ had been $0.9x_1 - 2x_2 \leq 1$, there would have been two separate vertices, as shown in Figure 4-6. Degeneracy occurs when two or more vertices coalesce into a single vertex.

To illustrate what happens, the Simplex Algorithm will be started at vertex

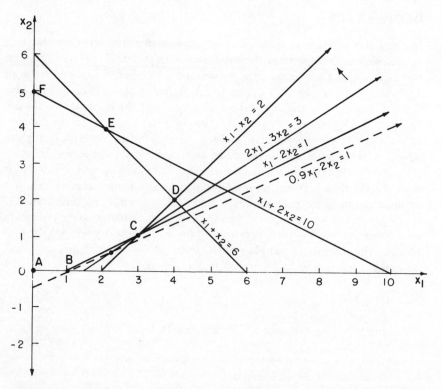

Figure 4-6. Geometric representation of the constraint equations for Example 4-4.

A and move through B and C to D, where the optimal solution is $p = 10$ for $x_1 = 4$ and $x_2 = 2$. Using the slack variables as the initially feasible basis gives:

Vertex A

$$2x_1 + x_2 \qquad\qquad\qquad\qquad = p \qquad p = 0$$

$$x_1 + 2x_2 + x_3 \qquad\qquad\qquad = 10 \qquad x_3 = 10$$

$$x_1 + x_2 \qquad + x_4 \qquad\qquad\quad = 6 \qquad x_4 = 6$$

$$x_1 - x_2 \qquad\qquad + x_5 \qquad\quad = 2 \qquad x_5 = 2$$

$$\rightarrow \quad x_1 - 2x_2 \qquad\qquad\qquad + x_6 \quad\;\; = 1 \qquad x_6 = 1$$

$$2x_1 - 3x_2 \qquad\qquad\qquad\qquad + x_7 = 3 \qquad x_7 = 3$$

x_1 is selected to enter the basis, and x_6 leaves the basis.

Performing the algebraic manipulations, we obtain the following results for vertex B:

Vertex B

$$5x_2 \qquad\qquad -2x_6 \qquad = p - 2 \qquad p = 2$$

$$4x_2 + x_3 \qquad\quad - x_6 \qquad = 9 \qquad x_3 = 9$$

$$3x_2 \quad + x_4 \qquad - x_6 \qquad = 5 \qquad x_4 = 5$$

$$\rightarrow \quad x_2 \qquad\qquad + x_5 - x_6 \qquad = 1 \qquad x_5 = 1$$

$$x_1 - 2x_2 \qquad\qquad + x_6 \qquad = 1 \qquad x_1 = 1$$

$$\text{Used} \rightarrow \quad x_2 \qquad\qquad - 2x_6 + x_7 = 1 \qquad x_7 = 1$$

x_2 is selected to enter the basis, and either the equation with x_5 or the equation with x_7 can be used for the algebraic manipulations. The following calculations use the equation with x_7 and then use the one with x_5 to illustrate the effect of these decisions. (In a computer program the decision would be made rather arbitrarily, e.g., by selecting the one with the lower subscript.)

Performing the algebraic manipulations to have x_7 leave the basis gives:

$$
\begin{array}{llr}
 & & \text{Vertex } C \\
 & +8x_6 - 5x_7 = p - 7 & p = 7 \\
x_3 & +7x_6 - 4x_7 = 5 & x_3 = 5 \\
x_4 + & 5x_6 - 3x_7 = 2 & x_4 = 2 \\
 & x_5 + x_6 - x_7 = 0 & x_5 = 0 \\
x_1 + & -3x_6 + 2x_7 = 3 & x_1 = 3 \\
x_2 & -2x_6 + x_7 = 1 & x_2 = 1
\end{array}
$$

The right-hand side of the third constraint equation is 0, and this causes $x_5 = 0$, which contradicts the fact that variables in the basis are to be greater than zero. However, the procedure is to continue with the Simplex Method, selecting x_6 to enter the basis, and the third constraint equation is used for the algebraic manipulations to have positive (or zero) right-hand sides. x_5 leaves the basis, and the result is:

$$
\begin{array}{llr}
 & & \text{Vertex } C \\
 -8x_5 & +3x_7 = p - 7 & p = 7 \\
x_3 \quad -7x_5 & +3x_7 = 5 & x_3 = 5 \\
x_4 - 5x_5 & +2x_7 = 2 & x_4 = 2 \\
 x_5 + x_6 & - x_7 = 0 & x_6 = 0 \\
x_1 \quad +3x_5 & - x_7 = 3 & x_1 = 3 \\
x_2 \quad +2x_5 & - x_7 = 1 & x_2 = 1
\end{array}
$$

There was no improvement in the objective function, and the Simplex Method did not move from vertex C. The procedure is continued having x_7 enter the basis and x_4 leave the basis. The results of the algebraic manipulations are:

$$
\begin{array}{llr}
 & & \text{Vertex } D \\
 -3/2x_4 - \tfrac{1}{2}x_5 & = p - 10 & p = 10 \\
x_3 - 3/2x_4 + \tfrac{1}{2}x_5 & = 2 & x_3 = 2
\end{array}
$$

$$\tfrac{1}{2}x_4 - \tfrac{5}{2}x_5 \qquad\qquad + x_7 = \quad 1 \qquad x_7 = 1$$

$$\tfrac{1}{2}x_4 - \tfrac{3}{2}x_5 + \quad x_6 \qquad\qquad = \quad 1 \qquad x_6 = 1$$

$$x_1 \qquad\quad + \tfrac{1}{2}x_4 + \tfrac{1}{2}x_5 \qquad = \quad 4 \qquad x_1 = 4$$

$$x_2 \quad + \tfrac{1}{2}x_4 - \tfrac{1}{2}x_5 \qquad = \quad 2 \qquad x_2 = 2$$

The maximum has been reached, because the coefficients of the variables in the objective function are all negative. The Simplex Algorithm was unaffected by the right-hand side of one of the equations becoming zero during the application of the algorithm.

Now returning to vertex B and selecting x_5 to enter the basis, the result of the manipulations is:

Vertex C

$$-5x_5 + 3x_6 \qquad = p - 7 \qquad p = 7$$

$$x_3 \quad -4x_5 + 3x_6 \qquad = \quad 5 \qquad x_3 = 5$$

$$\rightarrow \qquad x_4 - 3x_5 + 2x_6 \qquad = \quad 2 \qquad x_4 = 2$$

$$x_2 \qquad + \; x_5 - x_6 \qquad = \quad 1 \qquad x_2 = 1$$

$$x_1 \qquad\quad + 2x_5 - x_6 \qquad = \quad 3 \qquad x_1 = 3$$

$$- \; x_5 - \; x_6 + x_7 = \quad 0 \qquad x_7 = 0$$

Selecting x_6 to enter the basis and x_4 to leave the basis, the result of the manipulations is the optimum given at vertex D previously. Consequently using x_5 there is an improvement in the objective function, and one fewer applications of the Simplex Algorithm were required.

Unfortunately, the effect of a constraint equation selection with degeneracy cannot be predicted in advance for large problems, and an arbitrary selection is made, as previously mentioned. In conclusion, degeneracy is not unusual, but it has yet to affect the solution of linear programming problems in industrial applications.

ARTIFICIAL VARIABLES

To start a linear programming problem it is necessary to have an initially feasible basis as required in step 3 of the Simplex Method and as shown in equation (4–9b). In the illustrations up to now, we have been able to use the slack variables as the initially feasible basis. However, the constraints generally are not in such a convenient form, so another procedure is used, artificial variables. In this technique a new variable, an artificial variable, is added to each constraint equation to give an initial feasible basis to start the solution. This is permissible, and it can be shown that the optimal solution to the original problem is the optimal solution to the problem with artificial variables. However, it is necessary to modify the objective function to ensure that all the artificial variables leave the basis. This is accomplished by adding terms to the objective functions that consist of the product of each artificial variable and a negative coefficient that can be made arbitrarily large in magnitude for the case of maximizing the objective function. Thus, this will ensure that the artificial variables are the first ones to leave the basis during the application of the Simplex Method.

At this point it is reasonable to question if this would not be a significant amount of computations for convenience only. The answer would be yes if only one small linear programming problem were to be solved. However, this is not usually the case, and the margin for error is reduced significantly by avoiding manipulation of the constraint equations in a large problem. In fact, large linear programming codes require only the specification of the values of the coefficients in the objective function and the coefficients, right-hand sides, and the types of inequalities of the constraint equations to obtain an optimal solution. These programs can solve linear programming problems having thousands of constraints and thousands of variables (12). Consequently, developing a linear model of a plant or a process is the main effort required, and then one of the available general linear programming codes can be used to obtain the optimal solution. Also, most major companies have a group that includes experts in using linear programming, and also, there are firms that specialize in industrial applications of linear programming.

The following example illustrates the use of artificial variables as they might be employed in a computer program. The technique is sometimes called the "big M method."

EXAMPLE 4–5 (8)

Solve the following linear programming problem using artificial variables:

$$\text{Minimize:} \quad x_1 + 3x_2$$

$$\text{Subject to:} \quad x_1 + 4x_2 \geq 24$$

$$5x_1 + x_2 \geq 25$$

I.E. ¡≠ to Zero

Slack variables x_3 and x_4 and artificial variables a_1 and a_2 are introduced as shown below. The artificial variables will be the initially feasible basis, because the slack variable would give negative values and algebraic manipulations would be required to have x_1 and x_2 be the initially feasible basis. In the objective function M is the coefficient of the artificial variables a_1 and a_2, and M can be made arbitrarily large to drive a_1 and a_2 from the basis:

Minimize: $x_1 + 3x_2$ $+ Ma_1 + Ma_2 = c$

n - m
6 - 2 = 4
4 vars are Zero at a time

Subject to: $x_1 + 4x_2 - x_3$ (*Surplus vars*) $+ a_1 \qquad = 24$

$5x_1 + x_2$ (*Surplus vars*) $- x_4$ $+ a_2 = 25$

x_1
x_2 ≤ 0
x_3
x_4

The two constraints equations are used to eliminate a_1 and a_2 from the objective function. This is step 4 in the Simplex Method, and the objective function is a large number, $49M$, as shown below:

$(1 - 6M)x_1 + (3 - 5M)x_2 + Mx_3 + Mx_4$ $= c - 49M \quad c = 49M$

$x_1 + \qquad 4x_2 - x_3 \qquad - a_1 \qquad = 24 \qquad a_1 = 24$ *²⁴/₁*

$5x_1 + \qquad x_2 \qquad - x_4 + a_2 = 25 \qquad a_2 = 25$ *²⁵/₅*

Applying the Simplex Algorithm, x_1 enters the basis because it has the negative coefficient that is largest in magnitude. The second constraint equation is used to perform the algebraic manipulations, and a_2 leaves the basis. Performing the manipulations gives:

$(14/5 - 19/5M)x_2 + Mx_3 + (1/5 - 1/5M)x_4$
$\qquad\qquad\qquad - (1/5 - 6/5M)a_2 = c - 19M - 5$

$19/5x_2 - x_3 + \qquad 1/5x_4 \quad + a_1 \qquad - 1/5a_2 = 19$

$x_1 \qquad + 1/5x_2 \qquad\qquad - 1/5x_4 \quad + \qquad\qquad 1/5a_2 = 5$

$c = 19M + 5 \qquad a_1 = 19 \qquad\qquad x_1 = 5$

Continuing with the Simplex Algorithm, x_2 enters the basis. The first constraint equation is used for the algebraic manipulations, and a_1 leaves the basis. Performing the manipulations gives:

$$14/19x_3 + 5/95x_4 + (-14/19 + M)a_1 \qquad + (-5/95 + M)a_2 = c - 19$$

$$x_2 - 5/19x_3 + 1/19x_4 + \qquad 5/19a_1 - \qquad 1/19a_2 = 5$$

$$x_1 + \qquad 1/19x_3 - 18/95x_4 - \qquad 1/19a_1 + \qquad 20/95a_2 = 4$$

$$c = 19 \qquad x_1 = 4 \qquad x_2 = 5$$

Now the terms containing the artificial variables a_1 and a_2 can be dropped from the objective function and the constraint equations. The reason is that they both have large positive coefficients in the objective function and will not reenter the basis. The problem is continued without them to reduce computational effort. However, for this problem the optimum has been reached, all the coefficients in the objective function being positive, and no further reduction can be obtained. $\qquad\qquad$ *For minimum*

In addition to the infeasible difficulty discussed on page 84, there is another problem that can be encountered in linear programming, an *unbounded problem*, which is usually caused by a blunder. In this situation, the constraint equations do not confine the variables to finite values. This is illustrated by changing the linear programming problem in Example 4–5 from one of minimizing $x_1 + 3x_2$ to maximizing $x_1 + 3x_2$ subject to the constraints given in the problem. The constraints are of the greater than or equal to type, and they are satisfied with values of $x_1 \geq 4$ and $x_2 \geq 5$. Then for maximizing the objective function, the values of x_1 and x_2 could be increased without bounds to have the objective function also increase without bonds. Thus, the problem is said to be unbounded.

FORMULATING THE LINEAR PROGRAMMING PROBLEM—A SIMPLE REFINERY

To this point in the discussion of linear programming, the emphasis has been on the solution of problems by the Simplex Method. In this section procedures will be presented for the formulation of the linear programming problem for a plant or process. This will include developing the objective function from the cost or profit of the process or plant and the constraint equations from the availability of raw materials, the demand for products, and equipment capacity limitations and conversion capabilities. A simple petroleum refinery will be used as an example to illustrate these procedures. Also an optimal solution will be obtained using a large linear programming code to illustrate the use of one of these types of programs available on a large computer. In the following section the optimal solution of the general linear programming problem will be extended to a sensitivity analysis, and these results will be illustrated using the information computed from the large linear programming code for the simple refinery example.

Figure 4-7 shows the flow diagram for the simple petroleum refinery, and Table 4-2 defines the name of each of the process streams. There are only three process units in this refinery, and these are a crude oil atmospheric distillation column, a catalytic cracking unit, and a catalytic reformer. The crude oil distillation column separates the crude oil into five streams: fuel gas, straight-run gasoline, straight-run naphtha, straight-run distillate, and straight-run fuel oil. Part of the straight-run naphtha is processed through the catalytic reformer to improve its quality, i.e., increase the octane number. Also parts of the straight-run distillate and straight-run fuel oil are processed through the catalytic cracking unit to improve their quality so they can be blended into gasoline. The refinery produces four products: premium gasoline, regular gasoline, diesel fuel, and fuel oil. Even for this simple refinery there are 33 flow rates for which the optimal values have to be determined. This small problem points out one of the difficulties of large linear programming problems. The formulation of the problem is quite straightforward. However,

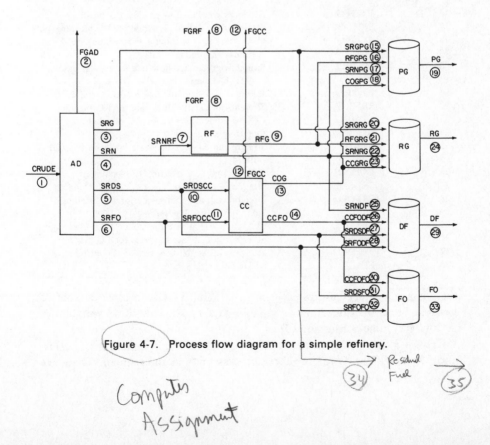

Figure 4-7. Process flow diagram for a simple refinery.

Table 4-2. Definition of the Names of the Process Streams for the Simple Petroleum Refinery.

NO.	NAME	DEFINITION (FLOW RATES ARE IN BARRELS PER DAY)
1	CRUDE	Crude oil flow rate to the atmospheric crude distillation column (AD)
2	FGAD	Fuel gas flow rate from AD
3	SRG	Straight-run gasoline flow rate from AD
4	SRN	Straight-run naphtha flow rate from AD
5	SRDS	Straight-run distillate flow rate from AD
6	SRFO	Straight-run fuel oil flow rate from AD
7	SRNRF	Straight-run naphtha feed rate to the reformer (RF)
8	FGRF	Fuel gas flow rate from the reformer
9	RFG	Reformer gasoline flow rate
10	SRDSCC	Straight-run distillate flow rate to the catalytic cracking unit (CCU)
11	SRFOCC	Straight-run fuel oil flow rate to the CCU
12	FGCC	Fuel gas flow rate from the CCU
13	CCG	Gasoline flow rate from CCU
14	CCFO	Fuel oil flow rate from CCU
15	SRGPG	Straight-run gasoline flow rate for premium gasoline (PG) blending
16	RFGPG	Reformer gasoline flow rate for PG blending
17	SRNPG	Straight-run naphtha flow rate for PG blending
18	CCGPG	CCU gasoline flow rate for PG blending
19	PG	Premium gasoline flow rate
20	SRGRG	Straight-run gasoline flow rate for regular gasoline (RG) blending
21	RFGRG	Reformer gasoline flow rate for RG blending
22	SRNRG	Straight-run naphtha flow rate for RG blending
23	CCGRG	CCU gasoline flow rate for RG blending
24	RG	Regular gasoline flow rate
25	SRNDF	Straight-run naphtha flow rate for diesel fuel (DF) blending
26	CCFODF	CCU fuel oil flow rate for DF blending
27	SRDSDF	Straight-run distillate flow rate for DF blending
28	SRFODF	Straight-run fuel oil flow rate for DF blending
29	DF	No. 2 diesel fuel flow rate
30	CCFOFO	CCU fuel oil flow rate for fuel oil (FO) blending
31	SRDSFO	Straight-run distillate flow rate for FO blending
32	SRFOFO	Straight-run fuel oil flow rate for FO blending
33	FO	No. 6 fuel oil flow rate

there is a major accounting problem in keeping track of a large number of variables, and the collection of reliable data to go with these variables is usually very time-consuming (9).

Table 4-3 lists the capacities, operating costs, process stream, mass yields, and volumetric yields for the three process units in the refinery. These are

Table 4-3. Capacities, Operating Costs, and Volumetric Yields for the Refinery Process Units.

UNIT	CAPACITY (BBL/DAY)	OPERATING COST ($/BBL)	INPUT	OUTPUT	MASS YIELD OF OUTPUT STREAM (LB/LB)	VOLUMETRIC YIELDS OF OUTPUT STREAMS (BBL/BBL)
Crude oil	100,000	1.00	CRUDE	FGAD	0.029	35.42
Atmospheric				SRG	0.236	0.270
Distillation				SRN	0.223	0.236
Column				SRDS	0.087	0.087
				SRFO	0.426	0.372
Catalytic	25,000	2.50	SRNRF	FGRF	0.138	158.7
Reformer				RFG	0.862	0.928
Catalytic	30,000	2.20	SRDSCC	FGCC	0.273	336.9
Cracking				CCG	0.536	0.619
Unit				CCFO	0.191	0.189
			SRFOCC	FGCC	0.277	386.4
				CCG	0.527	0.688
				CCFO	0.196	0.220

typical of a medium-size refinery in the Gulf Coast area. The mass yields were taken from those reported by Aronofsky, Dutton, and Tayyabkhan (10) and were converted to volumetric yields by using API gravity data. The operating costs were furnished by the technical division of a major oil company that has refineries on the Gulf Coast.

The quality specification and physical properties are given in Table 4-4

Table 4-4. Quality Specifications and Physical Properties for Products and Intermediate Streams for the Refinery.

STREAM	MOTOR OCTANE NUMBER	VAPOR PRESSURE (MM HG)	DENSITY (LB/BBL)	SULFUR CONTENT (LB/BBL)
Premium gasoline	≥93.0	≤12.7	–	–
Regular gasoline	≥87.0	≤12.7	–	–
Diesel fuel	–	–	≤306.0	≤0.5
Fuel oil	–	–	≤352.0	≤3.0
SRG	78.5	18.4	–	–
RFG	104.0	2.57	–	–
SNR	65.0	6.54	272.0	0.283
CCG	93.7	6.90	–	–
CCFO	–	–	294.4	0.353
SRDS	–	–	292.0	0.526
SRFO	–	–	295.0	0.980

Table 4-5. Crude Oil Cost and Product Sales Prices for the Petroleum Refinery.

Gulf Coast crude oil	$32.00/bbl
Premium gasoline	$45.36/bbl
Regular gasoline	$43.68/bbl
No. 2 diesel fuel	$40.32/bbl
No. 6 fuel oil	$13.14/bbl
Fuel gas	$ 3.50/MSCF or $ 0.01965/bbl

(handwritten) PIMS

(handwritten) 32 crude ↓ op cost   w/ cat cracking

	CRUDE	FGAD	SRG	SRN	SRDS	SRFO	SRNRF	FGRF	RFG	SRDSCC	SRFOCC	FGCC	CCG	CCFO	SRGPG	RFGPG	SRNPG	CCGPG	PG
Objective Function	-33.0	.01965					-2.50	.01965		-2.20	-2.20	.01965							45.36
Crude Availability	1.0																		
Products																			
Premium Gasoline																			
Min. PG Prod.																			1.0
PG Blending															1.0	1.0	1.0	1.0	-1.0
PG Octane Rating															78.5	104.0	65.0	93.7	-93.0
PG Vapor Press.															18.4	2.57	6.54	6.90	-12.7
Regular Gasoline																			
Min. RG Prod.																			
RG Blending																			
RG Octane Rating																			
RG Vapor Press.																			
Diesel Fuel																			
Min. DF Prod.																			
DF Blending																			
DF Density Spec.																			
DF Sulfur Spec.																			
Fuel Oil																			
Min. FO Prod.																			
FO Blending																			
FO Density Spec.																			
FO Sulfur Spec.																			
Process Units																			
Atm. Distillation																			
AD Capacity	1.0																		
FGAD Yield	35.42	-1.0																	
SRG Yield	0.270		-1.0																
SRN Yield	0.237			-1.0															
SRDS Yield	0.087				-1.0														
SRFO Yield	0.372					-1.0													
Reformer																			
RF Capacity							1.0												
FGRF Yield							158.7	-1.0											
RFG Yield							0.928		-1.0										
Catalytic Cracker																			
CC Capacity										1.0	1.0								
FGCC Yield										336.9	386.4	-1.0							
CCG Yield										0.619	0.688		-1.0						
CCFO Yield										0.189	0.220			-1.0					
Stream Splits																			
SRG			1.0												-1.0				
SRN				1.0			-1.0										-1.0		
SRDS					1.0					-1.0									
SRFO						1.0					-1.0								
RFG									1.0							-1.0			
CCG													1.0					-1.0	
CCFO														1.0					-1.0

Figure 4-8. Refinery objective function and constraint equations.

(handwritten annotations)

-- Residual Fuel / min RF Prod / RT Blending

1 ≥ 5000 RF min / RFBlend

1 - 1 = 0 RFBlend (In = out)

for the process streams, and the crude oil cost and the product sales prices are given in Table 4-5. The data in Table 4-4 were reported by Aronofsky et al. (29), and the cost and prices in Table 4-5 were obtained from the *Oil and Gas Journal* (11). The information given in Tables 4-3, 4-4, and 4-5 is required to construct the objective function and the constraint equations for the linear programming model of the refinery.

It is standard practice to present the linear programming problem for the refinery in matrix form, as shown in Figure 4-8. In the first row the coefficients of the terms in the objective function are listed under their corresponding variables. The sales prices are shown as positive, and the costs are shown as negative, so the problem is formulated to maximize the profit. These numbers were taken from Table 4-5, and it was convenient to combine the crude cost ($32.00/barrel) with the operating cost of the crude oil atmospheric distillation column ($1.00/barrel) to show a total cost of $33.00 per

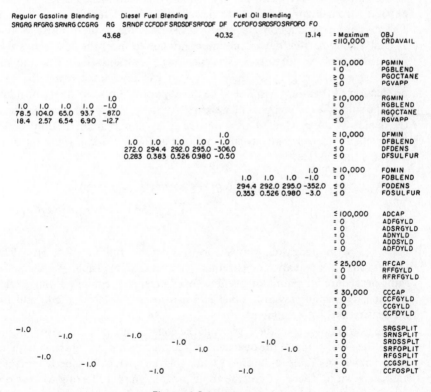

Figure 4-8 *(continued)*

barrel of crude oil processed in Figure 4-7. Consequently, the first row of Figure 4-8 represents the objective function given below:

$$-33.0 \text{ CRUDE} + 0.01965 \text{ FGAD} - 2.50 \text{ SRNRF} + 0.01965 \text{ FGRF}$$

$$- 2.20 \text{ SRDSCC} - 2.20 \text{ SRFOCC} + 0.01965 \text{ FGCC} + 45.36 \text{ PG}$$

$$+ 43.68 \text{ RG} + 40.32 \text{ DF} + 13.14 \text{ FO}$$

The constraint equations begin with the second row in Figure 4-8. They are grouped in terms of quality and quantity constraints on the crude and products, in terms of the performance of the process unit using the volumetric yields, and in terms of the stream splits among the process units and blending into the products.

The second row is the crude availability constraint limiting the refinery to 110,000 barrels/day. This is followed by the four quantity and quality constraints associated with each product. These are the daily production and blending requirements and two quality constraints. These have been extracted from Figure 4-8 and are shown in Table 4-6 for the four products. The minimum production constraint states that the refinery must produce at least 10,000 barrels/day of premium gasoline to meet the company's marketing division's requirements. The blending constraints state that the sum of the streams going to produce premium gasoline, must equal the daily production of premium gasoline. The quality constraints use linear blending, and the sum of each component weighted by its quality must meet or exceed the quality of the product. This is illustrated by the premium gasoline octane rating blending constraint, which is written as the following, using the information from the matrix:

$$78.5 \text{ SRGPG} + 104.0 \text{ RFGPG} + 65.0 \text{ SRNPG} + 93.7 \text{ CCGPC}$$

$$- 93.0 \text{ PG} \geq 0 \quad (4\text{-}11)$$

Here the premium gasoline must have an octane number of at least 93.0. Corresponding inequality constraints are specified in Table 4-6 using the same procedure for premium gasoline vapor pressure, regular gasoline octane number and vapor pressure, diesel fuel density and sulfur content, and fuel oil density and sulfur content.

The next set of information, given in the constraint equation matrix, Figure 4-8, is the description of the operation of the process unit using the volumetric yield shown in Table 4-3. This section of the matrix has been extracted and is shown in Table 4-7 for the three process units. Referring to the volumetric yields for the crude oil distillation column, these data state that 35.42

Table 4-6. Quantity and Quality Constraints for the Refinery
Products.

Premium gasoline

	SRGPC	RFGPG	SRNPG	CCGPG	PG	RHS
Min. PG production					1.0	≥10,000
PG blending	1.0	1.0	1.0	1.0	−1.0	=0
PG octane rating	78.5	104.0	65.0	93.7	−93.0	≥0
PG vapor pressure	18.4	2.57	6.54	6.90	−12.7	≤0

Regular gasoline

	SRGRG	RFGRG	SRNRG	CCGRG	RG	RHS
Min. RG production					1.0	≥10,000
RG blending	1.0	1.0	1.0	1.0	−1.0	=0
RG octane rating	78.5	104.0	65.0	93.7	−87.0	≥0
RG vapor pressure	18.4	2.57	6.54	6.90	−12.7	≤0

Diesel fuel

	SRNDF	CCFODF	SRDSDF	SRFODF	DF	RHS
Min. DF production					1.0	≥10,000
DF blending	1.0	1.0	1.0	1.0	−1.0	=0
DF density spec.	272.0	294.4	292.0	295.0	−306.0	≤0
DF sulfur spec.	0.283	0.353	0.526	0.980	−0.50	≤0

Fuel oil

	CCFOFO	SRDSFO	SRFOFO	FO	RHS
Min. FO production				1.0	≥10,000
FO blending	1.0	1.0	1.0	−1.0	=0
FO density spec.	294.4	292.0	295.0	−352.0	≤0
FO sulfur spec.	0.353	0.526	0.980	−3.0	≤0

times the volumetric flow rate of crude produces the flow rate of fuel gas
from the distillation column, FGAD, i.e.:

$$35.42 \; CRUDE - FGAD = 0 \qquad (4\text{--}12)$$

Corresponding yields of the other products from the crude oil distillation
are determined the same way. For the catalytic reformer the yield of the
fuel gas (FGRF) and the reformer gasoline (RFG) are given by the following
equations:

$$158.7 \; SRNRF - FGRF = 0 \qquad (4\text{--}13)$$

$$0.928 \; SRNRF - RFG = 0 \qquad (4\text{--}14)$$

Table 4-7. Process Unit Material Balances Using Volumetric Yields.

Crude oil atmospheric distillation column

	CRUDE	FGAD	SRG	SRN	SRDS	SRFO	RHS
AD capacity	1.0						≤100,000
FGAD yield	35.42	−1.0					=0
SRG yield	0.270		−1.0				=0
SRN yield	0.236			−1.0			=0
SRDS yield	0.086				−1.0		=0
SRFO yield	0.372					−1.0	=0

Catalytic reformer

	SRNRF	FGRF	RFG	RHS
RF capacity	1.0			≤25,000
FGRF yield	158.7	−1.0		=0
RFG yield	0.928		−1.0	=0

Catalytic cracking unit

	SRDSCC	SRFOCC	FGCC	CCG	CCFO	RHS
CC capacity	1.0	1.0				≤30,000
FGCC yield	336.9	386.4	−1.0			=0
CCG yield	0.619	0.688		−1.0		=0
CCFO yield	0.189	0.220			−1.0	=0

Similar equations are used in the matrix of Figure 4-8 and are summarized in Table 4-7 for the catalytic cracking unit.

The use of volumetric yields to give linear equations to describe the performance of the process units is required for linear programming. The results will be satisfactory as long as the volumetric yields precisely describe the performance of these process units. These volumetric yields are a function of the operating conditions of the unit, e.g., temperature, feed flow rate, catalyst activity, etc. Consequently, to have an optimal solution these volumetric yields must represent the best performance of the individual process units. To account for changes in volumetric yields with operating conditions, sometimes a separate simulation program is coupled to the linear programming code to furnish best values of the volumetric yields. Then an iterative procedure is used to converge optimal linear programming flow rates with corresponding values of volumetric yields from the simulation program. (See Figure 6-5.)

The last group of terms in Figure 4-8 gives the material balance around points where streams split among process units and blend into products.

The stream to be divided is given a coefficient of 1, and the resulting streams have a coefficient -1. For example, the straight-run naphtha from the crude oil distillation is split into four streams. One is sent to the catalytic reformer, and the other three are used in blending premium gasoline, regular gasoline, and diesel fuel. The equation for this split is:

$$SRN - SRNRF - SRNPG - SRNRG - SRNDF = 0 \qquad (4-15)$$

There are a total of seven stream splits, as shown in Figure 4-8.

This information is now available to determine the optimum operating conditions of the refinery. The optimal solution was obtained using the Mathematical Programming System Extended (MPSX) program run on the IBM 4341. The format used by this linear programming code has become an industry standard according to Murtagh (12) and is not restricted to the MPS series of codes developed originally for IBM computers. Consequently, we will also describe the input procedure for the code because of its more general nature. Also, we will use these refinery results to illustrate the additional information that can be obtained from sensitivity analysis.

SOLVING THE LINEAR PROGRAMMING PROBLEM FOR THE SIMPLE REFINERY

Having constructed the linear programming problem matrix, we are now ready to solve the problem using a large linear programming computer program. The input and output for these programs have become relatively standard (12), making the study of one beneficial in the use of any of the others. The solution of the simple refinery has been obtained using the IBM Mathematical Programming System Extended (MPSX). The detailed documentation is given in IBM manuals (15, 16) and by Murtagh (12) on the use of the program, and the following outlines its use for the refinery problem. The MPSX control program used to solve the problem is given in Table 4-8. The first two commands, PROGRAM and INITIALZ, define the beginning of the program and set up standard default values for many of the optional program parameters. TITLE writes the character string between the quotation marks at the top of every page of output. The four MOVE commands give user-specified names to the input data (XDATA), internal machine code version of the problem (XPBNAME), objective function (XOBJ), and right-hand-side vector (XRHS). Next, CONVERT calls a routine to convert the input data from binary coded decimal (BCD), or communications format, into machine code for use by the program, and BCDOUT has the input data printed. The next three commands, SETUP, CRASH, and PRIMAL, indicate that the objective function is to be maximized, a starting basis is

**Table 4-8.   Mathematical Programming System Control
Program for the Simple Refinery.**

```
PROGRAM

INITIALZ

TITLE('SIMPLE REFINERY MODEL')

MOVE(XDATA,'REFINERY')

MOVE(XPBNAME,'REFINERY')

MOVE(XOBJ,'OBJ')

MOVE(XRHS,'RHS')

CONVERT('SUMMARY')

BCDOUT

SETUP('MAX')

CRASH

PRIMAL

SOLUTION

RANGE

EXIT

PEND
```

to be created, and the primal method is to be used to solve the problem.
Output from PRIMAL is in machine code, so SOLUTION is called to produce
BCD output of the solution. The RANGE command is used in the sensitivity
analysis to determine the range over which the variables, right-hand sides,
and coefficients may vary without changing the basis. The last two statements,
EXIT and PEND, signal the end of the control program and return control
to the computer's operating system.

Input to the MPSX program is divided into four sections: NAME, ROWS,
COLUMNS, and RHS. The first two are shown in Table 4-9. The NAME
section is a single line containing the identifier, NAME, and the user-defined
name for the block of input data that follows. (MPSX has provisions for
keeping track of several problems during execution of the control program.)
When the program is run its looks for input data with the same name as

Table 4-9. MPSX Input NAME and ROWS Sections.

NAME		REFINERY
ROWS		
N	OBJ	
L	CRDAVAIL	
G	PGMIN	
E	PGBLEND	
G	PGOCTANE	
L	PGVAPP	
G	RGMIN	
E	RGBLEND	
G	RGOCTANE	
L	RGVAPP	
G	DFMIN	
E	DFBLEND	
L	DFDENS	
L	DFSULFUR	
G	FOMIN	
E	FOBLEND	
L	FODENS	
L	FOSULFUR	
L	ADCAP	
E	ADFCYLD	
E	ADSRGYLD	
E	ADNYLD	
E	ADDSYLD	
E	ADFOYLD	
L	RFCAP	
E	RFFGYLD	
E	RFRFGYLD	
L	CCCAP	
E	CCFGYLD	
E	CCGYLD	
E	CCFOYLD	
E	SRGSPLIT	
E	SRNSPLIT	
E	SRDSSPLT	
E	SRFOSPLT	
E	RFGSPLIT	
E	CCGSPLIT	
E	CCFOSPLT	

that stored in the internal variable XDATA. The ROWS section contains the name of every row in the model, preceded by a letter indicating whether it is a nonconstrained row (N), the objective function, a less-than-or-equal-to constraint (L), a greater-than-or-equal-to constraint (G), or an equality constraint (E).

The COLUMNS section of the input data is shown in Table 4-10. It is a listing of the nonzero elements in each column of the problem matrix (Figure

Table 4-10.   MPSX Input COLUMNS Section.

COLUMNS				
CRUDE	OBJ	-33.0	CRDAVAIL	1.0
CRUDE	ADCAP	1.0	ADFGYLD	35.42
CRUDE	ADSRGYLD	0.270	ADNYLD	0.237
CRUDE	ADDSYLD	0.087	ADFOYLD	0.372
FGAD	OBJ	0.01965	ADFGYLD	-1.0
SRG	ADSRGYLD	-1.0	SRGSPLIT	1.0
SRN	ADNYLD	-1.0	SRNSPLIT	1.0
SRDS	ADDSYLD	-1.0	SRDSSPLT	1.0
SRFO	ADFOYLD	-1.0	SRFOSPLT	1.0
SRNRF	OBJ	-2.50	RFCAP	1.0
SRNRF	RFFGYLD	158.7	RFRFGYLD	0.928
SRNRF	SRNSPLIT	-1.0		
FGRF	OBJ	0.01965	FGRFYLD	-1.0
RFG	RFRFGYLD	-1.0	RFGSPLIT	1.0
SRDSCC	OBJ	-2.20	CCCAP	1.0
SRDSCC	CCFGYLD	336.9	CCGYLD	0.619
SRDSCC	CCFOYLD	0.189	SRDSSPLT	-1.0
SRFOCC	OBJ	-2.20	CCCAP	1.0
SRFOCC	CCFGYLD	386.4	CCGYLD	0.688
SRFOCC	CCFOYLD	0.2197	SRFOSPLT	-1.0
FGCC	OBJ	0.01965	CCFGYLD	-1.0
CCG	CCGYLD	-1.0	CCGSPLIT	1.0
CCFO	CCFOYLD	-1.0	CCFOSPLT	1.0
SRGPG	PGBLEND	1.0	PGOCTANE	78.5
SRGPG	PGVAPP	18.4	SRGSPLIT	-1.0
RFGPG	PGBLEND	1.0	PGOCTANE	104.0
RFGPG	PGVAPP	2.57	RFGSPLIT	-1.0
SRNPG	PGBLEND	1.0	PGOCTANE	65.0
SRNPG	PGVAPP	6.54	SRNSPLIT	-1.0
CCGPG	PGBLEND	1.0	PGOCTANE	93.7
CCGPG	PGVAPP	6.90	CCGSPLIT	-1.0
PG	OBJ	45.36	PGMIN	1.0
PG	PGBLEND	-1.0	PGOCTANE	-93.0
PG	PGVAPP	-12.7		
SRGRG	RGBLEND	1.0	RGOCTANE	78.5
SRGRG	RGVAPP	18.4	SRGSPLIT	-1.0
RFGRG	RGBLEND	1.0	RGOCTANE	104.0
RFGRG	RGVAPP	2.57	RFGSPLIT	-1.0
SRNRG	RGBLEND	1.0	RGOCTANE	65.0
SRNRG	RGVAPP	6.54	SRNSPLIT	-1.0
CCGRG	RGBLEND	1.0	RGOCTANE	93.7
CCGRG	RGVAPP	6.90	CCGSPLIT	-1.0
RG	OBJ	43.68	RGMIN	1.0
RG	RGBLEND	-1.0	RGOCTANE	-87.0
RG	RGVAPP	-12.7		
SRNDF	DFBLEND	1.0	DFDENS	272.0
SRNDF	DFSULFUR	0.283	SRNSPLIT	-1.0
CCFODF	DFBLEND	1.0	DFDENS	294.4
CCFODF	DFSULFUR	0.353	CCFOSPLT	-1.0
SRDSDF	DFBLEND	1.0	DFDENS	292.0

Table 4-10. Continued

SRDSDF	DFSULFUR	0.526	SRDSSPLT	-1.0
SRFODF	DFBLEND	1.0	DFDENS	295.0
SRFODF	DFSULFUR	0.98	SRFOSPLT	-1.0
DF	OBJ	40.32	DFMIN	1.0
DF	DFBLEND	-1.0	DFDENS	-306.0
DF	DFSULFUR	-0.5		
CCFOFO	FOBLEND	1.0	FODENS	294.4
CCFOFO	FOSULFUR	0.353	CCFOSPLT	-1.0
SRDSFO	FOBLEND	1.0	FODENS	292.0
SRDSFO	FOSULFUR	0.526	SRDSSPLT	-1.0
SRFOFO	FOBLEND	1.0	FODENS	295.0
SRFOFO	FOSULFUR	0.98	SRFOSPLT	-1.0
FO	OBJ	13.14	FOMIN	1.0
FO	FOBLEND	-1.0	FODENS	-352.0
FO	FOSULFUR	-3.00		

4-8). Each line contains a column name followed by up to two row names and their corresponding coefficients from Figure 4-8.

The last input section is shown in Table 4-11. Here, the right-hand-side coefficients are entered in the same way that the coefficients for each column were entered in the COLUMNS section, i.e., only the nonzero elements. The end of the data block is followed by an ENDATA Card.

The solution to the refinery problem is presented in Table 4-12(a) and (b), as listed in the printout from the MPSX program. It is divided into two sections, the first providing information about the constraints (rows), and the second giving information about the refinery stream variables (columns).

In the ROWS section there are eight columns of output. The first is the internal identification number given to each row by the program. The second column is the name given to the rows in the input data. Next is the AT column that contains a pair of code letters to indicate the status of each row in the optimal solution. Constraint rows in the basis have the code

Table 4-11. MPSX Input Right-Hand Side Section.

RHS					
	RHS	CRDAVAIL	110000.0	PGMIN	10000.0
	RHS	RGMIN	10000.0	DFMIN	10000.0
	RHS	FOMIN	10000.0	ADCAP	100000.0
	RHS	RFCAP	25000.0	CCCAP	30000.0
ENDATA					

Table 4-12(a) MPSX Output for Optimal Solution, Section 1—Rows.

NUMBER	...ROW..	AT	...ACTIVITY...	SLACK ACTIVITY	..LOWER LIMIT.	..UPPER LIMIT.	.DUAL ACTIVITY
1	OBJ	BS	701823.4	-701823.4	NONE	NONE	1.000
2	CRDAVAIL	BS	100000.0	10000.0	NONE	110000.0	.
3	PGMIN	BS	47113.2	-37113.2	10000.0	NONE	.
4	PGBLEND	EQ	.	.	NONE	NONE	19.320
5	PGOCTANE	LL	.	.	NONE	NONE	.280
6	PGVAPP	BS	-188607.2	188607.2	NONE	NONE	.
7	RGMIN	BS	22520.4	12520.4	10000.0	NONE	.
8	RGBLEND	EQ	.	.	NONE	NONE	19.320
9	RGOCTANE	LL	.	.	NONE	NONE	.280
10	RGVAPP	UL	.	.	NONE	NONE	.
11	DFMIN	BS	12491.0	-2491.0	10000.0	NONE	.
12	DFBLEND	EQ	.	.	NONE	NONE	40.320
13	DFDENS	BS	-165458.8	165458.8	NONE	NONE	.
14	DFSULFUR	UL	.	.	NONE	NONE	.
15	FOMIN	LL	10000.0	.	10000.0	NONE	27.180
16	FOBLEND	EQ	.	.	NONE	NONE	40.320
17	FODENS	BS	-571996.8	571996.8	NONE	NONE	.
18	FOSULFUR	BS	-22286.7	22286.7	NONE	NONE	.
19	ADCAP	UL	100000.0	.	NONE	100000.0	-8.154
20	ADFGYLD	EQ	.	.	.	.	0.01965
21	ADSRGYLD	EQ	.	.	.	.	41.300
22	ADNYLD	EQ	.	.	.	.	45.571
23	ADDSYLD	EQ	.	.	.	.	40.320
24	ADFOYLD	EQ	.	.	.	.	40.320
25	RFCAP	BS	23700.0	1300.0	NONE	25000.0	.
26	FGRFYLD	EQ	.	.	.	.	0.01965
27	RFRFGYLD	EQ	.	.	.	.	48.440
28	CCCAP	UL	30000.0	.	NONE	30000.0	-5.274
29	CCFGYLD	EQ	.	.	.	.	0.01965
30	CCGYLD	EQ	.	.	.	.	45.5560
31	CCFOYLD	EQ	.	.	.	.	40.3200
32	SRGSPLIT	EQ	.	.	.	.	41.3000
33	SRNSPLIT	EQ	.	.	.	.	45.5708
34	SRDSSPLIT	EQ	.	.	.	.	40.320
35	SRFOSPLIT	EQ	.	.	.	.	40.320
36	RFGSPLIT	EQ	.	.	.	.	48.440
37	CCGSPLIT	EQ	.	.	.	.	45.556
38	CCFOSPLIT	EQ	.	.	.	.	40.320

Table 4-12(b). MPSX Output for Optimal Solution, Section 2— Columns.

NUMBER	.COLUMN.	AT	...ACTIVITY....	...INPUT COST..	..LOWER LIMIT.	..UPPER LIMIT.	.REDUCED COST.
39	CRUDE	BS	100000.0	-33.00	.	NONE	.
40	FGAD	BS	3542000.0	0.01965	.	NONE	.
41	SRG	BS	27000.0	.	.	NONE	.
42	SRN	BS	23700.0	.	.	NONE	.
43	SRDS	BS	8700.0	.	.	NONE	.
44	SRFO	BS	37200.0	.	.	NONE	.
45	SRNRF	BS	23700.0	-2.50	.	NONE	.
46	FGRF	BS	3761190.0	0.01965	.	NONE	.
47	RFG	BS	21993.6	.	.	NONE	-5.354
48	SRDSCC	LL	.	-2.20	.	NONE	.
49	SRFOCC	BS	30000.0	-2.20	.	NONE	.
50	FGCC	BS	11592000.0	0.01965	.	NONE	.
51	CCG	BS	20640.0	.	.	NONE	.
52	CCFO	BS	6591.0	.	.	NONE	.
53	SRGPG	BS	13852.0	.	.	NONE	.
54	RFGPG	BS	17240.0	.	.	NONE	-8.051
55	SRNPG	LL	.	.	.	NONE	.
56	CCGPG	BS	16021.1	.	.	NONE	.
57	PG	BS	47113.2	45.36	.	NONE	.
58	SRGRG	BS	13148.0	.	.	NONE	.
59	RFGRG	BS	4753.6	.	.	NONE	-8.051
60	SRNRG	LL	.	.	.	NONE	.
61	CCGRG	BS	4618.8	.	.	NONE	.
62	RG	BS	22520.4	43.68	.	NONE	.
63	SRNDF	LL	.	.	.	NONE	-5.251
64	CCFODF	BS	3263.0	.	.	NONE	.
65	SRDSDF	BS	8700.0	.	.	NONE	.
66	SRFODF	BS	528.0	.	.	NONE	.
67	DF	BS	12491.0	40.32	.	NONE	.
68	CCFOFO	LL	.	.	.	NONE	.
69	SRDSFO	BS	3328.0	.	.	NONE	.
70	SRFOFO	BS	6672.0	13.14	.	NONE	.
71	FO	BS	10000.0	.	.	NONE	.

BS, nonbasis inequality constraints that have reached their upper or lower limits have the code UL or LL, and equality constraints have the status code EQ. The fourth column is the row activity, as defined by the equation:

$$\text{Activity}_i = \sum_{j=1}^{m} a_{ij}x_j$$

This is the optimal value of the left-hand side of the constraint equations. However, it is computed by subtracting the slack variable from the right-hand side. The column labeled SLACK ACTIVITY contains the value of the slack variable for each row. The next three columns are associated with sensitivity analysis. The sixth and seventh columns show the lower and upper limits placed on the row activities. The final column, DUAL ACTIVITY, gives Lagrange Multipliers, which are also called the *Simplex multipliers, shadow prices,* and *implicit prices.* As will be seen subsequently in sensitivity analysis, they will relate changes in the activity to changes in the objective function. Also, the dot in the table means zero, the same convention used in the Simplex Tableau.

Examination of this section of output shows that the activity (or value) of the objective function (row 1, OBJ) is 701,823.4, i.e., the maximum profit for the refinery is $701,823.40 per day. Checking the rows that are at their lower limits, LL, for production constraints, one finds that only row 15, FOMIN, is at its lower limit of 10,000 barrels/day, indicating that only the minimum required amount of fuel oil should be produced. However, row 3, PGMIN, row 7, RGMIN, and row 11, DFMIN, are all above their lower limits with values of 47,113 barrels/day for premium gasoline, 22,520 barrels/day for regular gasoline, and 12,491 barrels/day for diesel fuel. More will be said about the information in this table when sensitivity analysis is discussed.

The COLUMNS section of the solution also has eight columns. The first three are analogous to the first three in the ROWS section, i.e., an interval identification number, name of the column, and whether the variable is in the basis BS or is at its upper or lower limit, UL or LL. The fourth column, ACTIVITY, contains the optimal value for each variable. The objective function cost coefficients are listed in the column INPUT COST. REDUCED COST is the amount by which the objective function will be increased per unit increase in each nonbasis variable and is part of the sensitivity analysis. It is given by c_j' of equation (4–29).

For this simple refinery mode, there were 33 variables whose optimal value were determined, and 38 constraint equations were satisfied. For an actual refinery there would be thousands of constraint equations, but they would be developed in the same fashion as described here. As can be seen, the model (constraint equations) was simple, and only one set of operating conditions was considered for the catalytic cracking unit, catalytic reformer, and the crude distillation column.

If the optimal flow rates do not match the corresponding values for volumetric yields, a search can be performed by repeating the problem to obtain a match of the optimal flow rates and volumetric yields. This has to be performed using a separate simulation program that generates volumetric yields from flow rate through the process units. (See Figure 6-5.) Thus, the linear model of the plant can be made to account for nonlinear process operations. Another procedure, successive linear programming, uses linear programming iteratively, also, and it will be discussed in Chapter 6. The state of industrial practice using both linear programming and successive linear programming is described by Smith and Bonner (13) for configuration of new refineries and chemical plants, plant expansions, economic evaluation of investment alternatives, assessment of new technology, operating plans for existing plants, variation in feeds, costing and distribution of products, evaluation of processing and exchange agreements, forecasting of industry trends, and economic impact of regulatory changes.

MPSX Section
Ignore

SENSITIVITY ANALYSIS

Having obtained the optimal solution for a linear programming problem, it would be desirable to know how much the cost coefficients could change, for example, before it is necessary to resolve the problem. In fact there are five areas that should be examined for their effect on the optimal solution. These are:

1. changes in the right-hand side of the constraint equations, b_i
2. changes in the coefficients of the objective function, c_j
3. changes in the coefficients of the constraint equations, a_{ij}
4. addition of new variables
5. addition of more constraint equations

Changes in the right-hand side of the constraint equations correspond to changes in the maximum capacity of a process unit or the availability of a raw material, for example. Changes in the coefficients of the objective function correspond to changes of the cost or the sale price of the products, and changes in the coefficients of the constraint equations correspond to changes in volumetric yields of a process. Addition of new variables and constraint equations correspond to the addition of new process units in the plant. It is valuable to know how these various coefficients and parameters can vary without changing the optimal solution, and this may reduce the number of times the linear programming problem must be solved.

Prior to doing this postoptimal analysis, we must develop some preliminary mathematical expressions for the analysis of the effect of the above five areas on the optimal solution. These are the inverse of the optimal basis and the Lagrange Multipliers. To obtain the matrix called the inverse of the optimal basis, $\mathbf{A}^{-1}$, consider that the optimal basis has been found by the previously described Simplex Method. There are m constraint equations and n variables as given by equations 4–1a, b, and c. For convenience, the nonzero variables in the optimal basis have been rearranged to go from 1 to m ($x_1^*, x_2^*, \cdots,$ $x_m^*, 0, 0, \cdots, 0$); and there are $(n - m)$ variables not in the basis whose value is zero. The optimal solution to this linear programming problem is indicated below, where $\mathbf{x}^*$ contains only the m nonzero basis variables:

$$p^* = \mathbf{c}^T \mathbf{x}^* = \underset{\mathbf{x}}{opt}\, \mathbf{c}^T \mathbf{x} \qquad (4\text{–}16)$$

and

$$\mathbf{A}\, \mathbf{x}^* = \mathbf{b} \qquad (4\text{–}17)$$

To solve for $\mathbf{x}^*$, both sides of the above equation are multiplied by the inverse of the optimal basis, $\mathbf{A}^{-1}$ whose elements are β_{ij} and obtain

$$\mathbf{x}^* = \mathbf{A}^{-1}\mathbf{b} \qquad (4\text{–}18)$$

It should be noted that $\mathbf{A}^{-1}$ may be obtained from the last step of the Simplex Method if all the constraint equations required slack variables. If not, then it has to be obtained from the original formulation of the problem using the optimal basis found from the Simplex Method.

The linear programming problem could be solved by the classical method of Lagrange Multipliers. However, the Simplex Method gives a systematic procedure for locating the optimal basis. Having located the optimal basis by the Simplex Method, we will use the Lagrange Multiplier formulation and the inverse of the optimal basis to determine the effect of change in the right-hand side on the optimal solution. Consequently, it is necessary to compute the values of the Lagrange Multipliers as follows. Multiplying each constraint equation, (4–1b), by the Lagrange Multiplier λ_i and adding to the objective function equation (4–1a), gives the following equation:

(handwritten top: maximize — logyfo)
(handwritten: minimiz)

(handwritten left: Coeffs)

$$L = \left[c_1 + \sum_{i=1}^{m} a_{i1} \lambda_i\right] x_1 + \left[c_2 + \sum_{i-1}^{m} a_{i2} \lambda_i\right] x_2 + \cdots$$

$$+ \left[c_m + \sum_{i=1}^{m} a_{im} \lambda_i\right] x_m + \left[c_{m+1} + \sum_{i=1}^{m} a_{im+1} \lambda_i\right] x_{m+1} + \cdots \quad (4\text{–}19)$$

$$+ \left[c_n + \sum_{i-1}^{m} a_{in} \lambda_i\right] x_n = p + \sum_{i=1}^{m} b_i \lambda_i = 0$$

(handwritten: $L = P = -\sum_{i=1}^{m} \lambda_i b_i$)

where x_1 to x_m are positive numbers, i.e., values of the variables in the basis, and x_{m+1} to x_n are zero, i.e., values of the variables that are not in the basis.

To solve this problem by classical methods, the partial derivatives of p with respect to the independent variables and the Lagrange Multipliers would be set equal to zero. Taking the partial derivatives of p with respect to the Lagrange Multipliers just gives the constraint equations, and taking the partial derivatives with respect to the independent variables, x_j^* $(j = 1, 2, \cdots m)$ gives:

(handwritten left: Calculate Lagrange Multipliers)

$$\frac{\partial p}{\partial x_j} = \left[c_j + \sum_{i-1}^{m} a_{ij} \lambda_i\right] = 0 \qquad \text{for } j = 1, 2, \cdots, m \qquad (4\text{–}20)$$

and x_j^* for $j = m + 1, \cdots, n$ is zero, since $\mathbf{x}^*$ is the optimal solution.

The values of the Lagrange Multipliers are obtained from the solution of equation (4–20). Written in matrix notation, equation (4–20) is:

(handwritten: $\sum_{i=1}^{m} a_{ij} \lambda_i = -c_{ij}$)

$$\mathbf{c} + \mathbf{A}^T \boldsymbol{\lambda} = 0 \qquad
\begin{bmatrix} a_{11} & a_{21} & & a_{m1} \\ & & & \\ a_{1m} & & & a_{nm} \end{bmatrix}
\begin{bmatrix} \lambda_1 \\ \\ \lambda_m \end{bmatrix} = \begin{bmatrix} c_1 \\ \\ c_m \end{bmatrix} \qquad (4\text{–}21)$$

where $\mathbf{A}^T$ is the transpose of the matrix $\mathbf{A}$.

Using the matrix identity $[\mathbf{A}^T]^{-1} = [\mathbf{A}^{-1}]^T$ and solving for the Lagrange Multipliers gives:

(handwritten: $\lambda_i = -\sum_{j=1}^{m} \beta_{ij} c_j$)

$$\boxed{\boldsymbol{\lambda} = -[\mathbf{A}^{-1}]^T \, \mathbf{c}} \qquad (4\text{–}22)$$

In terms of the elements of the inverse of the optimal basis β_{ik}, equation (4–22) can be written as:

$$\lambda_i = - \sum_{k=1}^{m} \beta_{ki} c_k \qquad \text{for } i = 1, 2, \cdots, m \qquad (4\text{–}23)$$

With this as background, the effect of the five changes on the optimal solution can be determined. The inverse of the optimal basis $\mathbf{A}^{-1}$ and the

Lagrange Multipliers will be used to evaluate these changes. The following example illustrates the computation of the inverse of the optimal basis and the Lagrange Multipliers.

EXAMPLE 4–6

Solve the following problem by the Simplex Method, and compute the inverse of the optimal basis and the Lagrange Multipliers:

$$\text{Maximize: } 2x_1 + x_2 + x_3$$

$$\text{Subject to: } x_1 + x_2 + x_3 \leq 10$$

$$x_1 + 5x_2 + x_3 \geq 20$$

Adding slack variables gives:

$$\text{Maximize: } 2x_1 + x_2 + x_3 \qquad = p$$

$$\text{Subject to: } x_1 + x_2 + x_3 + x_4 \qquad = 10$$

$$x_1 + 5x_2 + x_3 \qquad = x_5 \qquad = 20$$

An initially feasible basis is not available, and either artificial variables or algebraic manipulations must be performed to obtain one. Algebraic manipulations are used to have x_1 and x_2 be the variables in the basis. The result is:

$$-x_3 - 9/4x_4 - 13/20x_5 = p - 17\tfrac{1}{2} \qquad p = 17\tfrac{1}{2}$$

$$x_1 \quad + x_3 + 5/4x_4 + \quad 1/4x_5 = \quad 7\tfrac{1}{2} \qquad x_1 = \ 7\tfrac{1}{2}$$

$$x_2 \quad - \tfrac{1}{4}x_4 - \quad 1/4x_5 = \quad 2\tfrac{1}{2} \qquad x_2 = \ 2\tfrac{1}{2}$$

$$x_3 = \ 0$$

$$x_4 = \ 0$$

$$x_5 = \ 0$$

This is the optimum, for all the coefficients of the nonbasic variables in the objective function are negative. With the optimal solution known, the original problem now takes the form:

$$\text{Maximize: } 2x_1 + x_2 = 17\frac{1}{2}$$

$$\text{Subject to: } x_1 + x_2 = 10$$

$$x_1 + 5x_2 = 20$$

The inverse of the optimal basis is computed using the cofactor method

$$\mathbf{A}^{-1} = \frac{1}{|\mathbf{A}|} \|\mathbf{A}_{ji}\|$$

where $\|\mathbf{A}_{ji}\| = \|\mathbf{A}_{ij}\|^T$ and $\|\mathbf{A}_{ij}\|$ are the cofactors of the matrix $\mathbf{A}$ (8).

$$\mathbf{A} = \begin{bmatrix} 1 & 1 \\ 1 & 5 \end{bmatrix} \quad |\mathbf{A}| = 5 - 1 = 4 \quad \|\mathbf{A}_{ji}\| = \left\| \begin{matrix} 5 & -1 \\ -1 & 1 \end{matrix} \right\|$$

$$\mathbf{A}^{-1} = \begin{bmatrix} 5/4 & -\frac{1}{4} \\ -\frac{1}{4} & \frac{1}{4} \end{bmatrix} \quad \text{and} \quad \mathbf{A}^{-1}A = \begin{bmatrix} 5/4 & -\frac{1}{4} \\ -\frac{1}{4} & \frac{1}{4} \end{bmatrix} \begin{bmatrix} 1 & 1 \\ 1 & 5 \end{bmatrix} = \begin{bmatrix} 1 & 0 \\ 0 & 1 \end{bmatrix}$$

The Lagrange Multipliers are computed using equation (4–22)

$$\lambda = -[\mathbf{A}^{-1}]^T \mathbf{c}$$

$$\begin{bmatrix} \lambda_1 \\ \lambda_2 \end{bmatrix} = -\begin{bmatrix} 5/4 & -\frac{1}{4} \\ -\frac{1}{4} & \frac{1}{4} \end{bmatrix} \begin{bmatrix} 2 \\ 1 \end{bmatrix} = -\begin{bmatrix} 9/4 \\ -\frac{1}{4} \end{bmatrix}$$

or

$$\lambda_1 = -9/4 \quad \text{and} \quad \lambda_2 = \frac{1}{4}$$

Changes in the Right-Hand Side of the Constraint Equations:

Changes in the right-hand side of the constraint equations, i.e., changes in the b_i's, will cause changes in the values of the variables in the optimal solution, the x_j's. For an optimal solution to remain optimal, the x_j's cannot become negative. Equation (4–18) will be used to evaluate changes in the x_j's caused by changes in the b_i's. The jth component of equation 4–18 is used.

$$x^* = A_{opt}^{-1} b$$

$$x_j^* = \sum_{i=1}^{m} \beta_{ji} b_i \qquad \text{for } j = 1, 2, \cdots, m \qquad (4\text{–}24)$$

For a change in b_i of an amount Δb_i, the new value of x_j^*, called $x_{j,\text{ new}}^*$ is:

$$x^*_{j,\text{ new}} = \sum_{i=1}^{m} \beta_{ji}\,(b_i + \Delta b_i)$$

and

$$x^*_{j,\text{ new}} = x^*_j + \sum_{i=1}^{m} \beta_{ji}\,\Delta b_i \qquad \text{for } j = 1, 2, \cdots, m \qquad (4\text{-}25)$$

For the optimal solution $\mathbf{x}^*$ to remain optimal, the values of $x^*_{j,\text{ new}}$ must not become negative. The problem must be resolved if any of the $x^*_{j,\text{ new}}$'s becomes negative.

The change in the value of the objective function for changes in the b_i's, is computed using equation (4–19). Because the left-hand side of equation (4–19) is zero at the optimum, it can be written as:

$$p^* = -\sum_{i=1}^{m} b_i \lambda_i \qquad (4\text{-}26)$$

Using the same procedure for the change Δb_i, the change in the value of the objective function is:

$$p^*_{\text{new}} = -\sum_{i=1}^{m} (b_i + \Delta b_i)\,\lambda_i$$

$$p^*_{\text{new}} = p^* - \sum_{i=1}^{m} \lambda_i\,\Delta b_i \qquad (4\text{-}27)$$

Need to calculate λ_i's

It is from this equation that the Lagrange Multipliers receive the name *shadow prices*, for they have dimensions of dollars per unit and are used to compute the new value of the objective function from changes in the b_i's. This is called a *marginal cost calculation*.

Generally, in large linear programming computer programs, part of the computations includes the calculation of $x^*_{j,\text{ new}}$ and p^*_{new} for upper and lower limits on the b_i's. Also, values of the Δb_i's can be computed that will give the largest possible change in the x^*_j's, i.e., $x_{j,\text{ new}} = 0$. Simultaneous changes in the right-hand side of the constraint equations can be performed using the 100% rule, and this procedure is described by Bradley et al. (19).

EXAMPLE 4–7

For the problem given in Example 4–6, find the new optimal solution for $\Delta b_1 = -5$ without resolving the problem. Using equation (4–25) to compute the changes in the x_i's gives:

$$x_{1,\text{new}} = x_1 + \beta_{11}\,\Delta b_1 + \beta_{12}\,\Delta b_2$$

$$x_{2,\text{new}} = x_2 + \beta_{21}\,\Delta b_1 + \beta_{22}\,\Delta b_2$$

substituting in the values for $\Delta b_1 = -5$ and $\Delta b_2 = 0$ gives

$$x_{1,\text{new}} = 7\tfrac{1}{2} + 5/4(-5) \quad = 5/4$$

$$x_{2,\text{new}} = 2\tfrac{1}{2} + (1-\tfrac{1}{4})(-5) = 15/4$$

Using equation (4–27), the change in the objective function is computed as:

$$p^*_{\text{new}} = p^* - [\lambda_1\,\Delta b_1 + \lambda_2\,\Delta b_2] = 17\tfrac{1}{2} - (-9/4)(-5)$$

$$p^*_{\text{new}} = 25/4$$

Changes in the right-hand side of the constraint equations are part of the sensitivity analysis of the MPSX program. In Table 4-12(a) the smallest and largest values of the right-hand side of the constraint equations are given for the optimal solution to remain optimal as LOWER LIMIT and UPPER LIMIT. Also the Lagrange Multipliers were computed, and these are called the DUAL ACTIVITY in the MPSX nomenclature of Table 4-12(a). In this table NONE indicates that there is no bound, and a dot indicates that the value was zero. Correspondingly, in Table 4-12(b) the upper and lower limits on the variables are given. In this case the dot indicates that the lower bound was zero, and NONE indicates that there was no upper bound on the variable because BOUNDS was not used.

Changes in the Coefficients of the Objective Function: It is necessary to consider the effect on the optimal solution of changes in the cost coefficients of the variables in the basis and those not in the basis also. Referring to equation (4–19), the coefficients of the variables that are not in the basis, i.e., $x_{m+1}, \ldots, x_n$ must remain negative for maximization.

$$C_j^{'} = \left[c_j + \sum_{i=1}^{m} a_{ij}\lambda_i \right] < 0 \qquad \text{for } j = m+1, \cdots, n \qquad (4\text{–}28)$$

If a coefficient becomes positive from a change in the cost coefficients, it would be profitable to have that variable enter the basis.

The values of the Lagrange Multipliers are affected by changes in the cost coefficients of the variables in the basis, since they are related by equation (4–23). The term in the brackets in equation (4–28) is named the reduced cost (19), and it is convenient to define this term as c_j' to obtain the equation that accounts for the effect of changes in cost coefficients on the optimal solution:

$$c_j' = \left[c_j + \sum_{i=1}^{m} a_{ij} \lambda_i \right] \quad \text{for } j = m+1, \cdots, n \qquad (4\text{-}29)$$

where c_j' must remain negative for the optimal solution to remain optimal for maximizing.

The Lagrange Multipliers, λ_i's, are eliminated from equation (4–29) by substituting equation (4–23) to give:

$$c_j' = c_j - \sum_{i=1}^{m} a_{ij} \sum_{k=1}^{m} \beta_{ki} c_k \quad \text{for } j = m+1, \cdots, n$$

or

$$c_j' = c_j - \sum_{k=1}^{m} \sum_{i=1}^{m} a_{ij} \beta_{ki} c_k \quad \text{for } j = m+1, \cdots, n \qquad (4\text{-}30)$$

For a change, Δc_j, in the nonbasic variable cost coefficient, c_j, and for a change, Δc_k, in the basic variables cost coefficient c_k, it can be shown that the following equation holds:

$$c_{j,\,\text{new}}' = c_j' + \Delta c_j - \sum_{k=1}^{m} \Delta c_k \sum_{i=1}^{m} a_{ij} \beta_{ki} \quad \text{for } j = m+1, \cdots, n \qquad (4\text{-}31)$$

When maximizing, the new coefficients must remain negative for the variables not in the basis to have the optimal solution remain optimal, i.e.:

$$c_{j,\,\text{new}}' < 0 \qquad (4\text{-}32)$$

If (4–32) does not hold, then a new optimal solution must be obtained by solving the linear programming problem with the new values of the cost coefficients.

If the optimal solution remains optimal, the new value of the objective function can be computed with the following equation:

$$p_{\text{new}}^* = p^* + \sum_{k=1}^{m} x_k \, \Delta c_k \qquad (4\text{-}33)$$

If the problem must be resolved, it is usually convenient to introduce an artificial variable and proceed from this point to the new optimal solution. Large linear programming codes usually have this provision. Also, they can calculate a range of values of the cost coefficients where the optimal solution remains optimal and the corresponding effect on the objective function. The procedure used is called the 100% rule and is described by Bradley et al. (19).

EXAMPLE 4–8

For the problem given in Example 4–6, compute the effect of changing the cost coefficient c_1 from 2 to 3 and c_3 from 1 to 4, i.e., $\Delta c_1 = 1$ and $\Delta c_3 = 3$. Using equation (4–31) produces the following results for $j = 3, 4, 5$ (since $\Delta c_2 = 0$):

$$c'_{3,\text{ new}} = c'_3 + \Delta c_3 - \Delta c_1 [a_{13}\beta_{11} + a_{23}\beta_{12}]$$

substituting

$$c'_{3,\text{ new}} = -1 + 3 - (1)[(1)(5/4) + (1)(-\tfrac{1}{4})] = 1$$

$$c'_{4,\text{ new}} = c'_4 + \Delta c_4 - \Delta c_1 [a_{14}\beta_{11} + a_{24}\beta_{12}]$$

substituting

$$c'_{4,\text{ new}} = -9/4 + 0 - (1)[(1)(5/4) + (0)(-\tfrac{1}{4})] = -13/4$$

$$c'_{5,\text{ new}} = c'_5 + \Delta c_5 - \Delta c_1 [a_{15}\beta_{11} + a_{25}\beta_{12}]$$

substituting

$$c'_{5,\text{ new}} = -\tfrac{1}{4} + 0 - (1)[(0)(5/4) + (-1)(-\tfrac{1}{4})] = -\tfrac{1}{2}$$

An improvement in the objective function can be obtained, for $c'_{3,\text{new}}$ is greater than zero. Increasing x_3 from zero to a positive number will increase the value of the objective function. However, the problem will have to be resolved.

In the MPSX program the RANGE command and the parametrics are used to find the range over which the variables, right-hand sides, and coefficients of the objective function and constraints may be varied without changing the basis for the optimal solution. Output from the RANGE command consists of four sections: sections 1 and 2 for rows and columns at their limit levels, and sections 3 and 4 for rows and columns at an intermediate level (in the basis), which will be described here. Further information is given in references (12, 15, and 16).

In Table 4-13 the RANGE output is shown for constraint rows at upper and lower limit levels. The first four columns have the same meaning as in

Table 4-13.   MPS Output, RANGE: Rows at Limit Level.

SECTION 1 - ROWS AT LIMIT LEVEL

NUMBER	...ROW..	AT	...ACTIVITY...	LOWER ACTIVITY UPPER ACTIVITY	...UNIT COST.. ...UNIT COST..	LIMITING PROCESS.	AT AT
4	PGBLEND	EQ	.	−1530.74 807.77	19.320 −19.320	SRGPG RGMIN	LL LL
5	PGOCTANE	LL	.	−75122.38 ·142358.38	0.28 −0.28	RGMIN SRGPG	LL LL
8	RGBLEND	EQ	.	−157.39 184.70	19.320 −19.320	CCGRG RFGRG	LL LL
9	RGOCTANE	LL	.	−18739.35 17326.68	0.280 −0.280	RFGRG CCGRG	LL LL
10	RGVAPP	UL	.	−16460.63 9533.63	. .	RFGRG CCGRG	LL LL
12	DFBLEND	EQ	.	−4091.76 541.56	40.320 −40.320	CCFODF DFDENS	LL UL
14	DFSULFUR	UL	.	−331.08 2045.89	. .	SRFODF CCFODF	LL LL
15	FOMIN	LL	10000.0	5652.8 12252.2	27.180 −27.180	CCFODF SRFODF	LL LL
16	FOBLEND	EQ	.	−4347.24 1941.99	40.320 −40.320	CCFOFO FODENS	LL UL
19	ADCAP	UL	100000.0	94572.99 105485.23	−8.154 8.154	DFMIN RFCAP	LL UL
20	ADFGYLD	EQ	.	−INFINITY 3541999.0	0.01965 −.01965	NONE FGAD	LL
21	ADSRGYLD	EQ	.	−26197.55 5180.85	41.300 −41.300	PGMIN RGMIN	UL LL
22	ADNYLD	EQ	.	−1300.0 13394.25	45.570 −45.570	RFCAP RFGPG	LL LL
23	ADDSYLD	EQ	.	−12733.73 2490.99	40.320 −40.320	SRFODF DFMIN	LL LL

Table 4-13. Continued

NUMBER	...ROW..	AT	...ACTIVITY...	LOWER ACTIVITY UPPER ACTIVITY	...UNIT COST.. ...UNIT COST..	LIMITING PROCESS.	AT AT
24	ADFOYLD	EQ	.	-4347.24 2252.22	40.320 -40.320	CCFOFO SRFODF	LL LL
26	FGRFYLD	EQ	.	-INFINITY 3761190.0	.01965 -.01965	NONE FGRF	 LL
27	RFRFGYLD	EQ	.	-6829.31 12429.87	48.440 -48.440	RGMIN RFGPG	LL LL
28	CCAP	UL	30000.00	25926.81 32886.36	-5.274 5.274	CCFOFO SRFODF	LL LL
29	CCFGYLD	EQ	.	-INFINITY 11591992.0	.01965 -.01965	NONE FGCC	 LL
30	CCGYLD	EQ	.	-107317.69 15646.77	45.556 -45.556	RGMIN CCGPG	LL LL
31	CCFOYLD	EQ	.	-28457.97 2252.22	40.320 -40.320	SRFOFO SRFODF	LL LL
32	SRGSPLIT	EQ	.	-26197.55 5180.85	41.300 -41.300	PGMIN RGMIN	LL LL
33	SRNSPLIT	EQ	.	-1300.0 13394.25	45.570 -45.570	RFCAP RFGPG	UL LL
34	SRDSSPLT	EQ	.	-12733.73 2490.9	40.320 -40.320	SRFODF DFMIN	LL LL
35	SRFOSPLT	EQ	.	-4347.24 2252.22	40.320 -40.320	CCFOFO SRFODF	LL LL
36	RFGSPLIT	EQ	.	-6829.87 12429.87	48.440 -48.440	RGMIN RFGPG	LL LL
37	CCGSPLIT	EQ	.	-107317.69 15646.77	45.556 -45.556	RGMIN CCGPG	LL LL
38	CCFOSPLT	EQ	.	-28457.97 2252.22	40.320 -40.320	SRFOFO SRFODF	LL LL

the output from SOLUTION. The next four have two entries for each row. LOWER ACTIVITY and UPPER ACTIVITY are the lower and upper bounds on the range of values that the row activity (right-hand side) may have. Because the slack variable for the row is zero at a limit level, the upper and lower activities are numerically equal to the bounds of the range that the right-hand sides may have. The two UNIT COST entries are the changes in the objective function per unit change of activity when moving from the solution activity to either the upper or lower bound. The column labeled LIMITING PROCESS contains the name of the row or column that will leave the basis if the activity bounds are violated. The status column, AT, indicates the status of the leaving row or column. For example, in line 15 of Table 4-13, the row FOMIN is at its lower limit, its activity value is 10,000, and the right-hand side may be set to any number between 5,652.8 and 12,252.2 without changing the basis. If FOMIN goes below 5,652.8, then CCFODF would leave the basis. If FOMIN exceeds 12,252.2, then SRFODF would leave the basis. The cost associated with a change in FOMIN is $27.18/bbl with profit decreasing for an increase in FOMIN.

Similar information is provided in Table 4-14 about the range over which the nonbasis activities (variables) at upper or lower limits may be varied without forcing the row or column in LIMITING PROCESS out of the basis. An additional column is included in the table, LOWER COST/UPPER COST to show the highest and lowest cost coefficients at which the variable will remain in the basis. If the objective function cost coefficient goes below the LOWER COST, the activity will increase to UPPER ACTIVITY. Similarly, if its cost goes above UPPER COST, the activity will be decreased to LOWER ACTIVITY.

The third section of output from the range study is given in Table 4-15. It contains information about constraints that are not at their limits and, therefore, are in the basis of the optimal solution. The column headings have the same meaning as the headings for section 1 except that here the LIMITING PROCESS will enter the basis.

The fourth section, shown in Table 4-16, gives the RANGE analysis of the columns in the basis. As in Table 4-15, the LIMITING PROCESS will enter the basis when activity is forced beyond the upper or lower activity bounds. The information of greatest interest here are the entries for columns with coefficients in the objective function. These are CRUDE(39), FGAD(40), SRNRF(45), FGRF(46), SRFOCC(49), FGCC(50), PG(57), RG(62), DF(67), and FO(71). Examining the first row in Table 4-16, one finds that if the cost coefficient becomes −41.097, the activity (crude flow rate) would be reduced from 100,000 to 94,831.2. Consequently, if the cost of crude oil is increased to $40.09/barrel (operating cost is $1.00/barrel), the refinery should reduce its throughput by only 5.2%. Also notice that the lower cost for premium gasoline (PG) is 44.082, while the input cost is 45.35. If the bulk sale price of premium gasoline were to drop to $44.08/barrel, it would be profitable for the refinery to produce 23,655 barrels/day, a drop of almost 50% from the maximum of 47,113 barrels/day currently produced. A similar analysis for fuel oil (FO) indicates that it will probably never be profitable to produce fuel oil, for the sale price would have to increase from $13.14 to $40.32/barrel before production should be increased above the minimum.

Changes in Coefficients of the Constraint Equations:
Referring to equation (4–29), it is seen that changes in the a_{ij}'s for the nonbasic variables

Table 4-14. MPS Output, RANGE: Columns at Limit Level.

SECTION 2 - COLUMNS AT LIMIT LEVEL

NUMBER	.COLUMN.	AT	..INPUT COST..	LOWER ACTIVITY / UPPER ACTIVITY	..UNIT COST.. / ..UNIT COST..	..LOWER COST.. / ..UPPER COST..	LIMITING PROCESS.	AT / AT
48	SRDSCC	LL	-2.20	-1964.99 / 4550.96	5.353 / -5.353	-INFINITY / 3.128	SRFODF / CCFOFO	LL / LL
55	SRNPG	LL	.	-1300.00 / 3725.88	8.051 / -8.051	-INFINITY / 8.046	RFCAP / SRGPG	UL / LL
60	SRNRG	LL	.	-615.85 / 543.39	8.051 / -8.051	-INFINITY / 8.046	RFGRG / CCGRG	LL / LL
63	SRNDF	LL	.	-1300.00 / 9428.02	5.250 / -5.250	-INFINITY / 5.251	RFCAP / CCFODF	UL / LL
69	SRDSFO	LL	.	-1913.74 / 4596.20	. / .	-INFINITY / 0.000	SRFODF / CCFOFO	UL / LL

135

Table 4-15. MPS Output, RANGE: Rows at Intermediate Level.

SECTION 3 - ROWS AT INTERMEDIATE LEVEL

NUMBER	..ROW..	AT	...ACTIVITY....	SLACK ACTIVITY	LOWER ACTIVITY / UPPER ACTIVITY	...UNIT COST.. / ...UNIT COST..	LIMITING PROCESS.	AT / AT
2	CRDAVAIL	BS	100000.0	10000.0	94572.98 / 100000.0	-8.154 / -INFINITY	ADCAP / NONE	UL
3	PGMIN	BS	47111.0	-37113.2	23655.1 / 47113.2	-1.278 / -INFINITY	SRNPG / NONE	LL
6	PGVAPP	BS	-188607.2	188607.2	-188607.16 / -172146.52	/ -INFINITY	NONE / RGVAPP	UL
7	RGMIN	BS	22520.4	-12520.4	21167.53 / 46246.79	32.710 / -1.264	ADCAP / SRNPG	LL / UL
11	DFMIN	BS	12490.9	-2490.9	9592.13 / 21919.02	-17.765 / -5.251	ADCAP / SRNDF	UL / LL
13	DFDENS	BS	-165458.8	165458.8	-165775.57 / -153666.96	. / .	DFSULFUR / ADCAP	UL / LL
17	FODENS	BS	-571996.8	571966.8	-583788.53 / -571679.93	. / .	FOMIN / DFSULFUR	LL / UL
18	FOSULFUR	BS	-22286.7	22286.7	-27917.23 / -21955.59	-10.872 / .	FOMIN / DFSULFUR	LL / UL
25	RFCAP	BS	23700.0	1300.0	14271.68 / 23700.00	-5.251 / -INFINITY	SRNDF / NONE	UL

Table 4-16. MPS Output, RANGE: Columns at Intermediate Levels.

SECTION 4 - COLUMNS AT INTERMEDIATE LEVEL

NUMBER	.COLUMN.	AT	...ACTIVITY....	..INPUT COST..	LOWER ACTIVITY / UPPER ACTIVITY	...UNIT COST.. / ...UNIT COST..	..LOWER COST.. / ..UPPER COST..	LIMITING PROCESS.	AT / AT
39	CRUDE	BS	100000.0	-33.0	94573.0 / 100000.0	-8.154 / -INFINITY	-41.154 / INFINITY	ADCAP / NONE	UL
40	FGAD	BS	3541999.0	.01965	3349774.0 / 3541999.0	-.2302 / -INFINITY	-0.210 / INFINITY	ADCAP / NONE	UL
41	SRG	BS	27000.0	.	25534.7 / 27000.0	-30.200 / -INFINITY	-30.201 / INFINITY	ADCAP / NONE	UL
42	SRN	BS	23699.9	.	22413.8 / 23699.9	-34.405 / -INFINITY	-34.405 / INFINITY	ADCAP / NONE	UL
43	SRDS	BS	8699.9	.	8227.8 / 8699.9	-93.726 / -INFINITY	-93.726 / INFINITY	ADCAP / NONE	UL
44	SRFO	BS	37199.9	.	35181.1 / 37199.9	-21.919 / -INFINITY	-21.919 / INFINITY	ADCAP / NONE	UL
45	SRNRF	BS	23699.9	-2.50	14271.9 / 23699.9	-5.251 / -INFINITY	-7.750 / INFINITY	SRNDF / NONE	UL
46	FGRF	BS	3761190.0	.01965	2264964.1 / 3761190.0	-.0331 / -INFINITY	-.0134 / INFINITY	SRNDF / NONE	LL
47	RFG	BS	21993.6	.	13244.4 / 21993.6	-5.658 / -INFINITY	-5.658 / INFINITY	SRNDF / NONE	UL
49	SRFOCC	BS	30000.0	-2.20	25926.8 / 30000.0	-5.274 / -INFINITY	-7.474 / INFINITY	CCCAP / NONE	UL
50	FGCC	BS	11591992.0	.01965	10018114.0 / 11591992.0	-.01365 / -INFINITY	.006 / INFINITY	CCCAP / NONE	UL

137

Table 4-16. Continued

NUMBER	COLUMN	AT	...ACTIVITY....	..INPUT COST..	LOWER ACTIVITY / UPPER ACTIVITY	...UNIT COST.. / ...UNIT COST..	..LOWER COST.. / ..UPPER COST..	LIMITING PROCESS.	AT / AT
51	CCG	BS	20640.0	.	17837.6 / 20640.0	-7.665 / -INFINITY	-7.665 / INFINITY	CCCAP / NONE	UL /
52	CCFO	BS	6590.9	.	5696.1 / 6591.0	-24.003 / -INFINITY	-24.003 / INFINITY	CCCAP / NONE	UL /
53	SRGPG	BS	13852.0	.	10510.6 / 17073.2	-1.309 / .	-1.309 / .	SRNRG / RGVAPP	LL / UL
54	RFGPG	BS	17240.0	.	12541.4 / 21993.6	-.931 / .	-.931 / .	SRNRG / RGVAPP	LL / UL
56	CCGPG	BS	16021.2	.	8046.4 / 20640.0	. / -.947	. / .947	RGVAPP / SRNRG	UL / LL
57	PG	BS	47113.2	45.36	23655.1 / 47113.2	-1.279 / -INFINITY	44.081 / INFINITY	SRNRG / NONE	LL /
58	SRGRG	BS	13148.0	.	9926.8 / 16489.4	-1.309 / .	1.309 / .	RGVAPP / SRNRG	UL / LL
59	RFGRG	BS	4753.6	.	-4796.2 / 8947.9	-1.043 / .	1.043 / .	RGVAPP / SRNRG	UL / LL
61	CCGRG	BS	4618.8	.	-12328.6 / 12593.6	-.947 / .	.947 / .	SRNRG / RGVAPP	LL / UL
62	RG	BS	22520.4	43.68	21167.5 / 46246.8	-32.710 / -1.264	10.970 / 44.944	ADCAP / SRNPG	LL / LL

Table 4-16. Continued

NUMBER	COLUMN.	AT	...ACTIVITY....	...INPUT COST..	LOWER ACTIVITY / UPPER ACTIVITY	..UNIT COST.. / ..UNIT COST..	..LOWER COST.. / ..UPPER COST..	LIMITING PROCESS.	AT AT
64	CCFODF	BS	3263.0	·	-1372.7 / 3791.0	-15.172 / ·	15.172 / -.000	SRNF / DFSULFUR	LL / UL
65	SRDSDF	BS	8700.0	·	4103.8 / 8700.0	-INFINITY / ·	.000 / INFINITY	SRDSFO / NONE	LL
66	SRFODF	BS	528.0	·	-2800.0 / 1796.2	· / ·	· / -.000	DFSULFUR / SRDSFO	UL / LL
67	DF	BS	12491.0	40.32	10000.0 / 21919.0	-17.765 / -5.250	22.555 / 45.570	ADCAP / SRNDF	UL / LL
68	CCFOFO	BS	3328.0	·	2800.0 / 6591.0	· / 15.172	.000 / 15.172	DFSULFUR / SRNDF	UL / LL
70	SRFOFO	BS	6672.0	·	5403.8 / 7200.0	· / ·	.000 / -.000	SRDSFO / DFSULFUR	LL / UL
71	FO	BS	10000.0	13.14	10000.0 / 12252.2	-INFINITY / -27.180	-INFINITY / 40.320	NONE / FOMIN	LL

140   OPTIMIZATION FOR ENGINEERING SYSTEMS

will cause changes in c'_j. For the optimal solution to remain optimal, $c'_j < 0$ when maximizing, and, if not, the problem must be resolved. To evaluate the changes in the coefficients of the constraint equations, a_{ij}, several pages of algebraic manipulations are required. This development is similar to the ones given here for the b_i's and c_j's and is discussed in detail by Garvin (3) and Gass (4), along with the subject of parametric programming, i.e., evaluating a set of ranges on the a_{ij}'s, b_i's, and c_j's where the optimal solution remains optimal. Due to space limitations, these results will not be given here. Also the MPSX code has the capability of making these evaluations, as previously mentioned.

Addition of New Variables: The effect of adding new variables can be determined by modifying equation (4–19). If k new variables are added to the problem, then k additional terms will be added to equation (4–19), and the coefficient of the kth term is:

Seldom
used

$$\left[c_{n+k} + \sum_{i=1}^{m} a_{i,n+k} \, \lambda_i \right] \tag{4–34}$$

Each of these k terms can be computed with the available information. If they are all less than zero, the original optimal solution remains at the maximum. If equation (4–34) is greater than zero, the solution can be improved, and the problem has to be resolved. Artificial variables are normally used to evaluate additional variables to obtain the new optimal solution.

Addition of More Constraint Equations: For the addition of more constraint equations, the procedure is to add artificial variables and proceed with the solution to the optimum. The artificial variables supply the canonical form for the solution. The following example shows the effect of adding an additional independent variable and an additional constraint equation to a linear programming problem to illustrate the application of the methods described above.

EXAMPLE 4–9

Solve the linear programming problem using the Simplex Method

$$\text{Minimize:} \quad x_1 - 3x_2$$

$$\text{Subject to:} \quad 3x_1 - x_2 \leq 7$$

$$-2x_1 + 4x_2 \leq 12$$

Introduce slack variables for an initially feasible basis, and ignore the terms in parentheses for now. This gives:

$$x_1 - 3x_2 \qquad (+2x_5) = c \quad c = 0$$

$$3x_1 - x_2 + x_3 \qquad (+2x_5) = 7 \quad x_3 = 7$$

$$-2x_1 + 4x_2 + x_4 \qquad = 12 \quad x_4 = 12$$

$$x_1 = 0$$

$$x_2 = 0$$

When the Simplex Method is applied, x_2 enters and x_4 leaves the basis. Performing the algebraic manipulations gives:

$$-0.5x_1 \qquad +0.75x_4 (+2x_5) = c + 9 \quad c = -9$$

$$2.5x_1 \qquad +x_3 + 0.25x_4 (+2x_5) = 10 \qquad x_3 = 10$$

$$-0.5x_1 + x_2 \qquad +0.25x_4 \qquad = 3 \qquad x_2 = 3$$

$$x_1 = 0$$

$$x_4 = 0$$

When the Simplex Method is applied, x_1 enters and x_3 leaves the basis, giving the following results:

$$0.2x_3 + 0.8x_4 (+2.4x_5) = c + 11 \quad c = -11$$

$$x_1 + 0.4x_3 + 0.1x_4 (-0.8x_5) = 4 \qquad x_1 = 4$$

$$x_2 + 0.2x_3 + 0.3x_4 (+0.4x_5) = 5 \qquad x_2 = 5$$

$$x_3 = 0$$

$$x_4 = 0$$

The optimal solution has been obtained, for all the coefficients of the variables in the objective function (not in the basis) are positive.

We compute the inverse of the optimal basis A^{-1} and the Lagrange Multipliers, having obtained the optimal solution as follows:

$$A = \begin{bmatrix} 3 & -1 \\ -2 & 4 \end{bmatrix} \quad |A| = 10 \quad \|A_{ij}\| = \begin{bmatrix} 4 & 2 \\ 1 & 3 \end{bmatrix}$$

$$A^{-1} = \begin{bmatrix} 2/5 & 1/10 \\ 1/5 & 3/10 \end{bmatrix}$$

For Lagrange Multipliers, equation (4–22) is used:

$$\lambda = -[A^{-1}]^T \cdot c$$

and substituting gives

$$\begin{bmatrix} \lambda_1 \\ \lambda_2 \end{bmatrix} = -\begin{bmatrix} 2/5 & 1/5 \\ 1/10 & 3/10 \end{bmatrix}\begin{bmatrix} 1 \\ -3 \end{bmatrix} = \begin{bmatrix} 1/5 \\ 4/5 \end{bmatrix}$$

If the first constraint equation is changed as follows by adding another variable x_5:

$$3x_1 - x_2 + 2x_5 \leq 7$$

and the objective function is changed by including x_5 as shown below:

$$x_1 - 3x_2 + 2x_5$$

determine how this addition of a new variable affects the optimal solution found previously. The linear programming problem now has the following form:

$$x_1 - 3x_2 + 2x_5 \qquad = c$$

$$3x_1 - x_2 + 2x_5 + x_3 \qquad = 7$$

$$-2x_1 + 4x_2 \qquad\qquad + x_4 = 12$$

To determine if the optimal solution remains optimal, equation (4–34) is used. For this problem $n = 4$, $k = 1$, and $m = 2$, and equation (4–34) has the form:

$$[c_5 + a_{1,5}\lambda_1 + a_{2,5}\lambda_2]$$

substituting gives:

$$[2 + 2(1/5) + 0(4/5)] = 2.4 > 0$$

The optimal solution remains optimal, for equation (4–34) is positive, and it is not necessary to resolve the problem. x_5 is not in the basis and has a value of zero.

The terms in parentheses show the solution with the additional variable included. As can be seen, the coefficient at the final step is the same as computed using equation (4–34).

Find the new optimal solution if the following constraint equation is added to the problem

$$-4x_1 + 3x_2 + 8x_5 + x_6 = 10$$

The constraint equation is added to the optimal solution set so the problem will not have to be completely solved and is:

$$
\begin{aligned}
0.2x_3 + 0.8x_4 + 2.4x_5 &= c + 11 \\
x_1 + \quad 0.4x_3 + 0.1x_4 - 0.8x_5 &= 4 \\
x_2 + 0.2x_3 + 0.3x_4 + 0.4x_5 &= 5 \\
-4x_1 + 3x_2 \quad\quad\quad + 8x_5 + x_6 &= 10
\end{aligned}
$$

x_6 is used as the variable in the basis from the additional constraint equation. x_1 and x_2 are eliminated from the added constraint equation by algebraic manipulation, which gives:

$$
\begin{aligned}
0.2x_3 + 0.8x_4 + 2.4x_5 &= c + 11 & c &= -11 \\
x_1 + 0.4x_3 + 0.1x_4 - 0.8x_5 &= 4 & x_1 &= 4 \\
x_2 + 0.2x_3 + 0.3x_4 + 0.4x_5 &= 5 & x_2 &= 5 \\
x_3 - 0.5x_4 + 10x_5 + x_6 &= 11 & x_6 &= 11 \\
& & x_4 &= 0 \\
& & x_5 &= 0
\end{aligned}
$$

The new optimal solution has been found, for all the coefficients in the objective function are positive. An artificial variable would normally have been used, especially in a computer program, to give a feasible basis and proceed to the optimum.

CLOSURE

In this chapter the study of linear programming was taken through the use of large computer codes to solve industrial problems. Sufficient background was provided to be able to formulate and solve linear programming problems for an industrial plant using one of the large linear programming codes and to interpret the optimal solution and associated sensitivity analysis. In addition, this background should provide the ability for independent reading on extensions of the subject.

The mathematical structure of the linear programming problem was introduced by solving a simple problem graphically. The solution was found to be at the intersection of constraint equations. The Simplex Algorithm was then presented, which showed the procedure of moving from one intersection of constraint equations (basic feasible solution) to another and having the objective function improve at each step until the optimum was reached. Having seen the Simplex Method in operation, we discussed the important theorems of linear programming, which guaranteed that the global optimum would be found for the linear objective function and linear constraints. Then methods were presented that illustrated how a process flow diagram and associated information could be converted to a linear programming problem to optimize an industrial process. This was illustrated with a simple petroleum refinery example, and the solution was obtained using a large standard linear programming code, Mathematical Programming System Extended (MPSX), on an IBM 4341 computer. The chapter concluded with a discussion of postoptimal analysis procedures that evaluated the sensitivity of the solution to changes in important parameters of the linear programming problem. This sensitivity analysis was illustrated using simple examples and results from the solution of the simple refinery using the MPSX code.

A list of selected references is given at the end of the chapter for information beyond that presented here. These texts include the following topics. The Revised Simplex Method is a modification of the Simplex Method that permits a more accurate and rapid solution using digital computers. The dual linear programming problem converts the original or primal problem into a corresponding dual problem that may be solved more readily than the original problem. Parametric programming is an extension of sensitivity analysis where ranges on the parameters a_{ij}'s, b_i's, and c_j's are computed directly considering more than one parameter at a time. Also, there are decomposition methods that take an extremely large problem and separate or decompose it into a series of smaller problems that can be solved with reasonable computer time and space. In addition, special techniques have been developed for a class of transportation and network problems that facilitate their solution. Linear programming has been extended to consider multiple conflicting criteria, i.e., more than one objective function, and this has been named *goal programming*. An important extension of linear programming is the case where the variables can take on only integer values, and this has been named *integer programming*. Moreover, linear programming and the theory of games have been interfaced to develop optimal strategies. Finally, almost all large computers have one or more advanced linear programming codes capable of solving problems with thousands of constraints and thousands of variables. It is a very time-consuming and tedious task to assemble and enter reliabile data correctly in using these programs. These codes, e.g., MPSX, are very efficient and use sparse matrix inversion techniques, methods for dealing with ill-conditioned matrices, structural data formats, and simplified input and output transformations. Also, they usually incorporate postoptimal ranging, generalized upper bounding, and parametric programming (9, 12). Again, the topics mentioned above are discussed in the articles and books in the references and the selected list of texts at the end of the chapter.

SELECTED LIST OF TEXTS ON LINEAR PROGRAMMING AND EXTENSIONS

Bazaraa, M. S., and J. J. Jarris, *Linear Programming and Network Flows,* John Wiley & Sons, Inc., New York (1977).

Charnes, A., and W. W. Cooper, *Management Models and Industrial Applications of Linear Programming,* Vols. 1 and 2, John Wiley & Sons, Inc., New York (1967).

Garfinkel, R. S., and G. L. Nemhauser, *Integer Programming,* John Wiley & Sons, Inc., New York (1972).

Glicksman, A. M., *An Introduction to Linear Programming and the Theory of Games,* John Wiley & Sons, Inc., New York (1963).

Greenberg, H., *Integer Programming,* Academic Press, New York (1971).

Hadley, G. H., *Linear Programming,* Addison-Wesley, Inc., Reading, Mass. (1962).

Land, A. H., and S. Powell, *Fortran Codes for Mathematical Programming: Linear, Quadratic and Discrete,* John Wiley & Sons, Inc., New York (1973).

Lasdon, L., *Optimization Theory for Large Systems,* Macmillan and Co., New York (1970).

Naylor, T. H., and E. T. Byrne, *Linear Programming Methods and Cases,* Wadsworth Publishing Co., Belmont, Calif. (1963).

Orchard-Hays, W., *Advanced Linear Programming Computing Techniques,* McGraw-Hill Book Co., New York (1968).

Papadimitriou, C. H., and K. Steiglitz, *Combinatorial Optimization: Algorithms and Complexity,* Prentice-Hall, Inc., Englewood Cliffs, N.J. (1982).

Schrage, L., *Linear Programming Models with LINDO,* Scientific Press, Palo Alto, Calif. (1981).

Taha, H. A., *Integer Programming: Theory, Applications and Computations,* Academic Press, New York (1975).

REFERENCES

1. Dantzig, G. B., *Linear Programming and Extensions,* Princeton University Press, Princeton, N.J. (1963).
2. *An Introduction to Linear Programming,* IBM Data Processing Application Manual E20—8171, IBM Corp., White Plains N.Y. (1964).
3. Garvin, W. W., *Introduction to Linear Programming,* McGraw-Hill Book Co., New York (1966).
4. *Ibid.,* p. 10.
5. *Ibid.,* p. 12.
6. *Ibid.,* p. 21.
7. Gass, S. I., *Linear Programming: Methods and Applications,* 5th Ed., McGraw-Hill Book Co., New York (1985).
8. Smith, C. L., R. W. Pike, and P. W. Murrill, *Formulation and Optimization of Mathematical Models,* International Textbook Co., Scranton, Pa. (1970).
9. Holtzman, A. G., *Mathematical Programming for Operations Researchers and Computer Scientists,* Ed. A. G. Holtzman, Marcel Dekker, Inc., New York (1981).
10. Aronofsky, J. S., J. M. Dutton, and M. T. Tayyabkhan, *Managerial Planning with Linear Programming in Process Industry Operations,* John Wiley & Sons, Inc., New York (1978).
11. Anonymous, *Oil and Gas Journal,* 394 (May 3, 1982).
12. Murtagh, B. A., *Advanced Linear Programming: Computation and Practice,* McGraw-Hill Book Co., New York (1981).
13. Smith, M. G., and J. S. Bonner, *Computer-Aided Process Plant Design,* Ed. M. E. Leesley, Gulf Publishing Co., Houston, p. 1335 (1982).
14. Stoecker, W. F., *Design of Thermal Systems,* 2nd Ed., McGraw-Hill Book Co., New York p. 271 (1980).
15. *IBM Mathematical Programming System Extended/370 (MPSX/370) Program Reference Manual,* SH19–1095-3, 4th Ed., IBM Corp., White Plains, N.Y. (1979).
16. *IBM Mathematical Programming System Extended/370 Primer,* GH19–1091-1, 2nd Ed., IBM Corp., White Plains, N.Y. (1979).
17. Ignizio, J. P., *Linear Programming in Single and Multiple Objective Systems,* Prentice-Hall, Inc., Englewood Cliffs, N.J. (1982).
18. Quandt, R. E., and H. W. Kuhn, "On Upper Bounds for the Number of Iterations in Solving Linear Programs," *Operations Research,* 12:161–5 (1964).
19. Bradley, S. P., A. C. Hax, and T. L. Magnanti, *Applied Mathematical Programming,* Addison-Wesley Publishing Co., Reading, Mass. p. 97 (1977).

PROBLEMS

4–1.   Solve the following problem by the Simplex Method:

$$\text{Maximize: } 6x_1 + x_2 = p$$

$$\text{Subject to: } 3x_1 + 5x_2 \leq 13$$

$$6x_1 + x_2 \leq 12$$

$$x_1 + 5x_2 \leq 10$$

Determine the range on x_1 and x_2 for which the optimal solution remains optimal. Explain. (Note: It is not necessary to use sensitivity analysis.)

4-2. Solve the following problem by the Simplex Method:

$$\text{Maximize: } x_1 + 2x_2 + 3x_3 - x_4 = p$$

$$\text{Subject to: } x_1 + 2x_2 + 3x_3 + x_5 = 15$$

$$2x_1 + x_2 + 5x_3 + x_6 = 20$$

$$x_1 + 2x_2 + x_3 + x_4 = 10$$

Start with x_4, x_5, and x_6 in the basis.

4-3. a. Solve the following problem by the Simplex Method:

$$\text{Maximize: } 2x_1 + x_2 = p$$

$$\text{Subject to: } x_1 + x_2 \le 6$$

$$x_1 - x_2 \le 2$$

$$x_1 + 2x_2 \le 10$$

$$x_1 - 2x_2 \le 1$$

b. Compute the inverse of the optimal basis, and the largest changes in b_i's for the optimal solution remain optimal.

4-4. Solve the following problem by the Simplex Method:

$$\text{Maximize: } 3x_1 + 2x_2 = p$$

$$\text{Subject to: } x_1 + x_2 \le 8$$

$$2x_1 + x_2 \le 10$$

4-5. a. Solve the following problem by the Simplex Method:

$$\text{Maximize: } x_1 + 2x_2 = p$$

$$\text{Subject to: } x_1 + 3x_2 \le 105$$

$$-x_1 + x_2 \leq 15$$

$$2x_1 + 3x_2 \leq 135$$

$$-3x_1 + 2x_2 \leq 15$$

b. Solve this problem by the classical theory using Lagrange Multipliers, and explain why Lagrange Multipliers are sometimes called "shadow" or "implicit" prices.

4–6. a. Solve the following problem by the Simplex Method using slack and artificial variables:

$$\text{Maximize:} \quad x_1 + 10x_2 = p$$

$$\text{Subject to:} -x_1 + \quad x_2 \geq 5$$

$$3x_1 + \quad x_2 \leq 15$$

b. Calculate the inverse of the optimal basis and the Lagrange Multipliers.

c. Calculate the largest changes in the right-hand side of the constraint equations (b_j's) for the optimal solution in part (a) to remain optimal.

4–7. Solve the following problem by the Simplex Method using the minimum number of slack and artificial variables needed for an initially feasible basis:

$$\text{Minimize:} \ 2x_1 + 4x_2 + \quad x_3 = c$$

$$\text{Subject to:} \quad x_1 + 2x_2 - \quad x_3 \leq 5$$

$$2x_1 - \quad x_2 + 2x_3 = 2$$

$$-x_1 + 2x_2 + 2x_3 \geq 1$$

4–8. a. Solve the following problem using the Simplex Method using an artificial variable x_6 in the second constraint equation and adding the term $-10^6 x_6$ to the objective function:

$$\text{Maximize:} \ 2x_1 + \quad x_2 + x_3 = p$$

$$\text{Subject to:} \ x_1 + \quad x_2 + x_3 \leq 10$$

$$x_1 + 5x_2 + x_3 \geq 20$$

b. Compute the effect of changing cost coefficient c_1 from 2 to 3, i.e., $\Delta c_1 = 1$, and c_3 from 1 to 4, i.e., $\Delta c_3 = 3$, using the results of Example 4–6.

c. Without resolving the problem, find the new optimal solution if the first constraint equation is changed to the following by using the results of Example 4–6:

$$x_1 + x_2 + x_3 \leq 5$$

Also, compute the new optimal values of x_1 and x_2 and value of the objective function.

4–9. Consider the following linear programming problem:

$$\text{Maximize: } 2x_1 + x_2 = p$$

$$\text{Subject to: } x_1 + 2x_2 \leq 10$$

$$2x_1 + 3x_2 \leq 12$$

$$3x_1 + x_2 \leq 15$$

$$x_1 + x_2 \geq 4$$

a. Solve the problem by the Simplex Method using slack variables in the first three equations and an artificial variable in the fourth constraint equation as the initially feasible basis.

b. The following matrix is the inverse of the optimal basis, $\mathbf{A}^{-1}$. Multiply this matrix by the matrix $\mathbf{A}$ to obtain the unit matrix $\mathbf{I}$:

$$\mathbf{A}^{-1} = \begin{bmatrix} 0 & -0.143 & 0.429 & 0 \\ 0 & 0.429 & -0.286 & 0 \\ 1 & -0.714 & 0.143 & 0 \\ 0 & 0.286 & 0.143 & -1 \end{bmatrix}$$

c. Compute the Lagrange Multipliers for the problem.

d. Compute the changes in the right-hand side of the constraint equations that will cause all the values of the variables in the basis to become zero.

4–10. [3] Consider the following problem based on a blending analysis:

$$\text{Minimize: } 50x_1 + 25x_2 = c$$

$$\text{Subject to: } \quad x_1 + 3x_2 \geq 8$$

$$3x_1 + 4x_2 \geq 19$$

$$3x_1 + x_2 \geq 7$$

a. Solve this problem by the Simplex Method.
b. Compute the inverse of the optimal basis and the Lagrange Multipliers.
c. Determine the effect on the optimal solution (variables and cost) if the right-hand side of the second constraint equations is changed from 19 to 21 and the right-hand side of the third constraint equations is changed from 7 to 8.
d. Show that the following must hold for the optimal solution to remain optimal, considering changes in the cost coefficients.

$$3/4 \leq c_1/c_2 \leq 3$$

4–11. Consider the following linear programming problem:

$$\text{Maximize: } x_1 + 9x_2 + x_3 = p$$

$$\text{Subject to: } x_1 + 2x_2 + 3x_3 \leq 9$$

$$3x_1 + 2x_2 + 2x_3 \leq 15$$

a. Solve this problem by the Simplex Method.
b. Compute the inverse of the optimal basis and the Lagrange Multipliers.
c. Determine the largest changes in the right-hand side and in the cost coefficients of the variables in the basis for the optimal solution to remain optimal.

4–12. Solve the following problem by the Simplex Method. To demonstrate your understanding of the use of slack and artificial variables, use the slack variable in the first two constraint equations and an artificial variable in the third constraint equation as the initially feasible basis:

$$\text{Maximize: } x_1 + 2x_2 = p$$

$$\text{Subject to: } -x_1 + x_2 \leq 2$$

$$x_1 + x_2 \leq 6$$

$$x_1 + x_2 \geq 1$$

4–13. a. Derive equation (4–31) from equation (4–30). Explain the significance of the terms in equation (4–31), and discuss the application of this equation in sensitivity analysis associated with coefficients of the variables in the objective function.

b. Starting with equation (4–25) show that the change in **b** that gives the limit on $\Delta\mathbf{b}$ for $x^*_{i, \text{ new}} = 0$ is equal to $-\Delta\mathbf{b}$.

4–14. In a power plant that is part of a chemical plant or refinery, both electricity and process steam (high- and low-pressure) can be produced. A typical power plant has constraints associated with turbine capacity, steam pressure and amounts, and electrical demand. In Stoecker (14) the following economic and process model is developed for a simple power plant producing electricity, high-pressure steam x_1, and low-pressure steam x_2:

$$\text{Maximize: } 0.16x_1 + 0.14x_2 = p$$

$$\text{Subject to:} \quad x_1 + \quad x_2 \leq 20$$

$$x_1 + \quad 4x_2 \leq 60$$

$$4x_1 + \quad 3x_2 \leq 72$$

Determine the optimal values of x_1 and x_2 and the maximum profit using the Simplex Method.

4–15. A company makes two levels of purity of a product that is sold in gallon containers. Product A is of higher purity than product B with profits of $0.40 per gallon made on A and $0.30 per gallon made on B. Product A requires twice the processing time of B, and the company can produce no more than a total of 1000 gallons per day of A and B. However, the raw material supply is sufficient for only 800 gallons per day of both A and B combined. Product A requires a container of which only 400 1-gallon containers per day are available, while there are 700 1-gallon containers per day available for B. Assuming all the product can be sold of both A and B, what volumes of each should be produced to maximize the profit? Solve the problem graphically and by the Simplex Method.

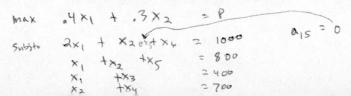

4–16. A wax concentrating plant, as shown below, receives feedstock with a low concentration of wax and refines it into a product with a high concentration of wax. In Stoecker (14) the selling prices of the products are x_1, $8 per hundred pounds, and x_2, $6 per hundred pounds; the raw material costs are x_3, $1.5 per hundred pounds, and x_4, $3 per hundred pounds.

The plant operates under the following constraints:

a. The same amount of wax leaves the plant as enters it.

b. The receiving facilities of the plant are limited to no more than a total of 800 pounds per hour.

c. The packaging facilities can accommodate a maximum of 600 pounds per hour of x_2 and 500 pounds per hour of x_1.

If the operating cost of the plant is constant, use the Simplex Algorithm to determine the purchase and production plan that results in the maximum profit.

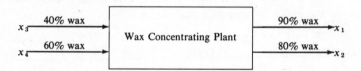

4–17. A company produces a product and a by-product, and production is limited by two constraints. One is on the availability of raw material, and the other is on the capacity of the processing equipment. The product requires 3.0 units of raw material and 2.0 units of processing capacity. The by-product requires 4.0 units of raw materials and 5.0 units of processing capacity. There is a total of 1700 units of raw material available and a total of 1600 units of processing capacity. The profit is $2.00 per unit for the product and $4.00 per unit for the by-product.

The economic model and constraints are:

Maximize: $2x_1 + 4x_2$

Subject to: $3x_1 + 4x_2 \leq 1700$ raw material constraint

$2x_1 + 5x_2 \leq 1600$ processing capacity constraint

a. Determine the maximum profit and the production of the product x_1 and by-product x_2 using the Simplex Method.

b. Calculate the inverse of the optimal basis and the Lagrange Multipliers.

c. i. If the total raw material available is increased from 1700 to 1701, determine the new product, by-product, and profit.

ii. If an additional 10 units of processing capacity can be obtained at a cost of $7, i.e., 1600 is increased to 1610, is this additional capacity worth obtaining?

d. A second by-product can be produced that requires 4.0 units of raw material and $3\frac{1}{3}$ units of processing capacity. Determine the profit that would have to be made on this by-product to consider its production.

4–18.[14] A chemical plant whose flow diagram is shown in Figure 4-9 manufactures ammonia, hydrochloric acid, urea, ammonium carbonate, and ammonia chloride from carbon dioxide, nitrogen, hydrogen, and chlorine. The x values in Figure 4-9 indicate flow rates in moles per hour.

The costs of the feedstocks are c_1, c_2, c_3, and c_4, and the values of the products are p_5, p_6, p_7, and p_8 in dollars per mole, where the subscript corresponds to that of the x value. In reactor 3 the ratios of molal flow rates are $m = 3x_7$ and $x_1 = 2x_7$, and, in other reactors, straightforward material balances apply. The capacity of reactor 1 is equal to or less than 2000 moles per hour of NH_3 and

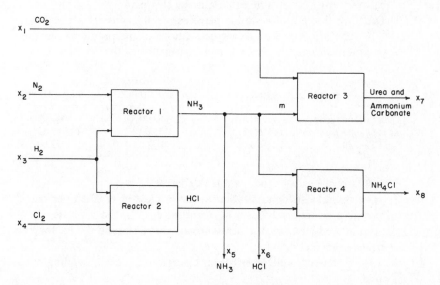

Figure 4-9. Flow diagram of chemical plant in Problem 4–18, after Stoecker (14).

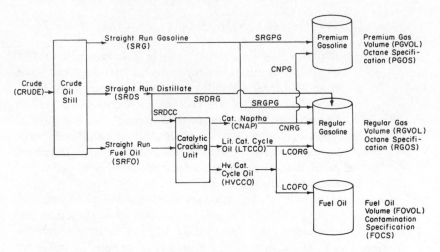

Figure 4-10. Flow diagram of a simple refinery (8).

the capacity of reactor 2 is equal to or less than 1500 moles per hour of HCl as given as Stoecker (14).

a. Develop the expression for the profit.

b. Write the constraint equations for this plant.

4–19. [8] The flow diagram of a simple petroleum refinery is shown in Figure 4-10. The prices and quality specifications of the products and their minimum production rates are given below:

PRODUCT	QUALITY	MINIMUM PRODUCTION (BBL/DAY)	PRICES ($/BBL)
Premium gasoline	≥ 91 Mon	25,000	$45.00
Regular gasoline	≥ 89 Mon	10,000	43.50
Fuel oil	≤ 55 Cont. no.	30,000	13.00

The current cost of crude is $32.00/barrel.

Operating cost for separation in the crude still is $0.25 per barrel for each product produced. The operating cost for the catalytic cracking unit is $0.10 for the straight-run distillate and $0.15 for the straight-run fuel oil.

The following table gives the specifications for each blending component:

COMPONENT	MON	CONT. NO.
Hv. Cat. cycle oil	–	59
Lt. Cat. cycle oil	88	50
Cat. naphtha	97	–
Straight-run distillate	84	–
Straight-run gasoline	92	–

The capacity of the catalytic cracking unit must not exceed 50,000 barrels/day, and the crude still is limited at 100,000 barrels/day. The crude is separated into three volume fractions in the crude still, 0.2 straight-run gasoline, 0.5 straight-run distillate, and 0.3 straight-run fuel oil. In the catalytic cracking unit a product distribution of 0.7 barrel of cat. naphtha, 0.4 light cat. cycle oil, and 0.2 barrel of heavy cat. cycle oil is obtained per barrel of straight-run distillate. The straight-run fuel oil product distribution is 0.1 barrel of cat. naphtha, 0.3 barrel of light cat. cycle oil, and 0.7 barrel of heavy cat. cycle oil.

Present a matrix representation of this simple refinery, similar to the one shown in Figure 4-8. Be sure to include the objective function and material balance, unit, and blending constraints.

4–20. For the results of the MPS optimization of the simple refinery, consider the following:

    a. Table 4-12(b) shows that the variable SRNPG is not in the basis. Compute the largest change in the cost coefficient of SRNPG for the optimal solution to remain optimal. Confirm that this is the correct answer by the sensitivity analysis results tabulated in the chapter.

    b. In Table 4-12(b) the fuel oil (FO) flow rate is at the optimal value of 10,000 barrels/day. Compute the change in the profit if the fuel oil flow rate is increased to 11,000 barrels/day using Lagrange Multipliers. Would this change cause the problem to be resolved according to the MPS results, why?

    c. The marketing department of the company requires a minimum of 5000 barrels/day of residual fuel, a new product. Residual fuel (RF) is straight run fuel oil (SRFO) directly from the atmospheric distillation column. The price is $10.00/barrel, and it is sold "as is." Give the modifications required to the matrix in Figure 4-8 to determine the optimum way to operate the refinery with this new product.

4–21. Prepare a matrix of the objective function and constraint equations from the process flow diagram for the contact process for sulfuric

acid like the one given in Figure 4-8 for the simple refinery. The
process flow diagram for the contact process is given in Figure
7-21. Use the following data, and assume that the units not included
below have fixed operating costs that do not effect the optimization.

Sales Prices and Raw Material Cost	($/lb)
Steam from boiler 1 (STB1)	0.012
Steam from boiler 2 (STB2)	0.012
Sulfuric acid (H2SO4)	0.050
Sulfur to burner (SULFUR)	0.025
Water to economizer (WATER)	0.006
Make-up water (MWATER)	0.006

Operating Costs	($/lb)
Steam from boiler 1 (STB1)	0.001
Steam from boiler 2 (STB2)	0.001
Air through dryer (DRYAIR)	0.005
Water to economizer (WATER)	0.001
Acid through acid cooler (H2SO4)	0.001
Acid through absorber (H2SO4)	00.01

Product Requirements and Raw Material Availability	(lb/hr)
Sulfuric acid (H2SO4)	30,000
Steam (STB1 + STB2)	40,000
Sulfur (SULFUR)	10,000

Process Unit Maximum Capacities	(lb/hr)
Waste heat boiler 1 (STB1)	25,000
Waste heat boiler 2 (STB2)	25,000
Acid cooler (H2SO4)	35,000
Dryer (DRYAIR)	150,000
Economizer (WATER)	60,000
Absorber (H2SO4)	35,000

Stream Split
Sulfuric acid production = 3.06 SULFUR

4-22.[17] In linear programming there is a dual problem that is obtained from
the original or primal problem. Many times the dual problem can
be solved with less difficulty than the primal one. The primal problem
and corresponding dual problem are stated below in a general form:

Primal problem		Dual problem	
Maximize:	$c^T x$	Minimize:	$b^T v$

Subject to: $\mathbf{A} \mathbf{x} \leq \mathbf{b}$ Subject to: $\mathbf{A}^T \mathbf{v} \geq \mathbf{c}^T$

$\mathbf{x} \geq 0$ $\mathbf{v} \geq 0$

The relationships between the primal and dual problems are summarized as follows. First, the dual of the dual is the primal problem. An $m \times n$ primal gives an $n \times m$ dual. For each primal constraint there is a dual variable and vice versa. For each primal variable there is a dual constraint and vice versa. The numerical value of the maximum of the primal is equal to the numerical value of the minimum of the dual. The solution of the dual problem is the Lagrange Multipliers of the primal problem.

a.   Give the primal problem of the following dual problem:

$$\text{Minimize: } 10v_1 + 15v_2$$

$$\text{Subject to: } \quad v_1 + \; 5v_2 \geq 8$$

$$v_1 + \quad v_2 \geq 4$$

b.   Solve the dual problem by the Simplex Method.
c.   Using the solution of the dual problem, determine the optimal values for the variables in the primal problem.

4–23.   The dual problem of linear programming can be obtained from the primal problem using Lagrange Multipliers. Using the form of the equations given in Problem 4–22 for the primal problem and, considering that slack variables have been added to the constraints, show that the Lagrangian function can be written as:

$$L(\mathbf{x}, \boldsymbol{\lambda}) = \mathbf{c}^T \mathbf{x} + \boldsymbol{\lambda}^T (\mathbf{A} \mathbf{x} - \mathbf{b})$$

Rearrange this equation to give the following form:

$$L(\mathbf{x}, \boldsymbol{\lambda}) = -\mathbf{b}^T \boldsymbol{\lambda} + \mathbf{x}(\mathbf{A}^T \boldsymbol{\lambda} + \mathbf{c}^T)$$

Justify that the following constrained optimization problem can be obtained from the Lagrangian function:

$$\text{Minimize: } \mathbf{b}^T \boldsymbol{\lambda}$$

$$\text{Subject to: } \mathbf{A}^T \boldsymbol{\lambda} \geq \mathbf{c}^T$$

This is the dual problem given in Problem 4–22. Note that the independent variables of the dual problem are the Lagrange Multipliers or "shadow prices" of the primal problem.

4–24. A primal programming can be converted into a dual problem as described in Problems 4–22 and 4–23. This approach is used when the dual problem is easier to solve than the primal problem. The general form of the primal problem and its dual was given in Problem 4–22.

    a. Solve the dual problem of the primal problem and its dual given below.

Primal problem:

Minimize: $10x_1 + 6x_2 + 8x_3$

Subject to: $x_1 + x_2 + 2x_3 \geq 2$

                $5x_1 + 3x_2 + 2x_3 \geq 1$

Dual problem:

Maximize: $2v_1 + v_2$

Subject to: $v_1 + 5v_2 \leq 10$

             $v_1 + 3v_2 \leq 6$

           $2v_1 + 2v_2 \leq 8$

    b. In this procedure the solution of the primal problem is the negative of the coefficients of the slack variables in the objective function of the final iteration of the Simplex Method of the dual problem, and the solution of the dual problem is the negative of the Lagrange Multipliers for the primal problem. Give the solution of the primal problem and the Lagrange Multipliers for the primal problem, and show that the minimum of the objective function of the primal problem is equal to the maximum of the objective function of the dual problem.

    c. In the primal problem give the matrix to be inverted to compute the inverse of the optimal basis.

    d. Compute the Lagrange Multipliers using equation (4–22), and show that they agree with the solution from the dual problem.

e. A new variable x_6 is added to the problem, as shown below:

Minimize: $10x_1 + 6x_2 + 8x_3 + \qquad 2x_6 = p$

Subject to: $x_1 + x_2 + 2x_3 + x_4 + \qquad 5x_6 = 2$

$$5x_1 + 3x_2 + 2x_3 \qquad + x_5 + 3x_6 = 1$$

Will the optimal solution remain optimal, or will the problem have to be resolved? Explain.

5
SINGLE-VARIABLE SEARCH TECHNIQUES

INTRODUCTION

In this and the next chapter, techniques are presented that are applicable to complex problems where the economic model and constraints can be in the form of a computer program or the process itself, in contrast to previous methods that required specific equations. The optimization problem is illustrated in Figure 5-1, where specifying inputs will produce outputs. The figure shows the general names associated with the inputs and outputs. Specifying the values of the independent variables determines the dependent variables. However, the values of the dependent variables could be affected by random error and parameters of the system. Also, a process example is given in the figure to illustrate these inputs and outputs. The dependent variable of product conversion is determined by the feed rate of the raw material and the temperature and pressure of the process. In addition, the parameter of feed composition and the random error associated with measuring the process inputs and outputs affect the value of this dependent variable. Other examples for different fields are given by Wilde (1).

In this chapter the effective interval elimination procedures for single-variable search methods will be emphasized. These methods rapidly reduce the interval containing the location of the optimum, using the minimax principle as the experiments are placed either sequentially or simultaneously. First, it will be necessary to define and describe search problems, search plans, unimodality, and the minimax principle briefly to establish a foundation for these techniques. In addition, other well-known single-variable methods will be presented, and they will be compared with the interval elimination procedures. Moreover, it will be seen that the multivariable search techniques of Chapter 6 will incorporate single-variable methods. Also, a computer program for the most important method is given in this chapter.

SEARCH PROBLEMS AND SEARCH PLANS

A search problem has been represented in Figure 5-1 as a "black box" for the process where the values of the economic model are computed by specifying inputs. Consequently, a search problem can be defined as an investigation that seeks the optimal value of a function. Search problems can be classified

BLACK BOX:

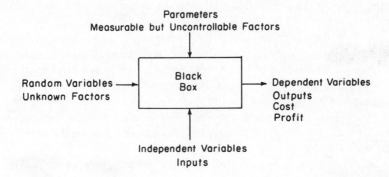

PROCESS EXAMPLE:

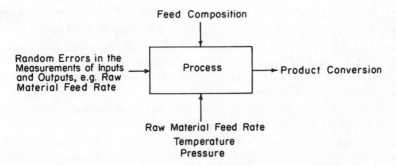

Figure 5-1. Representation of a search problem, after Wilde (1).

by the number of independent variables and by the absence or presence of random or experimental error.

Deterministic problems have no experimental error or random factors present. An example is the mathematical model of a process, where the outputs are calculated by a computer program from specified inputs. Stochastic problems have random error present, usually in the form of experimental errors from measuring the process variables. An example is a plant where there are experimental errors associated with laboratory and instrument measurements of the process flow rates and compositions.

For the solution of single-variable problems that do not have random error, there are powerful techniques based on the minimax principle. Unfortunately, comparable results are not available for multivariable problems except in the special case where the economic model is rectangular unimodal (2). To optimize stochastic problems, they are treated as deterministic with noise superimposed. The effect is to slow the search for the optimum, as discussed by Wilde (1).

To find the optimum of a search problem, a search plan is needed. A search plan is a set of instructions for performing n sets of experiments; $x_1, x_2, \cdots, x_n$, (values of the independent variables). An experiment consists of specifying one set of values of the independent variables, e.g., temperature, pressure, and raw material feed rate for a process, and determining the values of the outputs, e.g., product conversion. This could be done using the process itself or using a computer program of the mathematical model of the process for the evaluation of the dependent variables.

Search plans can be classified as either simultaneous or sequential. In a simultaneous search plan the locations of all the experiments are specified, and the outcome of the measurements is obtained at the same time. An example is the location of a set of thermocouples installed along the length of a fixed-bed reactor to determine the position of the hot spot (maximum temperature) in the catalyst bed while the process is in operation. In a sequential search plan the outcome of an experiment is determined before another experiment is made. Being able to base future experiments on past outcomes is a significant advantage. In fact, it can be shown that the advantage of sequential search plans over simultaneous search plans increases exponentially with the number of experiments (1).

We will begin by describing simultaneous search plans, and we will use these results to obtain sequential search plans. These plans, which are based on the minimax principle, are completely conservative, do not depend on luck, and rapidly reduce the interval that contains the optimum with relatively few measurements. Also, with the minimax principle the optimal search plan can be selected to find the optimum of the search problem.

UNIMODALITY

A function is unimodal if it has only one maximum or minimum in the region to be searched. Examples of unimodal functions are shown in Figure 5-2. As shown in the figure, a unimodal function can be continuous or discontinuous, have discontinuous first derivatives, or be defined only at discrete values of the dependent variable.

A unimodal function can be defined without using derivatives as follows. Let x_1 and x_2 ($>x_1$) be two experiments placed in the interval $a \leq x \leq b$, and let y_1 and y_2 be the results obtained from the profit function having a maximum at $y^* = y(x^*)$. Then y is unimodal if $x_2 < x^*$ implies that $y_1 < y_2$, and if $x_1 > x^*$ implies that $y_1 > y_2$. In other words, if the points

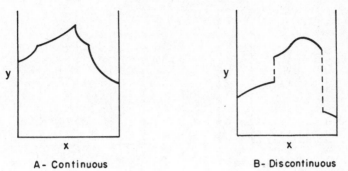

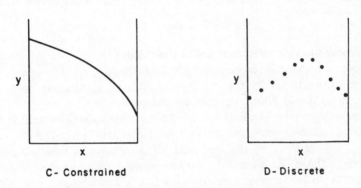

Figure 5-2. Examples of Unimodal Functions

are both on the same side of the optimum, then the one near the optimum has the higher values of y (1). This definition does not require a continuous function, and it will allow a search technique to be developed for unimodal discrete functions. Moreover, though search techniques are developed for unimodal functions, they will work on multimodal functions also. However, they will locate only one of the maxima or minima. In the following discussion all the functions are considered to be unimodal, and they have one maximum and one minimum either in the interval or on the boundary.

REDUCING THE INTERVAL OF UNCERTAINTY

Generally, we know the initial interval on the independent variable to be searched for the maximum of the profit function (or the minimum of the

Unimodal → Only 1 optimum

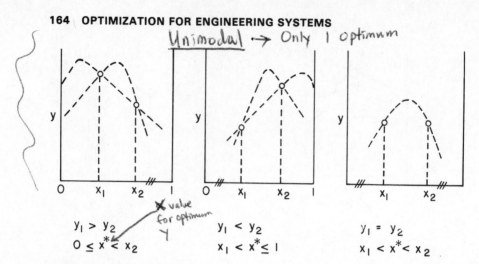

$y_1 > y_2$

$0 \leq x^* \leq x_2$

X value for optimum
y

$y_1 < y_2$

$x_1 < x^* \leq 1$

$y_1 = y_2$

$x_1 < x^* < x_2$

Figure 5-3. Eliminating part of the initial interval of uncertainty from the results of two experiments.

cost function). This interval is called the *initial interval of uncertainty,* and we need a systematic procedure to reduce the size of this interval. This can be accomplished by placing experiments and eliminating parts of the initial interval that do not contain the optimum.

Eliminating part of the initial interval of uncertainty is illustrated in Figure 5-3 for the three possible outcomes of two experiments placed on the interval $0 \leq x \leq 1$. If $y_1 > y_2$ the maximum of the unimodal function could lie between 0 and x_1 or x_1 and x_2, as the dotted lines illustrate. However, it can not lie in the interval between x_2 and 1.0, and consequently, this part of the initial interval can be eliminated. Had the results of the experiments been $y_1 < y_2$, then the part of the interval between 0 and x_1 could be eliminated. In the unlikely but lucky event that $y_1 = y_2$, then the maximum must lie between x_1 and x_2, and the parts of the initial interval between 0 and x_1 and x_2 and 1.0 are eliminated, as shown in the figure.

If the numerical values of x_1 and x_2 had been given, this would have specified a two-experiment search plan. We would like to search with the best search plan and reduce the interval of uncertainty as much as possible with a specified number of experiments. Consequently, a measure of the effectiveness of search plans is needed, so the best one among all those possible can be selected, i.e., the optimal search plan to optimize the function.

MEASURING SEARCH EFFECTIVENESS (1)

To compare search plans, the measure of effectiveness must be independent of functions being optimized. This is required to eliminate functional depen-

y values   *x values*

dence, bias, and luck. Consequently, it is necessary to have the measure of
the effectiveness of search plans depend on the placement of the experiments,
but not on the outcomes of those experiments. Therefore, the criterion to
be used in comparing search plans is the size of the *largest* interval of uncertainty possible, having determined the location of the experiments. This does
not depend on the outcome of the experiments.

To illustrate this idea, let us compare the two search plans shown in Figure
5-4 for their effectiveness based on the largest interval of uncertainty having
specified the location of the experiments. In the first search plan three experi-

i_3 = Final Interval of Uncertainty

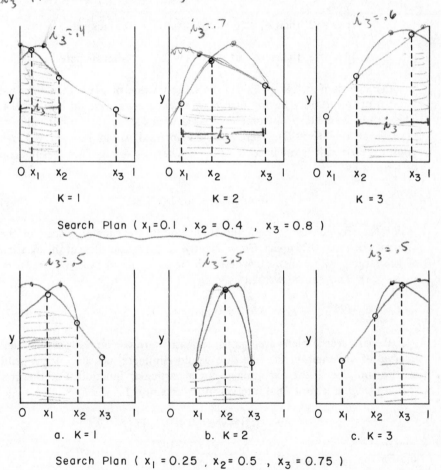

Search Plan ($x_1 = 0.1$, $x_2 = 0.4$, $x_3 = 0.8$)

Search Plan ($x_1 = 0.25$, $x_2 = 0.5$, $x_3 = 0.75$)

Figure 5-4.   Two three-experiment search plans ($x_1 = 0.1$, $x_2 = 0.4$, $x_3 = 0.8$) and
($x_1 = 0.25$, $x_2 = 0.5$, $x_3 = 0.75$). K is the index of the greatest outcome.

ments are located at $x_1 = 0.1$, $x_2 = 0.4$, $x_3 = 0.8$, on an initial unit interval. The possible outcomes of the function at these values are shown in Figure 5-4. Also shown in this figure is the second search plan with experiments located at $x_1 = 0.25$, $x_2 = 0.5$, $x_3 = 0.75$ on the same initial unit interval and the corresponding possible results of evaluating the function.

For the first search plan, the location of final interval of uncertainty, i_3, depends on the outcome of the experiments. Let K be the index of the best of the three results, and we have:

If $K = 1$, then $0 < x^* < x_2$ $i_3 = 0.4$ luckiest

If $K = 2$, then $x_1 < x^* < x_3$ $i_3 = 0.7$ unluckiest

If $K = 3$, then $x_1 < x^* < 1$ $i_3 = 0.6$ intermediate

In other words if x_1 $(K = 1)$ has the largest value of $y(x)$, then the final interval of uncertainty having placed three experiments would be $i_3 = 0.4$. This would be a lucky outcome compared with having the largest value of $y(x)$ be at x_2, $(K = 2)$ where the final interval would be $i_3 = 0.7$. An intermediate result is obtained for $K = 3$ where $i_3 = 0.6$. These results can be written as:

$$i_3 = [0.4, 0.7, 0.6] \text{ for } 1 \leq K \leq 3 \qquad (5\text{--}1)$$

For the second search plan the three points are equally spaced in the interval a distance 0.25 apart. Consequently, $i_3 = 0.5$ regardless of the location of the largest value of $y(x)$, whether it be at $x_1(K = 1)$, $x_2(K = 2)$, or $x_3(K = 3)$. This can be written as

$$i_3 = [0.5, 0.5, 0.5] \text{ for } 1 \leq K \leq 3 \qquad (5\text{--}2)$$

If the two search plans are compared, based on their largest possible final interval of uncertainty, the selection would eliminate luck and not depend on the outcome of the experiments for a particular function. For the first search plan the largest final interval of uncertainty, I_3, is:

$$I_3 = \max_{1 \leq K \leq 3} [i_3] = \max [0.4, 0.7, 0.6] = 0.7 \qquad (5\text{--}3)$$

and for the second search plan:

$$I_3 = \max_{1 \leq K \leq 3} [i_3] = \max [0.5, 0.5, 0.5] = 0.5 \qquad (5\text{--}4)$$

Consequently, the second search plan would be designated as the better of the two, because it has the smaller of the largest final intervals of uncertainty, i.e., $I_3 = 0.5$.

This discussion has illustrated that search plans should be compared on their largest final interval of uncertainty to have a consistent and conservative measure for comparison. This eliminates functional dependence and luck as factors in comparing search plans. Also, the example has served to define a nomenclature that can be used to discuss search plans with n experiments.

In general, a search plan with n experiments, x_n, specifies the size of all of the possible final intervals of uncertainty, as shown in Figure 5-5. This can be written as:

[handwritten: Experiments on either side of the experiment assumed to be a possible max (have max Y(x) out of the experiments)]

[handwritten: Final interval of uncertainty]

$$i_n = (x_{K+1} - x_{K-1}) \qquad \text{for } 1 \le K \le n \qquad \text{[handwritten: For 1 Search Plan]} \qquad (5\text{-}5)$$

and generates the i_n values for n experiments that are comparable to those of equations (5–1) and (5–2) for the two, three-experiment search plans. In equation (5–5) x_{K-1} and x_{K+1} are the two experiments on either side of the experiment x_K when it is considered to be the one to have the largest value of $y(x)$.

The results of the experiments determine the value of the best outcome $y(x_K)$ (and the index K) and the location and size of the final interval of uncertainty, i.e., the specific i_n that contains the best outcome x_K. However, we need to compare search plans, x_n, based on the largest final interval of uncertainty, I_n, which is independent of the outcome of the experiments. This can be written as:

[handwritten: Search plans x_n x_m etc]

[handwritten: K = The value for n that gives y(x) max of the x's (not the optimum)]

$$I_n(x_n) = \max_{1 \le K \le n} [i_n(x_n, K)] \qquad (5\text{-}6)$$

[handwritten: $i_K = x_{K+1} - x_{K-1}$]

[handwritten: $\vdash i_n = x_3 - x_1 \dashv \vdash i_n = x_5 - x_3 \dashv$ $\vdash i_n = I_0 - x_{n-1} \dashv$]

[handwritten: $\vdash i_n = x_2 - 0 \dashv \vdash i_n = x_4 - x_2 \dashv$ $\vdash i_n = x_n - x_{n-2} \dashv$]

[axis: 0 x_1 x_2 x_3 x_4 x_5 x_{n-2} x_{n-1} x_n I_0]
[K: 1 2 3 4 5 n-1 n]

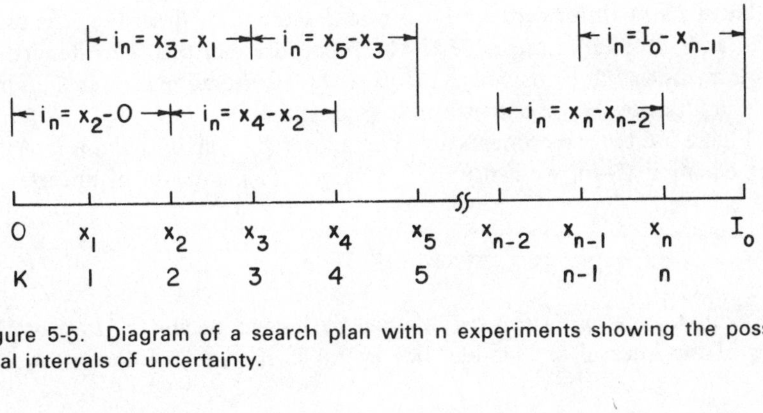

Figure 5-5. Diagram of a search plan with n experiments showing the possible final intervals of uncertainty.

This equation is a generalization of equations (5–3) and (5–4) for n experiments. It states that for a search plan $\mathbf{x}_n$, consider that each one of the n experiments could be the largest outcome, i.e., $1 \leq K \leq n$. This defines n possible final intervals of uncertainty i_n. From those values of i_n the largest one, I_n, is selected. This largest final interval of uncertainty is unique to this search plan and is independent of the outcome of the experiments.

MINIMAX PRINCIPLE (1)   *Best Search Plan*

Having decided to compare search plans based on their largest final interval of uncertainty, we want to select the best search plan $\mathbf{x}_n^*$, i.e., the one search plan that has the smallest of the largest final intervals of uncertainty. This is a statement of the minimax principle, which can be written as:

Smallest of the largest final intervals of uncertainty

Choose the Min of the max final Interval of uncertainty from each plan

$$I_n^* = I_n(\mathbf{x}_n^*) = \min_{\mathbf{x}_n} \, [I_n(\mathbf{x}_n)] \qquad (5–7)$$

Search plan w/ the Smallest of the largest intervals of uncertainty

and substituting equation (5–6) into (5–7) gives:

$$I_n^* = I_n(x_n^*) = \min_{\mathbf{x}_n} \left\{ \max_{1 \leq K \leq n} \, [i_n(\mathbf{x}_n, K)] \right\} \qquad (5–8)$$

largest of the intervals of uncertainty of all Search plans

Equation (5–8) is the mathematical statement of the minimax principle. It requires searching over all possible search plans $\mathbf{x}_n$ having n experiments to evaluate their largest final intervals of uncertainty I_n. Then the search plan with the smallest one is selected as best. To evaluate the largest final interval of uncertainty for each search plan, it is necessary to consider that each of the n experiments $x_1, x_2, \cdots, x_n$ may have the largest possible outcome $(1 \leq K \leq n)$. This will then enumerate the possible final intervals of uncertainty, i_n, from which the largest one can be selected.

Fig 5-4 ✓

This procedure sounds like a formidable task. However, it turns out to be relatively straightforward, and it is best illustrated by describing the cases of two and three experiments first. The procedure can then be extended to n experiment search plans where the experiments are all placed at the same time (simultaneously) or one at a time (sequentially).

In Figure 5-6 two experiments are shown located on an initial unit interval. Using equation (5–6), we can write the largest final interval of uncertainty I_2 as:

Example

$$I_2 = \max \, [x_2, \ 1 - x_1] \qquad (5–9)$$

The smallest value of I_2 can be obtained by having x_1 and x_2 as near the center of the interval as possible. For example, if $x_1 = 0.4$ and $x_2 = 0.8$,

$x_2 = .7$
$I_2 = .8$

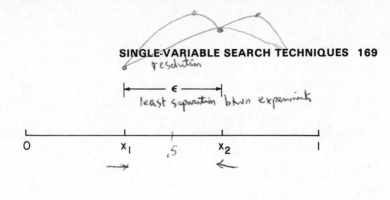

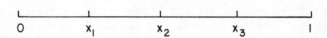

Figure 5-6. Search plans with two and three experiments on an initial unit interval.

then $I_2 = 0.8$, and if $x_1 = 0.49$ and $x_2 = 0.51$, then $I_2 = 0.51$. It is not possible to have $x_1 = x_2 = 0.5$ for $I_2 = 0.5$, because $x_1 = x_2 = 0.5$ is the same point. There would be only one outcome, and it would not be possible to tell which segment of the interval to eliminate. Consequently, to have the minimum value of I_2, we place the two experiments as close together as possible and still be able to detect a difference in the outcomes y_1 and y_2. This least separation between the experiments is called *resolution* and is indicated on the diagram in Figure 5-6 as ϵ. Consequently, the best search plan for two experiments is to place them symmetrically in the interval separated by the resolution, and the final interval will be obtained from equation (5–9) having $x_1 = 0.5 - \epsilon/2$ and $x_2 = 0.5 + \epsilon/2$.

$$I_2^* = 0.5 + \epsilon/2 \tag{5–10}$$

In Figure 5-6 three experiments are shown located on an initial unit interval. Using equation (5–6), we can write the largest final interval of uncertainty I_3 as:

$$I_3 = \max [x_2, x_3 - x_1, 1 - x_2] \tag{5–11}$$

Inspecting the above equation, it is seen that the value selected for x_2 controls the value of I_3. For example if $x_2 = 0.5$, then $1 - x_2 = 0.5$, and I_3 would have a value of 0.5, as long as the value of $(x_3 - x_1)$ was less than or equal to 0.5. In fact, the value of 0.5 for x_2 is the best in a minimax sense for the location of x_2. Then the minimum value of I_3 is 0.5, and x_1 and

x_3 can be located at any position as long as their difference does not exceed 0.5. A convenient way to place the three points is equally spaced in the interval with a separation of 0.25, i.e., uniform search.

If the two minimax search plans with two and three experiments are compared, the final intervals are as follows:

I_3 mxy $[x_2 (x_3 -1) (1-x_2)$

$$I_2^* = 0.5 + \epsilon/2 \tag{5-10}$$

$I^*_3 = max [.5, (x_3 - x_1) (1-.5)] = .5$

$$I_3^* = 0.5 \tag{5-12}$$

From these two equations we can see that placing one additional experiment reduces the final interval of uncertainty only by the amount of $\epsilon/2$. This is usually an insignificant interval reduction compared with the cost of placing another experiment. We will see that similar results will be obtained when n experiments are placed simultaneously.

SIMULTANEOUS SEARCH METHODS (2)

We will now extend the results to include k experiments placed simultaneously in an initial interval using the minimax principle. It will be necessary to consider the two cases of an odd and even number of experiments. It will be seen that only a small reduction in the final interval will be obtained with an additional experiment when going from an even number of experiments to an odd number. However, the spacing of an odd number of experiments uniformly in the interval will be attractive from the point of view of computational simplicity.

Beginning with the case of an odd number of experiments, it is convenient to use p pairs of experiments and have $k = 2p + 1$ total experiments. This is shown in Figure 5-7, where the initial interval is I_0, and it contains x_{2p+1} as the last one of k experiments. The possible final intervals of uncertainty are indicated in the figure also; and they consist of $(x_2 - 0)$, $(x_3 - x_1)$, $(x_4 - x_2)$, $\cdots$, $(x_{2p} - x_{2p-2})$, $(x_{2p+1} - x_{2p-1})$, $(I_0 - x_{2p})$.

The following set of equations can be written that relate even experimental points and the largest final interval of uncertainty I_k that is to be minimized:

$$x_2 - 0 \quad \leq I_k$$

$$x_4 - x_2 \quad \leq I_k$$

$$x_6 - x_4 \quad \leq I_k \tag{5-13}$$

$$\vdots$$

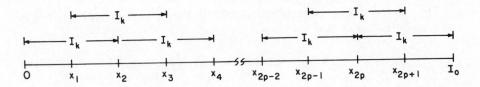

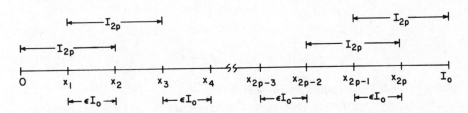

Figure 5-7. Minimax search plans for an odd and even number of experiments.

$$x_{2p} - x_{2p-2} \leq I_k$$

$$I_0 - x_{2p} \qquad \leq I_k$$

These $(p + 1)$ inequalities can be added to give the following equation:

$$I_0 \leq (p + 1)I_k \qquad\qquad (5\text{--}14)$$

This equation can be written as:

$$I_k \geq \frac{I_0}{(p + 1)} \qquad\qquad (5\text{--}15)$$

To satisfy the minimax principle, the minimum value of I_k must be selected, and this requires the equality be used in equation (5–15), i.e.

$$I_k^* = I_0/(p + 1) \qquad\qquad (5\text{--}16)$$

The optimal spacing of experiments requires that the even ones be placed an equal distance apart, i.e.:

$$x_{2h} = h\, I_k^* \quad \text{for } h = 1, 2, \cdots, p \qquad (5\text{–}17)$$

The odd experiments can be located between the even ones at any position, as long as they are no farther apart than I_k^*. Consequently, there is not a unique minimax search plan for an odd number of experiments. However, a computationally simple one is to distribute the experiments uniformly in the interval, as given by the following equation:

$$x_j = j\, I_k^*/2 \quad \text{for } j = 1, 2, 3, \cdots, k \qquad (5\text{–}18)$$

or

$$x_j = j\, I_0/2(p + 1) \quad \text{for } j = 1, 2, \cdots, k \qquad (5\text{–}19)$$

(handwritten: $(k=2p)$)

This procedure is called *uniform search*.

(handwritten margin: Even)

For an even number of experiments, a unique search plan will be obtained, search by uniform pairs. In this case there will be p pairs of experiments and a total of $2p$ experiments. This is shown in Figure 5–7 also, where the initial interval is I_0, and it contains x_{2p}, the last one of $2p$ experiments. Also, the possible final intervals of uncertainty I_{2p} are indicated in the figure and consist of $(x_2 - 0), (x_3 - x_1), \cdots, (x_{2p} - x_{2p-2}), (I_0 - x_{2p-1})$.

(handwritten margin: For Odd)

The following set of equations can be written that relate the even experimental points, as was done previously:

(handwritten annotations:
$i_1 = x_2 - 0 \le I_k$
$i_2 = x_4 - x_2 \le I_k$
$i_5 = x_6 - x_4 \le I_k$
$i_{2p-1} = x_{2p} - x_{2p-2} \le I_k$
$i_{2p+1} = I_0 - x_{2p} \le I_k$*)

(handwritten: Even)

$$
\begin{aligned}
i_1 &= x_2 - 0 &&\le I_{2p} \le I_k \\
i_3 &= x_4 - x_2 &&\le I_{2p} \le I_k \\
&\;\;\vdots \\
i_{2p_i} &= x_{2p} - x_{2p-2} &&\le I_{2p} \le I_k
\end{aligned}
\qquad (5\text{–}20)
$$

These p inequalities can be added to give the following equation:

(handwritten: $I_0 \le (p+1)\, I_k$)

$$x_{2p} \le p\, I_{2p} \le I_k \qquad (5\text{–}21)$$

The equation that includes the final interval I_0 involving the odd point, x_{2p-1} is:

(handwritten: $I_k \ge \dfrac{I_0}{(p+1)}$)

$$I_0 - x_{2p-1} \le I_{2p} \le I_k \qquad (5\text{–}22)$$

(handwritten:
$I_k^* = \dfrac{I_0}{(p+1)}$
$x_{2h} = h\, I_k^*$
$\text{for } h\ 1, 2, \cdots p$*)

Adding equation (5–21) and (5–22) gives:

$$I_0 + x_{2p} - x_{2p-1} \le (p+1) I_{2p} \qquad (5\text{–}23)$$

To satisfy the minimax principle, the minimum value of I_{2p} must be selected. To have the minimum value of I_{2p}, not only must the equality be selected, but the distance between the two experiments x_{2p} and x_{2p-1} must be as small as possible. This means that x_{2p} and x_{2p-1} must be separated by the resolution, as shown in Figure 5–7. The resolution is ϵI_0 and ϵ is a fraction of the initial interval. Thus, equation (5–23) becomes:

$$F_k = I_{2p} \ge \frac{I_0}{(p+1)} + \frac{(x_{2p} - x_{2p-1})}{(p+1)} \qquad I_0 + \epsilon I_0 = (p+1) I_{2p}^* \qquad (5\text{–}24)$$

Solving for I_{2p}^* gives:

Select equality $(x_{2p} - x_{2p-1}) = \epsilon I_0$

$$I_{2p}^* = (1 + \epsilon) I_0/(p+1) \qquad (5\text{–}25)$$

which is comparable to equation (5–16) for an odd number of experiments.

A unique search plan is obtained for an even number of experiments. For this search by uniform pairs, the even experiments are located throughout the interval according to equation (5–25) as:

$$x_{2h} = h(1+\epsilon) I_0/(p+1) \qquad \text{for } h = 1, 2, 3, \cdots, p \qquad (5\text{–}26)-$$

and the odd experiments are placed to the left of the even ones separated by a distance equal to the resolution, as shown below:

$$x_{2h-1} = x_{2h} - \epsilon I_0 \qquad \text{for } h = 1, 2, 3, \cdots, p \qquad (5\text{–}27)$$

Substituting for x_{2h} gives a convenient formula to compute the location of the odd experiments, which is comparable to equations (5–26) for the even experiments:

$$x_{2h-1} = [h - (p+1-h)\epsilon] I_0/(p+1) \qquad \text{for } h = 1, 2, 3, \cdots, p \qquad (5\text{–}28)-$$

A comparison of the equations for the final intervals of uncertainty for an even number of experiments and one additional experiments is given by rewriting equation (5–25) for an even number and equation (5–16) for an odd number as:

$$I_{2p}^* = \frac{I_0(1+\epsilon)}{p+1}$$

$$\text{Even: } I_{2p}^* = I_0/(p+1) + \epsilon I_0/(p+1) \qquad (5\text{–}29)$$

$$\text{Odd: } I_{2p+1}^* = I_0/(p+1) \qquad (5\text{–}30)$$

Search by Uniform Pairs

$$x_{2h} = h I_0 \frac{(1+\epsilon)}{p+1} \text{ for } h=1,2,\cdots p$$

$$x_{2h-1} = x_{2h} - \epsilon I_0$$

The placing of the additional experiment reduces the final interval by the amount of $\epsilon I_0/(p + 1)$. This normally would be a small number, and the additional experiment could involve significant expense. This must be weighed against the convenience of the use of uniform search, i.e., the odd minimax plan of distributing the experiments uniformly in the initial interval.

The following simple example illustrates the use of the results obtained for these minimax search plans.

EXAMPLE 5-1

Search for the maximum of the following function using search by uniform pairs with four experiments and uniform search with five experiments. The initial interval is $I_0 = 1.0$, and the resolution is $\epsilon = 0.05$. Compare the lengths and locations of the final intervals of uncertainty. Also compare the maximum values obtained with the optimum computed using the classical theory of maxima and minima.

$$\max: y = 3 + 6x - 4x^2 \quad \text{on} \quad 0 \leq x \leq 1.0$$

For four simultaneous experiments, their location is determined by equations (5–26) and (5–28), and for $h = 1$:

$$x_2 = (1 + \epsilon)\, I_0/(p + 1) = (1 + 0.05)(1)/(2 + 1) = 0.35$$

$$x_1 = [1 - (2 + 1 - 1)0.05](1)/(2 + 1) = 0.30$$

and x_1 and x_2 are separated by the resolution $\epsilon I_0 = 0.05$. The values of x_3 and x_4 are computed similarly and are:

$$x_3 = 0.65 \qquad x_4 = 0.70$$

Evaluating the function gives:

$$y(0.30) = 4.44$$

$$y(0.35) = 4.60$$

$$y(0.65) = 5.21$$

$$y(0.70) = 5.24$$

and the length and the location of the final interval of uncertainty are:

$$I_4^* = 0.35 \qquad 0.65 \le x^* \le 1$$

For five simultaneous experiments, their location is determined by equation (5–19):

$$x_1 = I_0/2(p + 1) = 1/2(2 + 1) = 1/6 \qquad \text{for } j = 1$$

The other values are computed similarly to give:

$$x_2 = 1/3$$

$$x_3 = 1/2$$

$$x_4 = 2/3$$

$$x_5 = 5/6$$

Evaluating the function gives:

$$y(1/6) = 3.89$$

$$y(1/3) = 4.56$$

$$y(1/2) = 5.00$$

$$y(2/3) = 5.22$$

$$y(5/6) = 5.22$$

and the length and location of the final interval of uncertainty are:

$$I_5^* = 1/3 \qquad 2/3 \le x^* \le 1$$

The difference in the final intervals of uncertainty between four and five experiments is $0.350 - 0.333 = 0.017$, and this is equal to $\epsilon I_0/(p + 1) = 0.05(1)/3 = 0.017$ from equations (5–29) and (5–30). Also using the classical theory of maxima and minima, the optimum is located at $x^* = 3/4$ with a value of $y(3/4) = 5.25$, which is compared with $y(0.70) = 5.24$, the largest value for four experiments, and $y(5/6) = 5.22$, the largest value for five experiments.

The preceding simple example has illustrated the use of the equations for simultaneous search. A more detailed discussion of these methods has been given by Wilde and Beightler (2) and includes a mathematical elaboration of resolution, distinguishability, and scaling. The topic of fictitious points will be discussed subsequently associated with lattice search. Now we will move to sequential search methods, using the concepts that have been developed for simultaneous search methods.

SEQUENTIAL SEARCH METHODS (2)

With a sequential search, it is possible to make use of previous information to locate subsequent experiments. The result is a significantly larger reduction in the final interval of uncertainty for the same number of experiments. The most efficient one of the sequential search plans is called *Fibonacci search*, from the famous sequence of numbers that appears in the equations of this procedure. This minimax method requires that the number of experiments be specified in advance, which may be inconvenient. Almost as efficient as Fibonacci search is *golden section search*, and this method does not require that the number of experiments be specified in advance. A third, related search plan, *lattice search*, is designed for functions that are defined only at discrete points. These methods, which place experiments one at a time, will be developed in the following paragraphs. However, the theory is available to place any number of experiments simultaneously in an interval and repeat this placement sequentially. These methods are called *even block, odd block,* and *golden block* search. Their description and minimax proofs are given by Wilde and Beightler (2) and Avriel (3). It is important to know that these other methods are available for use, but they will not be discussed here, for their application to the solution of industrial problems has been limited.

Fibonacci Search: This search technique is considered to be the best one of the minimax methods. It has the largest interval reduction of all of the procedures, but it requires that the number of experiments be specified in advance. The approach to developing this algorithm will be after that of Wilde (1) and Wilde and Beightler (2), where a dynamic programming approach is used. The derivation begins by placing the last two experiments optimally in the interval preceding the final interval of uncertainty. This is a simultaneous search with two experiments. Then the development determines the location of each preceding experiment to arrive at the location of the first two experiments.

In Figure 5-8 the locations of the last two experiments, x_n and x_{n-1}, are shown. They are placed symmetrically about the center of the interval preceding the final interval and are separated by a distance equal to the resolution, δI_n ($=\epsilon I_0$). The final interval is I_n, the one preceding it is I_{n-1}, and δ is the fractional resolution based on the final interval of uncertainty.

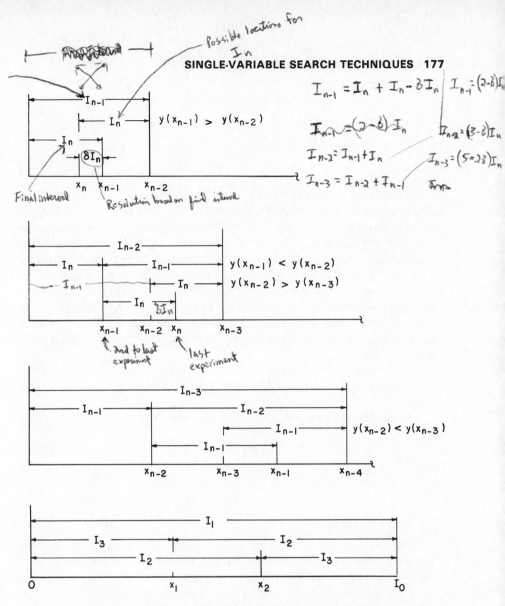

Figure 5-8. Locating experiments for Fibonacci search.

For convenience, at the start of the derivation one end of the interval I_{n-1} is the left boundary of the initial interval, I_0, and the other end must be the location of experiment x_{n-1}, i.e., $y(x_{n-1}) > y(x_{n-2})$ for maximizing.

Evaluating the results of experiments x_n and x_{n-1} will determine the location of the final interval, but not its length. The length of I_n is determined by the minimax simultaneous search of uniform pairs given by equation (5-10) for two experiments. This equation can be written as follows:

or

$$I_n = I_{n-1}/2 + \delta I_n /2$$

$$I_n = I_{n-1}/(2 - \delta) \tag{5-31}$$

We can now locate experiment x_{n-3} by considering that had $y(x_{n-1}) <$ $y(x_{n-2})$, then x_n would have been located to the right of x_{n-2} by a distance equal to δI_n for maximizing. This is shown in Figure 5-8, and experiment x_{n-3} has to be located a distance of I_{n-1} to the right of x_{n-1}. In addition, the final interval, I_n, could be located at any one of the four positions shown for I_n in Figure 5-8, depending on the outcomes of x_{n-2}, x_{n-1}, and x_n.

We can locate experiment x_{n-4} by considering that had $y(x_{n-2}) < y(x_{n-3})$, then x_{n-4} would have to be located to the right of x_{n-3} by a distance equal to I_{n-2}. This is shown in Figure 5-8 and ensures that the final interval is I_n. This also shows that the interval I_{n-2} is the sum of the final interval I_n and I_{n-1}, i.e.

$$I_{n-2} = I_n + I_{n-1} \tag{5-32}$$

This equation can be combined with equation (5–31) to give

$$I_{n-2} = I_n + (2 - \delta)I_n \tag{5-33}$$

or

$$I_{n-2} = (3 - \delta)I_n \tag{5-34}$$

This reasoning can be repeated to locate points x_{n-5}, x_{n-6}, $\cdots$, and the following results will be obtained, i.e., an interval is equal to the sum of the two following intervals:

$$I_{n-3} = I_{n-2} + I_{n-1}$$

$$I_{n-4} = I_{n-3} + I_{n-2}$$

$$I_{n-5} = I_{n-4} + I_{n-3} \tag{5-35}$$

$$\vdots$$

Repeated substitution of the equations determined like equation (5–34) gives the following results in terms of I_n for the equations (5–35):

$$I_{n-3} = (5 - 2\delta)I_n$$

$$I_{n-4} = (8 - 3\delta)I_n$$

$$I_{n-5} = (13 - 5\delta)I_n \tag{5-36}$$

$$\vdots$$

The generalization of equation (5–35) is:

$$I_{n-j} = I_{n-(j-1)} + I_{n-(j-2)} \tag{5-37}$$

and the generalization of equation (5–36) is:

$$I_{n-j} = (A_{j+2} - A_j \delta)I_n \tag{5-38}$$

The A_j's are a famous sequence of numbers dating back to 1202 (see Wilde (1) for details) and are called the *Fibonacci numbers*. The sequence can be generated by the following equations:

$$A_0 = 0$$

$$A_1 = 1 \tag{5-39}$$

$$A_n = A_{n-1} + A_{n-2}$$

and

n	0	1	2	3	4	5	6	7	8	9	10	11	12
A_n	0	1	1	2	3	5	8	13	21	34	55	89	144

which gives the first 12 values of the Fibonacci numbers.

We are now in a position to obtain the equation to calculate the length of the final interval of uncertainty, I_n, knowing the length of the initial interval, I_0, and to determine the placement of the first two experiments. The value of $n - j = 1$ is used in equation (5–38) to determine I_1 as given below:

$$I_1 = (A_{n+1} - A_{n-1}\delta)I_n \tag{5-40}$$

However, it is more convenient to have the equations in terms of the resolution based on the initial interval, ϵI_0. The substitution of $\epsilon I_0 = \delta I_n$ is made,

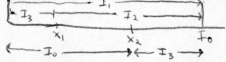

and I_1 is equal to I_0, because two experiments are required for interval reduction. Equation 5–40 becomes:

$$I_n = [(1 + \epsilon A_{n-1})/A_{n+1}] I_0 \qquad (5\text{–}41)$$

Thus, knowing the initial interval, I_0, the fractional resolution based on the initial interval, ϵ, and the number of experiments, n, we determine the length of the final interval of uncertainty, I_n, by equation (5–41). The location of this final interval is determined by the outcome of the experiments.

The location of the first two experiments can now be determined using equation (5–38). Both the first two experiments are needed to determine the part of the interval that is to be retained for further experiments. The first experiments are placed according to $n - j = 2$ or $j = n - 2$, and substituting into equation (5–38) gives:

$$I_2 = (A_n - A_{n-2}\delta)I_n \qquad (5\text{–}42)$$

Again, it is convenient to have the above equations in terms of the initial interval I_0 and the corresponding resolution ϵ. Making the substitution for $\delta I_n = \epsilon I_0$ and recognizing that x_2 can be located a distance I_2 from the left-hand side of the interval gives:

$$x_2 = I_2 = A_n I_n - \epsilon A_{n-2} I_0 \qquad (5\text{–}43)$$

The location of x_2 is shown in Figure 5-8, along with the location of x_1. The position for x_1 is symmetrically to x_2 a distance I_2 from the right-hand side of the interval. The position for x_1 can be computed by having $n - j = 3$ in equation (5–38). The result is:

$$x_1 = I_3 = (A_{n-1} - A_{n-3}\delta)I_n = A_{n-1}I_n - \epsilon A_{n-3}I_0 \qquad (5\text{–}44)$$

The procedure continues after the first two experiments are evaluated by discarding the interval that does not contain the optimum. The third experiment is placed in the interval symmetrically to the one in the interval. Evaluating this experiment permits discarding another section of the interval that does not contain the optimum. The procedure is continued by placing the remaining experiments symmetrically to the previous one with the best value until the final experiment is placed. This final experiment will be symmetric in the final interval with the previous one with the best value, and they will be separated by a distance equal to the resolution, $\epsilon I_0 = \delta I_n$. The following example illustrates the procedure using the function of Example 5–1.

EXAMPLE 5-2

Search for the maximum of the following function using Fibonacci search
with four experiments. The initial interval $I_0 = 1.0$ and the resolution $\epsilon =$
0.05:

$$\text{Maximize: } y = 3 + 6x - 4x^2$$

The final interval of uncertainty is computed using equation (5–41):

$$I_4 = [(1 + (0.05)(2)/5](1) = 0.22$$

The location of this interval will be determined by placing the experiments
and is shown on the line at the end of the problem. The location of the
second experiment is computed using equation (5–43):

$$x_2 = 3(0.22) - (0.05)(1)(1) = 0.610$$

The location of the first experiment is symmetrical to the second one, i.e.

$$x_1 = 1.0 - 0.61 = 0.39$$

The same results could be obtained using equation (5–44). Evaluating the
function gives:

$$y(0.39) = 4.732 \qquad y(0.61) = 5.172$$

The optimum lies in the interval $0.39 \le x^* \le 1.0$.
Experiment x_3 is placed symmetrically to x_2 in this interval as:

$$x_3 = 0.39 + (1 - 0.61) = 0.78$$

and

$$y(0.78) = 5.246$$

The optimum lies in the interval $0.61 \le x^* \le 1$.
Experiment x_4 is placed symmetrically to x_3 in this interval as:

$$x_4 = 0.61 + (1 - 0.78) = 0.83$$

and

$$y(0.83) = 5.244$$

The optimum lies in the region $0.61 \leq x^* \leq 0.83$, which is the location of the final interval computed at the beginning of the example.

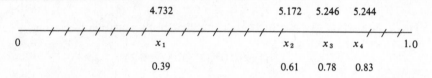

The classical theory solution was given in Example 5–1, and the optimum is located at $x = 3/4$ with a value of $y(3/4) = 5.25$. This is compared with the best value of 5.246 located at $x = 0.78$ with four sequential experiments using Fibonacci search.

A rapid interval reduction is obtained with Fibonacci search. This can be illustrated with a simplified form of equation (5–41) with $\epsilon = 0$, which is:

$$I_n = \frac{I_0}{A_{n+1}} \qquad X_1 = \frac{A_{n-1}}{A_{n+1}} I_0 \qquad X_2 = \frac{A_n}{A_{n+1}} I_0 \qquad (5\text{–}45)$$

(handwritten annotations)
$X_1 = \frac{55}{144} = .382$
$X_2 = \frac{89}{144} = .618$
$n = 11$
$A_{12} = 144$
$A_{11} = 89$
$A_{10} = 55$
$A_9 = 34$
$I_{11} = \frac{I_0}{144}$

For 11 experiments the initial interval is reduced by 144, because $A_{12} = 144$. This rapid reduction in the interval containing the optimum, along with the simple procedure of placing experiments symmetrically in the interval to continue the search, and its basis in the minimax principle, has made Fibonacci search one of the most widely used procedures. Table 5–1 gives a program for Fibonacci search, along with the input form Example 5–2 and the corresponding output.

The search technique to be discussed next is a modification of Fibonacci search. Golden section search sacrifices being a minimax technique to relax the requirement that the number of experiments be specified in advance.

This program performs a Fibonacci search to locate the maximum of the function given in the function FUNC in the interval between LBOUND and HBOUND. The input to this program is in free format, and it consists of the resolution desired (RESOL), the number of experiments (EXPNO), and the low and high bounds (LBOUND, HBOUND). The output includes the value of the function and the bounds on the interval of uncertainty for each application of the algorithm. The input and output shown with the

(handwritten annotations)
$$X_1 = \left[\frac{A_{n-1}}{A_{n+1}} + \epsilon \left(\frac{A_{n-1}^2}{A_{n+1}} - A_{n-3} \right) \right] I_0$$

$$X_2 = \left[\frac{A_n}{A_{n+1}} + \epsilon \left(\frac{A_{n-1} A_n}{A_{n+1}} - A_{n+1} \right) \right] I_0$$

Table 5-1.   Fortran Program with Sample Input and Output for a Fibonacci Search to Maximize the Function FUNC on the Interval from LBOUND to HBOUND.

```
C----------------------------------------------------------------
C
C      PROGRAM FIBON
C
C----------------------------------------------------------------
C
C      DESCRIPTION OF NOTATION:
C         RESOL :   RESOLUTION OF THE LAST EXPERIMENT
C         EXPNO :   NUMBER OF EXPERIMENTS TO BE PLACED IN INTERVAL
C         LBOUND:   LOW BOUND OF SEARCH INTERVAL
C         HBOUND:   HIGH BOUND OF SEARCH INTERVAL
C         FINTER:   FINAL INTERVAL LENGTH
C         DELTA :   LENGTH BETWEEN AN EXPERIMENT AND ITS BOUND
C         FINPT :   OPTIMAL EXPERIMENTAL VALUE
C----------------------------------------------------------------
       REAL  FIBO(100), INTER, FINTER, DELTA, TESTLB, TESTHB,
      1      RESOL, LBOUND, HBOUND, FINPT, LBVAL, HBVAL, FINVAL
       INTEGER  EXPNO, I, J, SWITCH
C----------------------------------------------------------------
C
C      READ IN AND ECHO PRINT INPUT DATA
C
C----------------------------------------------------------------
       READ (5,*) RESOL, EXPNO, LBOUND, HBOUND
       WRITE(6,60) RESOL,EXPNO,LBOUND,HBOUND
   60  FORMAT(/,5X,'INPUT DATA FOR FIBONNACCI SEARCH',
      *        /,5X,'RESO, EXPNO, LBOUND, HBOUND = ',F8.4,2X,I3,2(2X,F8.4) )
       WRITE(6,500)
  500  FORMAT(/,7X,'I',2X,'LBOUND ',2X,'HBOUND ',2X,'TESTLB',3X,'TESTHB'
      *  ,2X,' DELTA ',2X,' FINPT ',2X,' FINVAL')
C----------------------------------------------------------------
C
C      GENERATE (EXPNO + 1) FIBONACCI NUMBERS
C
C----------------------------------------------------------------
       FIBO(1)= 1.0
       FIBO(2)= 1.0
C
       J= EXPNO + 1
       DO 10 I=3, J
       FIBO(I)= FIBO(I-1) + FIBO(I-2)
   10  CONTINUE
C----------------------------------------------------------------
C
C      EVALUATE STARTING POINTS
C
C----------------------------------------------------------------
       INTER= HBOUND - LBOUND
       FINTER= (1+RESOL*FIBO(EXPNO-1))/FIBO(EXPNO+1)*INTER
       DELTA= FIBO(EXPNO-1)*FINTER-RESOL*FIBO(EXPNO-3)*INTER
```

5-37

Table 5-1. Continued

```
      TESTLB= LBOUND + DELTA
      TESTHB= HBOUND - DELTA
      FINPT = TESTLB
      FINVAL= FUNC(FINPT)
      WRITE(6,61)   LBOUND,HBOUND,TESTLB,TESTHB,DELTA,FINPT,FINVAL
   61 FORMAT(5X,'  1',7(F8.4,1X) )
C----------------------------------------------------------------
C
C     START FIBONNACCI SEARCH
C
C----------------------------------------------------------------
      J= EXPNO - 1
      DO 30 I=1, J
      K = I + 1
      LBVAL= FUNC(TESTLB)
      HBVAL= FUNC(TESTHB)
      IF (LBVAL.GE.HBVAL) GO TO 20
         LBOUND= TESTLB
         INTER = HBOUND - LBOUND
         DELTA = INTER - DELTA
         TESTLB= TESTHB
         TESTHB= HBOUND - DELTA
         SWITCH= 1
         GO TO 29
   20 CONTINUE
         HBOUND= TESTHB
         INTER = HBOUND - LBOUND
         DELTA = INTER - DELTA
         TESTHB= TESTLB
         TESTLB= LBOUND + DELTA
         SWITCH= 0
   29 CONTINUE
      IF (SWITCH.EQ.0) FINPT= TESTHB
      IF (SWITCH.EQ.1) FINPT= TESTLB
      FINVAL= FUNC(FINPT)
      WRITE(6,62)K,LBOUND,HBOUND,TESTLB,TESTHB,DELTA,FINPT,FINVAL
   62 FORMAT(5X,I3,7(F8.4,1X) )
   30 CONTINUE
C
      IF (SWITCH.EQ.0) FINPT= TESTHB
      IF (SWITCH.EQ.1) FINPT= TESTLB
      FINVAL= FUNC(FINPT)
C----------------------------------------------------------------
C
C     PRINT RESULTS
C
C----------------------------------------------------------------
      WRITE(6,63) FINPT, FINVAL
   63 FORMAT(/,5X,'OPTIMAL SOLUTION : ',
     &      /,5X,'                     X =',F10.4,
     &      /,5X,'OBJECTIVE FUNCTION =',F10.4)
```

5-38

Table 5-1.   Continued

```
      WRITE(6,64) LBOUND, HBOUND
 64   FORMAT(  5X,'FINAL INTERVAL OF UNCERTAINTY:', F10.4,
      &         ' TO ',F10.4)
 C
      STOP
      END
 C--------------------------------------------------------------------
 C
 C    EVALUATE OBJECTIVE FUNCTION
 C
 C--------------------------------------------------------------------
      FUNCTION FUNC(X)
      FUNC= 3 + 6*X - 4*X*X
      RETURN
      END
 ********************************************************************
```

```
      INPUT DATA FOR FIBONNACCI SEARCH
      RESO, EXPNO, LBOUND, HBOUND =    0.0500    4    0.0000    1.0000
```

I	LBOUND	HBOUND	TESTLB	TESTHB	DELTA	FINPT	FINVAL
1	0.0000	1.0000	0.3900	0.6100	0.3900	0.3900	4.7316
2	0.3900	1.0000	0.6100	0.7800	0.2200	0.6100	5.1716
3	0.6100	1.0000	0.7800	0.8300	0.1700	0.7800	5.2464
4	0.6100	0.8300	0.6600	0.7800	0.0500	0.7800	5.2464

```
      OPTIMAL SOLUTION :
                      X =     0.7800
      OBJECTIVE FUNCTION =    5.2464
      FINAL INTERVAL OF UNCERTAINTY:     0.6100 TO     0.8300
```

program are the results obtained using the problem in Example 5–2. To maximize a new function, supply the equation in the function FUNCT.

Golden Section Search: This method is used when the number of experiments is not known in advance. The search starts at essentially the same place as Fibonacci search when more than about six Fibonacci experiments are specified, i.e., x_1 and x_2 are located at the same position, $x_1 = 0.382$, $x_2 = 0.618$, based on a unit initial interval. The idea is to keep the procedure of placing experiments symmetrically in the interval to rapidly reduce the section that contains the optimum. To do this equation (5–37) is used, and the ratio of successive intervals is maintained constant. Dividing equation (5–37) by $I_{n\,(j-2)}$ gives:

$$\frac{I_1}{I_2} = \frac{I_2}{I_3} = \frac{I_3}{I_0} = \frac{I_{n-j}}{I_{n-(j-1)}} \qquad \frac{I_{n-(j-1)}}{I_{n-(j-2)}} = \tau$$

$$\frac{I_{n-j}}{I_{n-(j-2)}} = \frac{I_{n-(j-1)}}{I_{n-(j-2)}} + 1 = \tau + 1 \qquad (5\text{--}46)$$

$$\tau^2 = \tau + 1 \qquad \tau = 1.618033$$

The ratio of successive intervals τ as defined as:

$$\tau = \frac{I_{n-j}}{I_{n-(j-1)}} = \frac{I_{n-(j-1)}}{I_{n-(j-2)}} = \ldots = \frac{I_1}{I_2} \qquad (5\text{--}47)$$

Using the following relation

$$\frac{I_{n-j}}{I_{n-(j-2)}} = \frac{I_{n-j}}{I_{n-(j-1)}} \cdot \frac{I_{n-(j-1)}}{I_{n-(j-2)}} = \tau \cdot \tau = \tau^2 \qquad (5\text{--}48)$$

This equation can be combined with equation (5–46) to give:

$$\tau^2 = \tau + 1 \qquad (5\text{--}49)$$

The solution of this quadratic equation is given by Wilde (1) as:

$$\tau = (1 + \sqrt{5})/2 = 1.618033989 \ldots \qquad (5\text{--}50)$$

To begin the search, the second (or first) experiment is located, using equation (5–47), at:

$$x_2 = I_2 = I_1/\tau = I_0/\tau = 0.618 I_0 \qquad (5\text{--}51)$$

and the first (or second) experiment is located symmetrically in the interval as:

$$x_1 = I_0 - I_0/\tau = (1 - 1/\tau) I_0 = 0.382 I_0 \qquad (5\text{--}52)$$

and after n experiments the final interval of uncertainty is:

$$I_n = \frac{I_0}{\tau^{n-1}} \qquad (5\text{--}53)$$

The following example illustrates the procedure using the same function in the prior examples.

EXAMPLE 5–3

Search for the maximum of the following function using golden section search stopping after four experiments to compare with previous results. The initial interval is $I_0 = 1.0$

$$\frac{I_3}{I_1} = \left(\frac{I_3}{I_2}\right)\left(\frac{I_2}{I_1}\right) = \tau^2$$

$$I_3 = \frac{I_0}{\tau^2} = x_1$$

$$x_1 = .302 I_0$$

$$I_n = \frac{I_0}{\tau^{n-1}} = \left(A_{n+1} - A_{n-1}\right) I_n$$

Maximize: $y = 3 + 6x - 4x^2$

The final interval of uncertainty is computed using equation (5–53):

$$I_4 = 1/(1.618)^3 = 0.236$$

The location of the second experiment is computed using equation (5–51):

$$x_2 = I_0/\tau = 1/\tau = 0.618$$

and the first experiment is located symmetrically in the interval as:

$$x_1 = 1 - 0.618 = 0.382$$

Evaluating the function gives

$$y(0.382) = 4.71 \qquad y(0.618) = 5.18$$

The optimum lies in the interval $0.382 \le x^* \le 1.0$.
Experiment x_3 is placed symmetrically to x_2 in this interval as:

$$x_3 = 0.382 + (1 - 0.618) = 0.764$$

and

$$y(0.764) = 5.24$$

The optimum lies in the interval $0.618 \le x^* \le 1.0$.
Experiment x_4 is placed symmetrically to x_3 in this interval as:

$$x_4 = 0.618 + (1 - 0.764) = 0.854$$

and

$$y(0.854) = 5.20$$

The optimum lies in the region $0.618 \le x^* \le 0.854$, which is the location of the final interval computed at the beginning of the example. It is slightly larger, 0.236, than the Fibonacci final interval value of 0.220.

A rapid interval reduction was obtained with golden section search also. For 11 experiments the initial interval would be reduced by 123, compared with 144 for Fibonacci search. Both techniques have been widely used in industrial applications. In the next section we will briefly describe another extension of Fibonacci search, *called lattice search,* which applies to functions that are defined only at discrete values of the independent variables.

*ε = 0
Read*

→ Not on exam

→ only points, not a curve

Lattice Search. This method has been developed for the problem where the independent variable takes on only discrete values. Thus, it is necessary to have a search method that searches on these discrete values. Examples could be the determination of the optimum route for an aircraft or the optimum number of temperature or pressure measuring devices for a process.

The approach is to modify the Fibonacci search technique such that each experiment falls on a discrete value of the independent variable as the search proceeds. This means that the first two experiments must start on discrete values of the independent variable, called *lattice points,* and the final two experiments are adjacent to each other at lattice points.

Beginning with equation (5–41) it is simplified for $\epsilon = 0$, i.e., the resolution is zero. This gives the following equation:

$$I_n = I_0/A_{n+1} \tag{5–54}$$

For this equation I_0 is the number of lattice points plus 1, and I_n is equal to 1 to have the last two experiments adjacent to each other. However, these conditions overdetermine equation (5–54), and another approach is as follows. To have I_n be equal to 1, the number of experiments is determined by selecting the Fibonacci number A_{n+1}, which is equal to or greater than I_0 plus 1. Usually, the Fibonacci number will not match the comparable value of I_0 plus 1, and this value will have to be increased by adding fictitious points to I_0. These points are usually added to either the left or right end of the interval. However, they can be located in any convenient place as long as they are not one of the points that must be evaluated during the search.

To start the search, equation (5–43) is used with $\epsilon = 0$, i.e.:

$$x_2 = A_n I_n \tag{5–55}$$

Using equation (5–54) to have this equation in terms of I_0 gives:

$$x_2 = A_n (I_0/A_{n+1}) \tag{5–56}$$

Consequently, the second experiment is located at the lattice point corresponding to A_n. The first experiment is located symmetrically to x_2 in the initial interval. Then the function is evaluated at the two points, and the third and subsequent experiments are placed symmetrically in the interval remaining. The last two experiments will differ by one, and the optimum lattice point will have been located. The following example illustrates the procedure using the function of the previous examples and precision points.

EXAMPLE 5–4

Search for the maximum of the following function using lattice search and 20 precision points on the initial interval of $I_0 = 1.0$:

$$y = 3 + 6x - 4x^2$$

The precision points are given by the following equation:

$$x_i = 0.05i - 0.025 \qquad \text{for } i = 1, 2, \cdots, 20$$

The first point is $x_1 = 0.025$, and the last point is $x_{20} = 0.975$. The points are spaced on the line as shown at the end of the example. Using equation (5–54) to have I_n be 1.0, A_{n+1} is selected to be equal to $I_0 = 21$. In this case 21 is the Fibonacci number A_8, and no fictitious points are required. The second experiment is placed according to equation (5–56) at $x_2 = A_7 = 13$. The first experiment is placed symmetrically in the interval at $x_1 = 21 - 13 = 8$. The results are shown on the line at the end of the example for the remaining experiments:

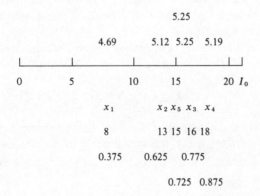

Evaluating the outcomes of the experiments, there is a tie between x_3 and x_5. Consequently, for this lattice search either lattice points 15 or 16 could be used as the optimal value.

A further discussion of this procedure is given by Wilde (1). Now our attention will turn to extending the use of these methods on an open interval in the next section.

OPEN INITIAL INTERVAL

Many multivariable search techniques search on a line in space as they attempt to move from a starting point through better points to arrive at an optimum, as will be seen in the next chapter. This requires a single-variable search, where one end of the interval is known, and the other is to be found in order to have the optimum bounded in the interval.

The approach is to attempt to place two experiments along the line of search to bound the optimum and, at the same time, have the experiments be in the correct position to continue a Fibonacci or golden section search. The compromise is one of attempting to select an interval that is large enough to ensure that the optimum is bounded, but no so large that excessive effort is required to reduce the interval to an acceptable final value. Also, if the optimum is not bounded with two experiments, provision can be made to have a third experiment placed such that it is in the proper position to continue the search. The second experiment would be used with the third one for the two required in the search technique. Once the optimum is bounded, then the previously described procedures are used to reduce the size of the interval to an acceptable value.

In addition to illustrating the above procedure for bounding an optimum in an open interval, we want to illustrate how this procedure can be used in a multivariable search procedure. The gradient line developed in Chapter 2 will be used for this purpose.

A line in space can be represented in vector notation by the following equation:

$$\mathbf{x} = \mathbf{a} + k(\mathbf{b} - \mathbf{a}) \tag{5-57}$$

where k is called the *parameter of the line*. The components of this vector equation can be written using the components of $\mathbf{x}$, and known points $\mathbf{a}$ and $\mathbf{b}$ as:

$$x_1 = a_1 + k(b_1 - a_1)$$

$$x_2 = a_2 + k(b_2 - a_2) \tag{5-58}$$

Get 1st 2 experiments to bound opt then cont w/ Fibonacci

$x_{R} = .618 I_o$

$x_1 = .382 I_o$

$x_2 = \dfrac{.618}{.382} x_1$

Pick x_1, Calculate x_2

$x_3 = \dfrac{.618}{.382} x_2$

$$\vdots$$

$$x_n = a_n + k(b_n - a_n)$$

For the value of $k = 0$, $\mathbf{x}$ is equal to $\mathbf{a}$ and for $k = 1$, $\mathbf{x}$ is equal to $\mathbf{b}$. Values of k between 0 and 1 generate values of $\mathbf{x}$ between $\mathbf{a}$ and $\mathbf{b}$, values of k greater than 1 generate values of $\mathbf{x}$ beyond $\mathbf{b}$, and values of k less than 1 generate values of $\mathbf{x}$ beyond $\mathbf{a}$.

The gradient line was given by equation (2–32) and is rewritten here using the plus sign to have the direction of steep ascent as:

$$\mathbf{x} = \mathbf{x_0} + k \ \nabla y(\mathbf{x_0}) \tag{5–59}$$

In this case values of the parameter k greater than 0 generate points $\mathbf{x}$ in the direction of steep ascent.

The problem of maximizing $y(\mathbf{x})$, a multivariable function, is converted to maximizing $y[\mathbf{x_0} + k \ \nabla y(\mathbf{x_0})]$, a function of k only, along the line of steep ascent starting at point $\mathbf{x_0}$. Consequently, there is an open interval along the gradient line beginning at $\mathbf{x_0}$, and it is necessary to bound the maximum by selecting two values of k. Then a Fibonacci or golden section search can be conducted on k to determine the location of final interval and values of $y(\mathbf{x})$ as previously described. The following simple example illustrates the use of Fibonacci search in placing experiments on a line in space.

EXAMPLE 5–5

The following is the equation of the direction of steep ascent (gradient line) for a function through the point $\mathbf{x_0}$ (1, 1, 0, 2). It has been determined that the maximum lies between $\mathbf{x_0}$ and the point $\mathbf{x_1}$(5, 2, 3, 7). Locate the position of the first two experiments for a Fibonacci search having five experiments, and determine the length of the final interval of uncertainty on each coordinate axis. The resolution can be taken as zero. The equation for the gradient line is:

$$\mathbf{x} = \mathbf{x_0} + k \ \nabla y(\mathbf{x_0})$$

$$x_1 = 1 + 4k$$

$$x_2 = 1 + 1k$$

$$x_3 = 0 + 3k$$

$$x_4 = 2 + 5k$$

For this problem $k = 1$ generates point $\mathbf{x}_1$ and $k = 0$ gives the starting point $\mathbf{x}_0$. Consequently, a Fibonacci search is to be conducted on the interval of $0 \leq k \leq 1$ with $n = 5$. Equation (5–41) is used for the final interval on k:

$$I_5 = I_0/A_6 = 1/8 = 0.125$$

Equations (5–43) and (5–44) are used to locate x_1 and x_2 on k.

$$x_2 = A_n/I_n = 5/8 = 0.625$$

$$x_1 = A_{n-1}/I_n = 3/8 = 0.375$$

Final interval of uncertainty:

Variable	Initial interval		Final interval
k	$0 \leq k \leq 1$	1	$0.125(1) = 0.125$
x_1	$1 \leq x_1 \leq 5$	4	$0.125(4) = 0.5$
x_2	$1 \leq x_2 \leq 2$	1	$0.125(1) = 0.125$
x_3	$0 \leq x_3 \leq 3$	3	$0.125(3) = 0.375$
x_4	$2 \leq x_4 \leq 7$	5	$0.125(5) = 0.725$

Locations of the first two experiments are:

First experiment	Second experiment
$x_1 = 1 + 4(0.375) = 2.5$	$x_1 = 1 + 4(0.625) = 3.5$
$x_2 = 1 + 1(0.375) = 1.375$	$x_2 = 1 + 1(0.625) = 1.625$
$x_3 = 0 + 3(0.375) = 1.125$	$x_3 = 0 + 3(0.625) = 1.875$
$x_4 = 2 + 5(0.375) = 3.875$	$x_4 = 2 + 5(0.625) = 5.125$

Depending on the outcome of these experiments, sections of the interval are discarded, and the remaining experiments are placed symmetrically in the remaining parts of the intervals to obtain the final interval computed above for each variable. The length of the final interval of uncertainty is usually different for each variable, and there may be one variable that ultimately specifies the number of experiments to have a sufficiently small final interval.

Golden section search will be used to illustrate the procedures to bound the optimum on an open interval. In this case it will not be necessary to specify the number of experiments, and a stopping criterion can be used based on the computed values of y_{n+1} and y_n, e.g., $|y[x_0 + k_{n+1}\nabla y(x_0)] - y[x_0 + k_n \nabla y(x_0)]| \leq s$, where s is a specified small number.

The first two experiments are located using equations (5–51) and (5–52), which are:

$$x_2 = 0.618\, I_0 \qquad\qquad (5\text{–}51)$$

$$x_1 = 0.382\, I_0 \qquad\qquad (5\text{–}52)$$

The problem is one of specifying I_0 sufficiently large that $y(x_1) > y(x_2)$ for maximizing to have the maximum bounded between 0 and x_2. If this does not happen, then x_2 will have to become x_1, and a third experiment will have to be placed. The location of this experiment is given by the following equation obtained using the two previous equations:

$$x_3 = 0.618(x_2/0.382) \qquad\qquad (5\text{–}60)$$

This should result in $y(x_2) > y(x_3)$, have the maximum bounded, and have x_2 and x_3 in the proper location to continue the search on the interval $x_1 \leq x^* \leq x_3$. Then golden section search can be conducted placing experiments symmetrically in the interval until the stopping criterion is reached.

Wilde and Beightler (2) have an expanded discussion of this procedure, giving the generalization of equation (5–60) for h measurements using Fibonacci research. Their conclusion is "that underestimation of the reduction ratio needed costs twice as many extra measurements as overestimation by the same amounts." The following example will illustrate the procedure for an unbounded function represented graphically.

EXAMPLE 5–6

An unbounded function is shown in Figure 5-9. It will be used to illustrate the location of the first two and four additional experiments of golden section

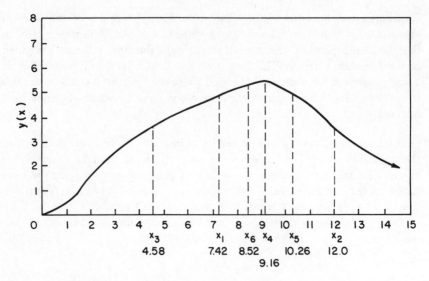

Figure 5-9. Golden section search with an unbounded function.

search. It is obvious from the function that one experiment must be greater than 9.0. This is information we would not have normally, but the problem still remains to select a value of I_0 using equations (5–51) and (5–52) such that the function is bounded with two experiments. Having selected a value of I_0 and computed x_1 and x_2, then the values of $y(x_1)$ and $y(x_2)$ can be readily evaluated using Figure 5–9. To simplify the procedure x_1 can be calculated directly from x_2 by combining equations (5–51) and (5–52) as

$$x_1 = 0.382(x_2/0.618)$$

Arbitrarily select $x_2 = 12.0$, and computing x_1, using the above equation, gives a value of $x_1 = 7.42$. The corresponding values of y are $y(7.42) = 4.9$ and $y(12.0) = 3.5$, and the maximum has been bounded. The remaining four experiments are placed symmetrically in the interval with the previous best value as shown in the figure. The final interval is $8.52 \leq x^* \leq 10.26$ with the value maximum of $y(9.16) = 5.3$ in this interval.

OTHER METHODS

There are several nonminimax techniques that have been used successfully for single-variable optimization. They involve fitting a polynomial to the profit function and computing the stationary points of the polynomial itera-

Line in Space

tively until a satisfactory optimum has been obtained. The polynomial is usually quadratic or at most cubic, and procedures can be incorporated to bound the optimum when the interval is open. These procedures will be reviewed, and further descriptions are given by Avriel (3), Beveridge and Schechter (6), and Himmelblau (7).

To have a quadratic fit of the profit (or cost) function, the coefficients of the function are evaluated by making three measurements. The quadratic equation can be written as:

$$y = ax^2 + bx + c \tag{5-61}$$

P9/90

The stationary point of the above equation is obtained by setting the first derivative equal to zero to give:

$y[x] = y[a + \alpha(b-a)]$

$$x^* = -b/2a \tag{5-62}$$

The values of a and b are determined by measurements at three points to determine $y(x_1)$, $y(x_2)$, and $y(x_3)$. Thus equation (5-61) can be written as:

$x = a + \alpha(b-a)$

$x_1 = a_1 + \alpha(b_1 - a_1)$

$x_2 = a_2 + \alpha(b_2 - a_2)$

$x_3 = a_3 + \alpha(b_3 - a_3)$

$\alpha = 0 \quad x = a$

$\alpha = 1 \quad x = b$

$$y(x_1) = ax_1^2 + bx_1 + c$$
$$y(x_2) = ax_2^2 + bx_2 + c \tag{5-63}$$
$$y(x_3) = ax_3^2 + bx_3 + c$$

which are three linear algebraic equations in a, b, and c. In matrix form they can be written as:

$a = \begin{pmatrix} 1 \\ 1 \\ 1 \end{pmatrix} \quad b = \begin{pmatrix} 2 \\ 3 \\ 4 \end{pmatrix}$

$\begin{pmatrix} x_1 \\ x_2 \\ x_3 \end{pmatrix} = \begin{pmatrix} 1 \\ 1 \\ 1 \end{pmatrix} + \alpha \begin{pmatrix} 2 \\ 3 \\ 4 \end{pmatrix}$

$$\begin{bmatrix} x_1^2 & x_1 & 1 \\ x_2^2 & x_2 & 1 \\ x_3^2 & x_3 & 1 \end{bmatrix} \begin{bmatrix} a \\ b \\ c \end{bmatrix} = \begin{bmatrix} y_1 \\ y_2 \\ y_3 \end{bmatrix} \tag{5-64}$$

$\alpha = .382 \quad \alpha = .618$

This set of equations can be solved for a and b, and the results are substituted into equations (5-62) to compute x^* the stationary point of the quadratic approximation to the profit function. The result is:

$\begin{bmatrix} x_1 \\ x_2 \\ x_3 \end{bmatrix} = \begin{bmatrix} 1 \\ 1 \\ 1 \end{bmatrix} + .382 \begin{bmatrix} 2 \\ 3 \\ 4 \end{bmatrix} = \begin{pmatrix} 1.767 \\ 2.146 \\ 2.524 \end{pmatrix} = x^1$

$$x^* = \frac{y_1(x_2^2 - x_3^2) + y_2(x_3^2 - x_1^2) + y_3(x_1^2 - x_2^2)}{2[y_1(x_2 - x_3) + y_2(x_3 - x_1) + y_3(x_1 - x_2)]} \tag{5-65}$$

$= \begin{bmatrix} 1 \\ 1 \\ 1 \end{bmatrix} + .618 \begin{bmatrix} 2 \\ 3 \\ 4 \end{bmatrix} = \begin{pmatrix} 2.236 \\ 2.854 \\ 3.427 \end{pmatrix} = x^2$

The procedure involves selecting three initial points and computing the optimum of the quadratic approximation, x^* by equation (5-65). Typically, the procedure continues using x^* as one of the next three points to repeat the application of equation (5–65). The point with the smallest value of y (for maximizing) is discarded. The procedure is repeated until a tolerance on the dependent variable is met, e.g., $|y_{n+1} - y_n| \leq s$, where s is a small number that is specified. However, there is a possibility that the procedure can oscillate around the optimum. In this case logic has to be incorporated into the computer program that recognizes when $y_{n+1} < y_n$ (when maximizing) and takes corrective action. An algorithm that incorporates these procedures, called *Powell's method,* is described by Himmelblau (7). The technique is generally called the *quadratic method* (3).

A complimentary procedure to be used with the quadratic method for an open interval to bound the optimum is described by Himmelblau (7) also. It is called the *DSC method* and is a logical procedure that takes an initial step, Δx, from the starting point to evaluate the function. It continues the search using increments $2\Delta x$, $4\Delta x$, $8\Delta x$, $\cdots$, until the optimum is bounded. These points provide the data for a second-order interpolation to estimate x^*. However, Himmelblau (7) states that, instead of using a second-order interpolation, it is better to shift to the quadratic method once the optimum has been bounded to have a more efficient algorithm.

A simple example illustrating the use of these algorithms is given by Himmelblau (7) and Beightler et al. (4). Also Wilde and Beightler (2) give the equation for a cubic approximation to the profit function.

It should be mentioned that the Armijo line search (11) has been used successfully with the multivariable search method, successive quadratic programming (12). This line search does not have minimax properties, but has been shown to converge to the minimum of a continuous function. Also, a sequence for the parameter of the gradient line has been shown to converge to the minimum of a continuous function. Further details are given in the article by Armijo (11) for these theorems and in the article by Beigler and Cuthrell (12) for applications with the successive quadratic programming algorithm for optimization of process simulators.

CLOSURE

In this chapter we began by describing search problems for background to single-variable and multivariable search techniques. Then the conservative, minimax, single-variable search procedures were developed and illustrated for both simultaneous and sequential applications. Also, the use of single-variable methods with multivariable problems was described, and this included techniques for open intervals. The chapter closed by reviewing the nonminimax sequential procedure of a quadratic fit to profit function and an associated algorithm to bound the optimum.

In summary, both the minimax and quadratic methods have been used effectively in industrial applications, and both have advocates in the literature. The minimax procedures tend to require more complicated computer programs, but offer the guarantee of locating the final interval containing the optimum in a specified number of steps for a unimodal function. The quadratic method procedures tend to have less complicated computer programs, but this depends on stopping and oscillation-prevention logic. Also, there is no guarantee of locating a specific interval containing the optimum in a specified number of steps. However a superlinear rate of convergence is claimed for them (8). As pointed out by Himmelblau (7), one of the more important evaluations of a single-variable method is how it performs when embedded in a multivariable procedure, and he presents some limited results that show no really significant advantage for either approach. Unfortunately, none of the multivariable procedures has been found clearly superior to the others, to let us extend these results for a comprehensive evaluation. For further information Avriel (3) has given a comprehensive, concise mathematical description of essentially all the single-variable methods, including the ones discussed here and others, such as the cubic method, Newton's method, secant method, and the block search techniques. Also, the related theorems on rates of convergence are given and discussed. In addition, McCormick (9) reports a new method for continuous function with continuous derivatives that may become important as evaluations of methods continue.

REFERENCES

1. Wilde, D. J., *Optimum Seeking Methods,* Prentice-Hall, Inc., Englewood Cliffs, N.J. (1964).
2. Wilde, D. J., and C. S. Beightler, *Foundations of Optimization,* Prentice-Hall Inc., Englewood Cliffs, N.J. (1967).
3. Avriel, M., *Nonlinear Programming, Analysis and Methods,* Prentice-Hall, Inc., Englewood Cliffs, N.J. (1976).
4. Beightler, C. S., D. T. Phillips, and D. J. Wilde, *Foundations of Optimization,* 2nd Ed., Prentice-Hall, Inc., Englewood Cliffs, N.J. (1969).
5. Kuester, J. L., and J. H. Mize, *Optimization Techniques with FORTRAN,* McGraw-Hill Book Co., New York (1973).
6. Beveridge, G. S., and R. S. Schechter, *Optimization: Theory and Practice,* McGraw-Hill Book Co., New York (1970).
7. Himmelblau, D. M., *Applied Nonlinear Programming,* McGraw-Hill Book Co., New York (1972).
8. Box, M. C., D. Davies, and W. H. Swann, *Nonlinear Optimization Techniques,* Oliver & Boyd Ltd., Edinburgh, Great Britain (1969).
9. McCormick, G. P., *Nonlinear Programming 4,* Ed. O. L. Mangasarian, R. R. Myer, and S. M. Robinson, Academic Press, New York, p. 223 (1981).
10. Stoecker, W. F., *Design of Thermal Systems,* McGraw-Hill Book Co., New York (1971).
11. Armijo, L., "Minimization of Functions Having Lipschitz Continuous First Partial Derivatives," *Pacific Journal of Mathematics,* 16(1):1 (1966).

12. Biegler, L. T., and J. E. Cuthrell, "Improved Infeasible Path Optimization for Sequential Modular Simulators-II: The Optimization Algorithm," *Computers & Chemical Engineering,* 9(3):257 (1985).

PROBLEMS

5–1.   Figure 5-10 gives the profit function is given for a sulfuric acid alkylation reactor as a function of feed rate and catalyst concentration. Plot the profit function as a function of feed rate for a constant catalyst concentration of 95%. Place six golden section experiments on the interval, giving their location, the corresponding value of the profit function, and the length and location of the final interval of uncertainty.

5–2.   Show that equation (5–43) for x_2 can be put in the following form in terms of ϵ and I_0:

$$x_2 = [1 + \epsilon(A_{n-1} + A_{n-2}A_{n-1}/A_n)](A_n/A_{n+1})I_0$$

5–3.   Derive equation (5–65) from equation (5–64).

5–4.   Compare the final intervals of uncertainty (initial being 1.0) for simultaneous elimination, Fibonacci search, and golden section search using 2, 5, and 10 experiments. Assume perfect resolution. Give conclusions from this comparison.

5–5.   Compare the anticipated performance of Fibonacci search and the quadratic method for the following types of unimodal, single-variable functions: quadratic, continuous, arbitrary, and discrete.

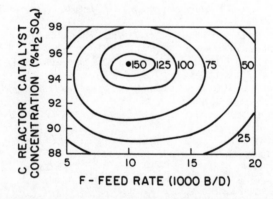

Figure 5-10.   Profit function for the operation of a sulfuric acid alkylation reactor as a function of catalyst concentration and feed rate.

5–6. In Bolzano's method (2) both the value of the function $y(x)$ and the first derivative of the function $y'(x)$ are evaluated at a point to eliminate the part of the line that does not contain the optimum. For a unimodal function the final interval I_n is given by the following equation for this method:

$$I_n = I_0/2^n$$

where n is the number of combined evaluations of $y(x)$ and $y'(x)$ that are made, and I_0 is the initial interval of uncertainty. Compare Bolzano's method with Fibonacci search and golden section search by computing the ratio of the final to the initial interval of uncertainty, I_n/I_0, for each of the three techniques using 5 and 10 for n with Bolzano's method and 10 experiments each with Fibonacci and golden section searches.

5–7. [1] The results of an eight-experiment simultaneous search plan for the interval $2 \le x^* \le 12$ is given below:

y	–	1.0	1.5	3.2	3.0	2.6	2.3	1.9	1.4	–
x	2	3.1	4.2	5.0	6.5	7.1	8.8	9.5	10.5	12

What are the possible final intervals of uncertainty, the maximum one and the one that contains the maximum values of y?

5–8. For Examples 5–2 and 5–3 determine the final interval by placing a fifth experiment by Fibonacci and golden section searches.

5–9.[10] Determine the maximum of the following function using golden section search on the initial interval shown:

$$y = 12x - 2x^2 \qquad \text{on} \qquad 0 \le x^* \le 10$$

Conduct the search until the difference between the two largest values of y is 0.01 or less. Give this largest value of y and the corresponding value of x. Compare this with the result obtained by using the classical theory of maxima and minima.

5–10.[10] An economic analysis of a proposed facility is being conducted to select an operating life such that the maximum uniform annual income is achieved. A short life results in high annual amortization costs, but the maintenance costs become excessive for a long life. The annual income after deducting all operating costs, except maintenance costs, is $180,000. The installed cost of the facility, C, is $500,000 borrowed at 10% interest compounded annually. The annual maintenance charges are evaluated using the product of the gradient present-worth factor and the capital-recovery factor. In the gradient present-worth method, there are no maintenance charges the first year, a cost M for the second year, $2M$ for the third year, $3M$ for the fourth year, etc. The second-year cost, M, for the problem is $10,000. The annual profit is given by the following equation:

$$P = 180,000 - \{[(i + 1)^N - 1 - iN]/i[(1 + i)^N - 1]\}M \\ - \{i(1 + i)^N/[(1 + i)^N - 1]\}C$$

where i is the interest rate and N is the number of years. Determine the number of years, N, that gives the maximum uniform annual income, P. For your convenience the following table gives the values of the coefficients of M and C for $i = 0.1$ as a function of N:

YEAR	COEFFICIENT OF M	C	YEAR	COEFFICIENT OF M	C
1	0	1.10	11	4.05	0.154
2	0.476	0.576	12	4.39	0.147
3	0.909	0.403	13	4.69	0.141
4	1.30	0.317	14	5.00	0.136
5	1.80	0.264	15	5.28	0.131
6	2.21	0.230	16	5.54	0.128
7	2.63	0.205	17	5.80	0.125
8	2.98	0.188	18	6.05	0.122
9	3.38	0.174	19	6.29	0.120
10	3.71	0.163	20	6.51	0.117

5–11. Find the maximum of the following open-ended function that represents a line in space from a multivariable search method using seven golden section search measurements including the last two that bound the function. Begin the bounding of the function with the first experiment at $\alpha = 1.0$, and continue until the function is bounded. Then proceed with five more golden section measurements to locate the maximum. Compare the best value found in the seven experiment golden section search with the exact value of the maximum computed using the classical theory of maxima and minima:

$$y = 2\alpha - \tfrac{1}{2}\alpha^2 \quad \text{on} \quad 0 \leq \alpha \leq \infty$$

5–12. It is proposed to recover the waste heat from exhaust gases leaving a furnace (flow rate, $m = 60,000$ lb/hr; heat capacity, $c_p = 0.25$

BTU/lb°F) at a temperature of $T_{in} = 500°F$ by installing a heat exchanger (overall heat transfer coefficient, $U = 4.0$ BTU/hr,ft²,°F) to produce steam at $T_s = 220°F$ from saturated liquid water at 220°F. The value of heat in the form of steam is $p = \$0.75$ per million BTU's, and the installed cost of the heat exchanger is $c = \$5.00$ per ft² of gas side area. The life of the installation is $n = 5$ years, and the interest rate is $i = 8.0\%$. The following equation gives the net profit P for the 5-year period from the sale of the steam and the cost of the heat exchanger. The exhaust gas temperature T_{out} can be between the upper and lower limits of 500 and 220°F.

$$P = pqn - cA(1+i)^n$$

where

$$q = mc_p(T_{in} - T_{out}) = UA\,\Delta T_{LM}$$

$$\Delta T_{LM} = \frac{(T_{in} - T_s) - (T_{out} - T_s)}{\ln\left(\dfrac{T_{in} - T_s}{T_{out} - T_s}\right)}$$

a. Derive the following equation for this design:

$$P = 225{,}270 - 492.8T_{out} + 3750\ln(T_{out} - 220)$$

b. Use a Fibonacci search with seven experiments to locate the optimal outlet temperature T_{out} to maximize the profit P on the interval of T_{out} from 220 to 500°F. Find the largest value of the profit and the size and location of the final interval of uncertainty for the fractional resolution based on the initial interval of $\epsilon = 0.01$.

c. Use analytical methods to determine the optimal profit and temperature.

5–13. a. The need to be able to distinguish between outcomes of experiments gives a relation between the final interval of uncertainty I_n and the fractional resolution ϵ based on the initial interval of uncertainty I_0. Referring to Figure 5-8, the experiments x_n, x_{n-1}, and x_{n-2} must all be separated by a distance of no less than ϵI_0 to be able to distinguish among their outcomes $y(x_n)$, $y(x_{n-1})$, and $y(x_{n-2})$. This can be expressed as:

$$I_n = x_{n-2} - x_n = (x_{n-2} - x_{n-1}) + (x_{n-1} - x_n) \geq 2\epsilon I_0$$

Using equations (5–39) and (5–41), show that the following inequality is obtained to relate the Fibonacci numbers and the fractional resolution ϵ:

$$A_{n-2} \leq 1/\epsilon$$

b. If a fractional resolution $\epsilon = 0.01$ is required, how many experiments are needed according to the results in part(a)?

c. Search for the maximum of the following function using a Fibonacci search with a fraction resolution of 0.05 on the interval $0 \leq x^* \leq 1$ using the criterion developed in (a) and (b):

$$y(x) = e^x - 2x^2$$

5–14. Demonstrate your understanding of the minimax principle by solving the following problems given by Wilde (1).

a. "You are convinced that your optimization professor is trying to fail you if he can get enough evidence to do so. You are trying to decide whether or not to read the assignment for next Thursday. If you read it and the professor gives a 10-minute quiz, you can expect to gain 10 points toward your final average. If there is no quiz, the knowledge you gained by reading the assignment will probably give you an extra 5 points on the next hour exam. You may go to the movies instead, and if there is no optimization quiz you will have 3 points worth of relaxation. But if there is a quiz and you haven't studied, your score will be 0 for the day, and the movie will be no consolation. *What should be your minimax decision?* If your professor is really out to get you, *what will he do?*"

b. "Suppose that you have a third alternative, namely, to study for an exam in another course. If then there is no optimization quiz, you can at least pick up 8 points in your other course. But if your optimization professor gives a quiz, your 0 in optimization will bring your average for the day down to 4 points. What should be your minimax strategy?"

6
MULTIVARIABLE OPTIMIZATION PROCEDURES

INTRODUCTION

This part of optimization is the most dynamic topic. As pointed out by Sargent (33) in 1979, relevant papers are being published at the rate of about 200 per month in more than 30 journals, not counting conference proceedings and special collections. A conference in 1979 added 450 papers to the list. Applications are varied and appear in almost every field.

Production codes for nonlinear optimization comparable to MPSX (Mathematical Programming System Extended) for linear programming are not available. However, over the past two decades, the capability to locate the optimum of a nonlinear economic model of a plant and to comply with several hundred constraints associated with the process models, unit capacities, raw material availabilities, and product demands has been developed in proprietary codes of major corporations (1). Generally available nonlinear codes for large problems have grown from university and government research programs on numerical experimentation with algorithms, and their documentation is somewhat limited (2). However, the theoretical foundations for these computer programs were developed in the 1960s, and, as with linear programming, the capability to solve optimization problems with increasing numbers of constraints has grown with improvements in computer hardware and software. However, there still is debate about which algorithms and/or computer codes are superior, and Lasdon (3) has recommended having several codes available that implement some of the more successful methods.

The effectiveness of a multivariable optimization procedure depends on several, interrelated things. These are the optimization theory, the algorithms to implement the theory, the computer program and programming language used for computations with the algorithms, the computer to run the program, and the optimization problems being solved. For example, in the area of multivariable, unconstrained search methods, several hundred algorithms have been used with various degrees of success. They have been programmed in FORTRAN mainly, run on various types of computers, and applied to a range of problems from simple algebraic expressions to plant simulation.

This chapter describes unconstrained and constrained multivariable search algorithms that have been successful in solving industrial optimization prob-

203

lems. Examples are given to illustrate these methods, and references to sources for computer programs are given for the methods. Also, references to recent and classic texts and articles are included for further information. For example, a two-volume set of books by Fletcher (4,5) is a recent comprehensive compilation of the mathematical aspects of nonlinear programming methods, as are the equally recent books by Gill et al. (6), McCormick (7), and Bertsedkas (50). The books by Reklaitis et al. (15), Vanderplaat (24), Haftka and Kamat (54), and Dennis and Schnabel (55) describe the theory and recent computational practice, and Avriel's book (9) gives a broad mathematical coverage of the subject. Finally, Wilde's book (10), *Optimum Seeking Methods,* the first book devoted to the subject, still contains valuable information in a very readable style.

In general form the nonlinear optimization problem can be stated as:

Optimize: $y(\mathbf{x})$

Subject to: $f_i(\mathbf{x}) = 0$ for $i = 1, 2, \cdots, h$ (6-1)

$f_i(\mathbf{x}) \geq 0$ $i = h + 1, \cdots, m$

There are n independent variables, $\mathbf{x} = (x_1, x_2, \cdots, x_n)$, m constraint equations, of which h are equality constraints. Also, the values of the x_j's can have upper and lower bounds specified. For this general form Avriel (11) points out that there is no unified approach to obtain the optimal solution of the nonlinear optimization problem comparable to the unifying role of the Simplex Method in linear programming. He states that the Simplex Method can efficiently solve a linear program in thousands of variables, but how to minimize an unconstrained nonlinear function with a few variables is an important question.

There are four classes of procedures for multivariable optimization applicable to nonlinear economic models with nonlinear constraints. These are multivariable search methods, multivariable elimination procedures, random search, and stochastic approximation procedures. Multivariable search methods are the most important and are discussed in detail. The capabilities and limitations of the other three methods are given in summary, with reference to other sources for more complete information.

Multivariable search methods can be thought of as encompassing the theory and algorithms of nonlinear programming along with the associated computational methods. These procedures use algorithms based on geometric or logical concepts to move rapidly from a starting point away from the optimum to a point near the optimum. Also, they attempt to satisfy the constraints associated with the problem and the Kuhn-Tucker conditions as they generate improved values of the economic model.

Multivariable elimination procedures are methods that reduce the feasible region (hypersurface of the independent variables) by discarding regions that are known *not* to contain the optimum. These are similar to minimax single-variable search methods in that they eliminate intervals on each of the independent variables. However, these methods are restricted to certain types of functions, e.g., strongly unimodal functions. Also, to locate the best value of the profit function with these procedures, the reduction in the range of the independent variables increases as the number of independent variables increases. This effect has been referred to as the *curse of dimensionality*, and has been illustrated by Wilde (10). The single-variable minimax interval elimination procedures are not useful in multidimensions, because only line segments are eliminated in those procedures, and there is a very large number of lines in a plane.

Random search is a method that places experiments randomly in the feasible region after it has been divided into a grid of discrete points. Knowing the number and location of the grid points, we can place a set of experiments randomly. Then we can determine with a certain probability that one of these points has a value of the profit function that is in a specified best fraction (top $x\%$). Unimodality is not required, and the number of independent variables is not directly a factor. In adaptive or creeping random search, experiments are placed randomly in a selected section of the feasible region, and a best value is located. Then another section of the feasible region is placed around this best value, and random experiments are placed again. This procedure is repeated until a stopping criterion is met. In essence, random search is used as a multivariable search method.

Stochastic approximation procedures are methods that apply to economic models that contain random error, e.g., the plant instead of a computer simulation of the plant. These techniques are similar to multivariable search methods, but they move slowly to avoid being confounded by the random error in the values of the economic model.

These four methods are described such that they can be applied to industrial problems. The most important and widely used multivariable search methods are given first, and then the other three procedures are discussed.

MULTIVARIABLE SEARCH METHODS OVERVIEW

Wilde (10) has proposed a strategy for multivariable search methods that contains some important ideas. This strategy has an opening gambit, a middle game, and an end game, which is analogous to the strategy of chess. In the opening gambit a starting point is selected. Then the middle game involves moving from this starting point to a point near the optimum as rapidly as possible. In the end game a quadratic fit to the economic model is performed to avoid stopping at a saddle point or sharp ridge.

Generally, selecting a starting point is not a problem, for the current design or plant operating conditions are usually known. If they are not available, then midpoints between the upper and lower limits on the independent variables can be used, and Wilde (10) has suggested others, such as the centroid and the minimax.

In the middle game a multivariable search method is used that moves rapidly from the starting point to a point that appears to be an optimum. Only enough explorations are performed at each step to obtain information useful to locate future experiments and to keep the method moving rapidly toward the optimum. The objective is to attain a series of improved values of the economic model with a minimum of computational effort.

The end game takes over once the middle game procedure has located what appears to be an optimum. A quadratic fit to the economic model at this best point is performed to determine if it is an optimum, rather than a saddle point or a ridge. The strategy has the middle game continue, if an optimum is not located, or stop, if one is found based on the quadratic approximation.

With these ideas in mind, multivariable search methods will be described that are middle game procedures applicable to unconstrained and constrained problems. One of the most frequently encountered unconstrained optimization problems is that of a nonlinear least-squares fit of a curve to experimental data. However, industrial optimization problems are constrained ones, almost without exception. Moreover, it will be seen that some constrained methods convert the problem into an unconstrained one, and then an unconstrained procedure is employed. Also, some of the more effective middle game procedures develop the information for the quadratic fit of the end game as they proceed from the starting point.

There are several hundred unconstrained multivariable search methods, but most of them are variations on a few concepts. These concepts can be used to classify the methods. Many techniques may be called *geometric methods,* for they use a local, geometric property to find a direction having an improved value of the economic model. Typically, derivative measurements are required. Two examples are the direction of steepest ascent (gradient search) and quadratic fit to the profit function (Newton's method). Other techniques can be called *logical methods,* for they use an algorithm based on a logical concept to find an improved direction of the profit function. Two examples are pattern search and flexible polyhedron search. Typically, derivative measurements are not required, and these types of procedures have been called *function comparison methods* (6). However, two methods that would not fit into these two categories readily are extensions of linear and quadratic programming. Here, linear programming, for example, is applied iteratively to a linearized version of the nonlinear constrained problem to move toward the optimum from a starting point. The methods are called *successive*, or sequential, *linear programming* and *successive*, or sequential, *quadratic programming*.

Another equally valid way to classify unconstrained methods has been given by Gill et al. (6). These categories are Newton, quasi-Newton, and conjugate gradient types, each with and without first or second derivatives, and functional comparison methods. Also, some of the quasi-Newton methods are called *variable metric* methods, and some of the conjugate gradient methods are called *conjugate direction* methods. They are all geometric methods, except for the functional comparison methods, which are logical methods.

There are essentially six types of procedures to solve constrained nonlinear optimization problems. Four of these methods convert the constrained problem into an unconstrained one, and then an unconstrained search procedure is applied. These four types are penalty or barrier functions methods; the augmented Lagrangian functions; generalized reduced gradients; and feasible directions, or projections, sometimes called methods of restricted movement. The other two are the previously mentioned procedures of successive, or sequential, linear and quadratic programming.

UNCONSTRAINED MULTIVARIABLE SEARCH METHODS

In this section on unconstrained multivariable search methods, several of the most effective and widely used methods are described. First, the quasi-Newton methods are given that have proved to be the most effective and more elaborate of the procedures. Then conjugate gradient and conjugate direction methods are illustrated with two examples. Finally, the popular function comparison procedure, pattern search, is presented, and assessments of these methods are presented as related to problems with constraints.

Before discussing the specifics of the methods, it is necessary to describe the desirable features of an algorithm. As mentioned previously, the algorithm should generate a sequence of values of x_k that move rapidly from the starting point x_0 to the neighborhood of the optimum x^*. Then the iterates x_k should converge to x^* and terminate when a convergence test is satisfied. Therefore, an important theoretical result for an algorithm would be a theorem that proves the sequence of values x_k generated by the algorithm converge to a local optimum. For example, the following theorem from Walsh (26) provides sufficient conditions for convergence of the method of steepest ascent (gradient search).

If the limit of the sequence $\{x_k\}$ of $x_{k+1} = x_k + \alpha \nabla y(x_{k,})$ is x^* for all x in a suitable neighborhood of x^*, then $y(x)$ has a local minimum at $x = x^*$.

The proof of this theorem is by contradiction.

As will be seen, the method of steepest ascent (gradient search) is not an effective method even though it will converge to an optimum eventually. The algorithm tends to zigzag, and the rate of convergence is significantly slower than other algorithms. Consequently, the rate, or order, of convergence of an algorithm is another important theoretical property. The rate of convergence of a sequence x_k for an algorithm as described by Fletcher (4) is in terms of the norm of the difference of a point in the sequence x_k and the optimum x^* i.e., $\|x_k - x^*\|$. If $\|x_{k+1} - x^*\|/\| x_k - x^*\| \to a$, then the rate of convergence is said to be linear or first-order if a ≥ 0. It is said to be superlinear if a $= 0$. For an algorithm, it is desirable to have the value of a as small as possible. For some algorithms it is possible to show that $\|x_{k+1} - x^*\|/\| x_k - x^*\|^2 \to a$, and for this case the rate of convergence is said to be quadratic or second-order. For the method of steepest ascent, Fletcher (4) states that the rate of convergence is a slow rate of linear convergence that depends on the largest and smallest eigenvalues of the Hessian matrix.

Another criterion often used to compare algorithms is their ability to locate the optimum of quadratic functions. This is called *quadratic termination.* The justification for using this criterion for comparison is that near an optimum the function can be "adequately approximated by a quadratic form," according to Bazaraa and Shetty (56). They claim that an algorithn that does not perform well in minimizing a quadratic function probably will not do well for a general nonlinear function, especially near the optimum.

There are several caveats about relying on theoretical results in judging algorithms. One is that the existence of convergence and rate of convergence results for any algorithm does not guarantee good performance in practice, according to Fletcher (4). One reason is that these theoretical results do not account for computer round-off error, which may be crucial. Both numerical experimentation with a variety of test functions and convergence and rate of convergence proofs are required to give a reliable indication of good performance. Also, as discussed by Gill et al. (6) conditions for achieving the theoretical rate of convergence may be rare, because an infinite sequence does not exist on a computer. Moreover, the absence of a theorem on the rate of convergence of an algorithm may be as much a measure of the difficulty of the proof as the inadequacy of the algorithm, according to Gill et al. (6).

Quasi-Newton Methods: These methods begin the search along a gradient line and use gradient information to build a quadratic fit to the economic model (profit function). Consequently, to understand these methods it is helpful to discuss the gradient search algorithm and Newton's method as background for the extension to the quasi-Newton algorithms. All the algorithms involve a line search given by the following equation:

$$\mathbf{x}_{k+1} = \mathbf{x}_k - \alpha \mathbf{H}_k \nabla y(\mathbf{x}_k) \qquad (6\text{-}2)$$

For gradient search $\mathbf{H}_k$ is $\mathbf{I}$, the unit matrix, and α is the parameter of the gradient line. For Newton's method $\mathbf{H}_k$ is the inverse of the Hessian matrix, $\mathbf{H}^{-1}$, and α is 1. For quasi-Newton methods $\mathbf{H}_k$ is a series of matrices beginning with the unit matrix, $\mathbf{I}$, and ending with the inverse of the Hessian matrix, $\mathbf{H}^{-1}$. The quasi-Newton algorithm that employs the BFGS (Broyden, Fletcher, Golfarb, Shanno) formula for updating the Hessian matrix is considered to be the most effective of the unconstrained multivariable search techniques, according to Fletcher (5). This formula is an extension of the DFP (Davidon, Fletcher, Powell) formula.

Gradient search, or the method of steepest ascent, was presented in Chapter 2 as an example of the application of the method of Lagrange Multipliers. However, let us consider briefly another approach to obtain this result, which should give added insight to the method. First, the profit function is expanded around point $\mathbf{x}_k$ in a Taylor series with only first-order terms as:

$$\text{Maximize: } y(\mathbf{x}) = y(\mathbf{x}_k) + \sum_{j=1}^{n} \frac{\partial y}{\partial x_j}(\mathbf{x}_k)(x_j - x_{jk}) \qquad (6\text{-}3)$$

In matrix notation, the above equation has the following form:

$$\text{Maximize: } y(\mathbf{x}) = y(\mathbf{x}_k) + \nabla y(\mathbf{x}_k)^T(\mathbf{x} - \mathbf{x}_k) \qquad (6\text{-}4)$$

Then to maximize $y(\mathbf{x})$, the largest value of $\nabla y(\mathbf{x}_k)^T(\mathbf{x} - \mathbf{x}_k)$ is to be used. When the largest value of $\nabla y(\mathbf{x}_k)^T(\mathbf{x} - \mathbf{x}_k)$ is determined, it has to be in the form of an equation that gives the way to change the individual x_j's to move in the direction of steepest ascent. This term can be written in vector notation as the dot product of two vectors:

$$\nabla y(\mathbf{x}_k) \cdot (\mathbf{x} - \mathbf{x}_k) = |\nabla y(\mathbf{x}_k)| \, |\mathbf{x} - \mathbf{x}_k| \cos \theta \qquad (6\text{-}5)$$

The magnitude of the gradient of $y(\mathbf{x}_k)$ at point $\mathbf{x}_k$, $|\nabla y(\mathbf{x}_k)|$, is known or can be measured at $\mathbf{x}_k$, and the magnitude of the vector $(\mathbf{x} - \mathbf{x}_k)$ is to be determined to maximize the dot product of the two vectors. In examining equation (6–5), the largest value of the dot product is with the value of $\theta = 0$ where cos (0) = 1. Consequently, the two vectors $\nabla y(\mathbf{x}_k)$ and $(\mathbf{x} - \mathbf{x}_k)$ are colinear and are proportional. This is given by the following equation:

$$(\mathbf{x} - \mathbf{x}_k) = \alpha \nabla y(\mathbf{x}_k) \tag{6–6}$$

where α is the proportionality constant and is also the parameter of the gradient line. Therefore, the gradient line, equation (6–6), can be written as:

$$\mathbf{x} = \mathbf{x}_k + \alpha \nabla y(\mathbf{x}_k) \tag{6–7}$$

Gradient search

The plus sign in the equation indicates the direction of steepest ascent, and using a negative sign in the equation would give the direction of steepest descent. However, these directions are actually steep ascent (descent) rather than steepest ascent (descent). Only if the optimization problem is scaled such that a unit change in each of the independent variables produces the same change in the profit function will the gradient move in the direction of steepest ascent. The procedures for scaling has been described in detail by Wilde (10) and Wilde and Beightler (12), and scaling is a problem encountered with all search methods.

The following short example illustrates the gradient method for a simple function with ellipsoidal contours. The zigzag behavior is observed as the algorithm moves from the starting point at (2, −2, 1) to the minimum at (0, 0, 0) of a function that is the sum of squares.

EXAMPLE 6–1

Search for the minimum of the following function using gradient search starting at point $\mathbf{x}_0 = (2, -2, 1)$.

$$y = 2x_1{}^2 + x_2{}^2 + 3x_3{}^2$$

The gradient line, equation (6–7), for point $\mathbf{x}_0$ is:

$$\boxed{\mathbf{x} = \mathbf{x}_0 + \alpha \nabla y(\mathbf{x}_0)}$$

and the three components of this equation are:

$$x_1 = x_{10} + \alpha \frac{\partial y}{\partial x}(\mathbf{x}_0)$$

change + to − signs for minimize
so α doesn't come out neg
for clarity

$$\begin{cases} x_2 = x_{20} + \alpha \dfrac{\partial y}{\partial x_2}(\mathbf{x}_0) \\[2mm] x_3 = x_{30} + \alpha \dfrac{\partial y}{\partial x_3}(\mathbf{x}_0) \end{cases}$$

Evaluating the partial derivatives gives:

$$\frac{\partial y}{\partial x_1} = 4x_1 \qquad \frac{\partial y}{\partial x_1}(\mathbf{x}_0) = 8 \qquad \frac{\partial y}{\partial x_2} = 2x_2 \qquad \frac{\partial y}{\partial x_2}(\mathbf{x}_0) = -4$$

$$\frac{\partial y}{\partial x_3} = 6x_3 \qquad \frac{\partial y}{\partial x_3}(\mathbf{x}_0) = 6$$

The gradient line is:

$$x_1 = 2 + 8\alpha$$

$$x_2 = -2 - 4\alpha$$

$$x_3 = 1 + 6\alpha$$

Tells how to change x_1 & x_2 to go in direction of steepest descent

If instead wanted to do Fibonacci (or Golden section) then $d_1 = .382\ I_0$, $\alpha_2 = .610\ I_0$, $\alpha_2 = d_1 \frac{.618}{.382}$

Converting $y(x_1,x_2,x_3)$ into $y(\alpha)$ for an exact line search gives:

$$y = 2(2 + 8\alpha)^2 + (-2 - 4\alpha)^2 + 3(1 + 6\alpha)^2$$

Analytical method

$$\frac{dy}{d\alpha} = 32(2 + 8\alpha) - 8(-2 - 4\alpha) + 36(1 + 6\alpha) = 0 \rightarrow \alpha^* = -0.23016$$

Computing point $\mathbf{x}_1$ using $\alpha^* = -0.23016$ gives:

$\alpha = +$ Direction of steepest ascent
$\alpha = -$ "   "   "   Descent

$$\begin{cases} x_1 = 2 + 8(-0.23016) = 0.15872 \\[2mm] x_2 = -2 - 4(-0.23016) = 1.0794 \\[2mm] x_3 = 1 + 6(-0.23016) = -0.38096 \end{cases}$$

Continuing, the partial derivatives are evaluated at $\mathbf{x}_1$ to give:

$$\frac{\partial y}{\partial x_1}(\mathbf{x}_1) = 4(0.15892) = 0.63488 \qquad \frac{\partial y}{\partial x_2}(\mathbf{x}_1) = 2(1.0794) = 2.1588$$

$$\frac{\partial y}{\partial x_3}(\mathbf{x}_1) = 6(-0.38096) = -2.2858$$

The gradient line at x_1 is:

$$x_1 = 0.15872 + 0.63688\alpha$$

$$x_2 = 1.0794 + 2.1588\alpha$$

$$x_3 = -0.38096 - 2.2858\alpha$$

The value of α that miminizes $y(\alpha)$ along the gradient line from x_1 is computed as was done previously, and the result is $\alpha^* = -0.2433$. Using this value of α, the point x_2 is computed as $(0.004524, 0.5542, 0.1752)$. Then, the search is continued along the gradient line from x_2 to x_3. These results and those from subsequent application of the algorithm are tabulated below, along with the previous results.

ITERATION	x_1	x_2	x_3	α	$y(x)$
0	2	-2	1		15.0
				-0.23016	
1	0.1587	1.0794	-0.3810		1.6510
				-0.2433	
2	0.004254	0.5542	0.1752		0.3993
				-0.2568	
3	-1.2×10^{-4}	0.2696	-0.0947		0.09959
				-0.2436	
4	3.4×10^{-6}	0.1383	0.04371		0.02486
				-0.2568	
5	0	0.06727	-0.02365		0.006203
				-0.2435	
6	0	0.03452	0.01090		0.001548
				-0.2570	
7	0	1.68×10^{-3}	-5.90×10^{-3}		2.8×10^{-4}
				-0.4999	
8	0	3.0×10^{-6}	1.0×10^{-6}		1.2×10^{-11}

A stopping criterion—having the independent variables be less than or equal to 1×10^{-3}—was used. Also, a criterion on the value of $y(x)$ could have been used.

Notice that the value of the parameter of the gradient line α is always negative. This indicates that the algorithm is moving in the direction of steepest descent. As the above results show, gradient search tends to take a zigzag path to the minimum of the function. This is typical of the performance of this algorithm.

In the development of Newton's method, the Taylor series expansion of $y(\mathbf{x})$ about $\mathbf{x}_k$ includes the second-order terms as shown below:

$$\text{Optimize: } y(\mathbf{x}) = y(\mathbf{x}_k) + \sum_{j=1}^{n} \frac{\partial y\;(\bar{\mathbf{x}}_k)}{\partial x_j}(x_j - x_{jk}) +$$

$$\qquad\qquad (6\text{--}8)$$

$$\frac{1}{2}\sum_{i=1}^{n}\sum_{j=1}^{n} \frac{\partial^2 y\;(\mathbf{x}_k)}{\partial x_i\,\partial x_j}(x_i - x_{ik})(x_j - x_{jk})$$

A more convenient way to write this equation is:

$$y(\mathbf{x}) = y(\mathbf{x}_k) + \nabla y(\mathbf{x}_k)^T(\mathbf{x} - \mathbf{x}_k) + \tfrac{1}{2}(\mathbf{x} - \mathbf{x}_k)^T\mathbf{H}(\mathbf{x} - \mathbf{x}_k) \qquad (6\text{--}9)$$

where $\mathbf{H}$ is the Hessian matrix, the matrix of second partial derivatives evaluated at the point $\mathbf{x}_k$, and $(\mathbf{x} - \mathbf{x}_k)^T$ is the row vector, which is the transpose of the column vector of the difference between the vector of independent variables $\mathbf{x}$ and the point $\mathbf{x}_k$ used for the Taylor Series expansion.

The algorithm is developed by locating the stationary point of equation (6–8) or (6–9) by setting the first partial derivatives with respect to $x_1, x_2, \cdots,$ x_n equal to zero. For equation (6–8) the result is:

$$\frac{\partial y}{\partial x_1} = \frac{\partial y\;(\mathbf{x}_k)}{\partial x_1} + \sum_{j=1}^{n} \frac{\partial^2 y\;(\mathbf{x}_k)}{\partial x_1\,\partial x_j}(x_j - x_{jk}) = 0$$

$$\vdots \qquad\qquad\qquad (6\text{--}10)$$

$$\frac{\partial y}{\partial x_n} = \frac{\partial y\;(\mathbf{x}_k)}{\partial x_n} + \sum_{j=1}^{n} \frac{\partial^2 y\;(\mathbf{x}_k)}{\partial x_n\,\partial x_j}(x_j - x_{jk}) = 0$$

which, when written in terms of the Hessian matrix, is:

$$\nabla y(\mathbf{x}_k) + \mathbf{H}(\mathbf{x} - \mathbf{x}_k) = 0 \qquad (6\text{--}11)$$

Then solving for $\mathbf{x}$, the optimum of the quadratic approximation, the following equation is obtained, which is the Newton's method algorithm:

$$\mathbf{x} = \mathbf{x}_k - \mathbf{H}^{-1}\nabla y(\mathbf{x}_k) \qquad (6\text{--}12)$$

Let mou work, 2nd partial
Derivs so
Quasi + trys to get rid of that

Comparing this equation with equation (6–2), it is seen that $\alpha = 1$ and $\mathbf{H}_k = \mathbf{H}^{-1}$, the inverse of the Hessian matrix. Also, a line search is not required for this method, because $\alpha = 1$. However, more computational effort is required for one iteration of this algorithm than for one iteration of gradient search, because the inverse of the Hessian matrix has to be evaluated in addition to the gradient vector. The same quadratic function of the gradient search algorithm example is used to illustrate Newton's method in the following example, and it shows the additional computations required.

EXAMPLE 6–2

Search for the minimum of the function from Example 6–1 using Newton's method starting at point $x_0 = (2, -2, 1)$:

$$y = 2x_1{}^2 + x_2{}^2 + 3x_3{}^2$$

From the previous example the gradient is:

$$\nabla y(x_0)^T = (8, -4, 6)$$

The Hessian matrix formed from the second partial derivatives evaluated at x_0 and its inverse are:

$$H_0 = \begin{bmatrix} 4 & 0 & 0 \\ 0 & 2 & 0 \\ 0 & 0 & 6 \end{bmatrix} \qquad H_0^{-1} = \begin{bmatrix} 1/4 & 0 & 0 \\ 0 & 1/2 & 0 \\ 0 & 0 & 1/6 \end{bmatrix}$$

The algorithm is given by equation (6–12), and for this example it is:

$$\begin{bmatrix} x_1 \\ x_2 \\ x_3 \end{bmatrix} = \begin{bmatrix} 2 \\ -2 \\ 1 \end{bmatrix} - \begin{bmatrix} 1/4 & 0 & 0 \\ 0 & 1/2 & 0 \\ 0 & 0 & 1/6 \end{bmatrix} \begin{bmatrix} 8 \\ -4 \\ 6 \end{bmatrix} = \begin{bmatrix} 0 \\ 0 \\ 0 \end{bmatrix}.$$

The minimum of the quadratic function is located with one application of the algorithm.

In Newton's method, if x_k is not close to x^*, it may happen that H^{-1} is not positive definite, and then the method may fail to converge in this case (26). However, if the starting point x_0 is sufficiently close to a local optimum x^*, the rate of convergence is second-order, as given by the following theorem from Fletcher (4).

If x_k is sufficiently close to x^* for some k, and if H^* is positive definite, then Newton's method is well defined for all k and converges at a second-order rate.

Quasi — Newton

The proof of the theorem has x_k in the neighborhood of x^* and uses induction.

Newton's method has the property of quadratic termination, as demonstrated by the example above. It arrives at the optimum of a quadratic function in a finite number of steps, one.

However, for nonlinear functions generally, Newton's method moves methodically toward the optimum, but the computational effort required to compute the inverse of the Hessian matrix at each iteration usually is excessive compared with other methods. Consequently, it is considered to be an inefficient middle game procedure for most problems.

To overcome these difficulties, quasi-Newton methods were developed which use the algorithm given by equation (6–2). They begin with a search along the gradient line, and only gradient measurements are required for H_k in subsequent applications of the algorithm given by equation (6–2). As the algorithm proceeds, a quadratic approximation to the profit function is developed only from the gradient measurements, and for a quadratic function of n independent variables, the optimum is reached after n applications of the algorithm.

Davidon developed the concept in 1959, and Fletcher and Powell, in 1963, extended the methodology. As discussed by Fletcher (4), there have been a number of other contributors to this area, also. The DFP (Davidon, Fletcher, Powell) algorithm has become the best known of the quasi-Newton (variable metric or large-step gradient) algorithms. Some of its properties are superlinear rate of convergence on general functions and quadratic termination using exact line searches on quadratic functions (4).

A number of variations of the functional form of the matrix H_k of equation (6–2) with the properties described above have been developed, and some *Best* of these have been tabulated by Himmelblau (8). However, as previously stated, the BFGS algorithm developed in 1970 is preferable to the others, and this is currently well accepted, according to Fletcher (4). The following paragraphs will describe the DFP and BFGS algorithms and illustrate each with an example. Convergence proofs and related information are given by Fletcher (4) and others (6, 7, 8, 9).

The DFP algorithm has the following form of equation (6–2) for minimizing the function $y(x)$:

$$x_{k+1} = x_k - \alpha_{k+1} H_k \nabla y(x_k) \qquad \text{Quasi Newton} \qquad (6\text{–}13)$$

Approx to Hessian matrix

where α_{k+1} is the parameter of the line through x_k, and H_k is given by the following equation (12):

$$H_o = \text{Identity matrix}$$

$$H_k = H_{k-1} + A_k + B_k \qquad (6\text{–}14)$$

$$X_{k+1} = X_k - H^{-1} \nabla y(x_k) \qquad \text{Newton's}$$

$$X_{k+1} = X_k + \alpha_{k+1} \nabla y(x_k) \qquad \text{Gradient Search}$$

The matrices $\mathbf{A}_k$ and $\mathbf{H}_k$ are given by the following equations:

$$\mathbf{A}_k = \frac{(\mathbf{x}_k - \mathbf{x}_{k-1})(\mathbf{x}_k - \mathbf{x}_{k-1})^T}{(\mathbf{x}_k - \mathbf{x}_{k-1})^T(\nabla y(\mathbf{x}_k) - \nabla y(\mathbf{x}_{k-1}))} \qquad (6\text{--}15)$$

$$\mathbf{B}_k = \frac{\mathbf{H}_{k-1}(\nabla y(\mathbf{x}_k) - \nabla y(\mathbf{x}_{k-1}))(\nabla y(\mathbf{x}_k) - \nabla y(\mathbf{x}_{k-1}))^T\mathbf{H}_{k-1}^T}{(\nabla y(\mathbf{x}_k) - \nabla y(\mathbf{x}_{k-1}))^T\mathbf{H}_{k-1}(\nabla y(\mathbf{x}_k) - \nabla y(\mathbf{x}_{k-1}))} \qquad (6\text{--}16)$$

The algorithm begins with a search along the gradient line from the starting point $\mathbf{x}_0$, as given by the following equation obtained from equation (6–13), with $k = 0$.

$$\mathbf{x}_1 = \mathbf{x}_0 - \alpha_1\mathbf{H}_0\nabla y(\mathbf{x}_0) \qquad (6\text{--}17)$$

where $\mathbf{H}_0 = \mathbf{I}$ is the unit matrix. This equation is the same as equation (6–7) for the gradient line. The algorithm continues using equation (6–13) until a stopping criterion is met. However, for a quadratic function with n independent variables, the method converges to the optimum after n iterations (quadratic termination) if exact line searches are used.

The matrices $\mathbf{A}_k$ and $\mathbf{B}_k$ have been constructed so their sums would have the specific properties shown below (12):

$$\left\{\sum_{k-1}^{n} \mathbf{A}_k = \mathbf{H}^{-1}\right. \qquad \overset{\wedge}{\underset{k=1}{\sum}} H_k = H^{-1} \qquad (6\text{--}18)$$

$$\left\{\sum_{k=1}^{n} \mathbf{B}_k = -\mathbf{H}_0 = -\mathbf{I}\right. \quad \textit{Identity matrix} \qquad (6\text{--}19)$$

The sum of the n matrices $\mathbf{A}_k$ generate the inverse of the Hessian matrix $\mathbf{H}^{-1}$ to have equation (6–13) be the same as Newton's method, equation (6–12), at the end of n iterations. The sum of the matrices $\mathbf{B}_k$ generates the negative of the unit matrix $\mathbf{I}$ at the end of m iterations to cancel the first step of the algorithm when $\mathbf{I}$ was used for $\mathbf{H}_0$ in equation (6–17).

The development of the algorithm and the proofs for the rate of convergence and quadratic termination are given by Fletcher (4). Also, the procedure is applicable to and effective on nonlinear functions. According to Fletcher (4), for general functions it preserves positive definite $\mathbf{H}_k$ matrices, and thus the descent property holds. Also, it has a superlinear rate of convergence, and it converges to the global minimum of strictly convex functions if exact line searches are used.

The following example illustrates the use of the DFP algorithm for a quadratic function with three independent variables. Consequently, the optimum is reached with three applications of the algorithm.

EXAMPLE 6–3 (14)

Determine the minimum of the following function using the DFP algorithm starting at $x_0^T = (0, 0, 0)$:

$$\text{Minimize: } 5x_1^2 + 2x_2^2 + 2x_3^2 + 2x_1x_2 + 2x_2x_3 - 2x_1x_3 - 6x_3$$

Performing the appropriate partial differentiation, we obtain the gradient vector $\nabla y(x)$ and the Hessian matrix:

$$\nabla y(x) = \begin{bmatrix} 10x_1 + 2x_2 - 2x_3 \\ 2x_1 + 4x_2 + 2x_3 \\ -2x_1 + 2x_2 + 4x_3 - 6 \end{bmatrix} \qquad H = \begin{bmatrix} 10 & 2 & -2 \\ 2 & 4 & 2 \\ -2 & 2 & 4 \end{bmatrix}$$

Using equation (6–17) to start the algorithm gives:

$$\begin{bmatrix} x_{11} \\ x_{21} \\ x_{31} \end{bmatrix} = \begin{bmatrix} 0 \\ 0 \\ 0 \end{bmatrix} - \alpha_1 \begin{bmatrix} 1 & 0 & 0 \\ 0 & 1 & 0 \\ 0 & 0 & 1 \end{bmatrix} \begin{bmatrix} 0 \\ 0 \\ -6 \end{bmatrix} = \begin{bmatrix} 0 \\ 0 \\ 6\alpha_1 \end{bmatrix} = \begin{bmatrix} 0 \\ 0 \\ 3/2 \end{bmatrix}$$

The optimal value of α_1 is determined by an exact line search using $x_1 = 0$, $x_2 = 0$, $x_3 = 6\alpha_1$, as follows:

$$y(\alpha_1) = 2(6\alpha_1)^2 - 6(6\alpha_1) = 72\alpha_1^2 - 36\alpha_1$$

$$\frac{dy}{d\alpha_1} = 144\alpha_1 - 36 = 0 \rightarrow \alpha_1 = 1/4$$

The value of x_1 is computed by substituting for α_1 in the previous equation:

$$x_1^T = (0, 0, 3/2) \qquad \nabla y(x_1)^T = (-3, 3, 0) \qquad \nabla y(x_0)^T = (0, 0, -6)$$

The algorithm continues using equations (6–13) and (6–14) for $k = 1$:

$$x_2 = x_1 - \alpha_2 H_1 \nabla y(x_1)$$

or

$$\begin{bmatrix} x_{12} \\ x_{22} \\ x_{32} \end{bmatrix} = \begin{bmatrix} 0 \\ 0 \\ 3/2 \end{bmatrix} - \alpha_2 \begin{bmatrix} 5/6 & 1/6 & 1/3 \\ 1/6 & 5/6 & -1/3 \\ 1/3 & -1/3 & 7/12 \end{bmatrix} \begin{bmatrix} -3 \\ 3 \\ 0 \end{bmatrix} = \begin{bmatrix} 2\alpha_2 \\ -2\alpha_2 \\ 3/2 + 2\alpha_2 \end{bmatrix} = \begin{bmatrix} 1 \\ -1 \\ 5/2 \end{bmatrix}$$

where

$$\mathbf{H}_1 = \mathbf{H}_0 + \mathbf{A}_1 + \mathbf{B}_1$$

and $\mathbf{A}_1$ and $\mathbf{B}_1$ are given by equations (6–15) and (6–16):

$$\mathbf{A}_1 = \begin{bmatrix} 0 \\ 0 \\ 3/2 \end{bmatrix} \begin{bmatrix} 0 & 0 & 3/2 \end{bmatrix} \Bigg/ \begin{bmatrix} 0 & 0 & 3/2 \end{bmatrix} \begin{bmatrix} -3 \\ 3 \\ 6 \end{bmatrix} = \begin{bmatrix} 0 & 0 & 0 \\ 0 & 0 & 0 \\ 0 & 0 & 1/4 \end{bmatrix}$$

$$\mathbf{B}_1 = - \frac{\begin{bmatrix} 1 & 0 & 0 \\ 0 & 1 & 0 \\ 0 & 0 & 1 \end{bmatrix} \begin{bmatrix} -3 \\ 3 \\ 6 \end{bmatrix} \begin{bmatrix} -3 & 3 & 6 \end{bmatrix} \begin{bmatrix} 1 & 0 & 0 \\ 0 & 1 & 0 \\ 0 & 0 & 1 \end{bmatrix}}{\begin{bmatrix} -3 & 3 & 6 \end{bmatrix} \begin{bmatrix} 1 & 0 & 0 \\ 0 & 1 & 0 \\ 0 & 0 & 1 \end{bmatrix} \begin{bmatrix} -3 \\ 3 \\ 6 \end{bmatrix}} = \begin{bmatrix} -1/6 & 1/6 & 1/3 \\ 1/6 & -1/6 & -1/3 \\ 1/3 & -1/3 & -2/3 \end{bmatrix}$$

$$\mathbf{H}_1 = \begin{bmatrix} 1 & 0 & 0 \\ 0 & 1 & 0 \\ 0 & 0 & 1 \end{bmatrix} + \begin{bmatrix} 0 & 0 & 0 \\ 0 & 0 & 0 \\ 0 & 0 & 1/4 \end{bmatrix} + \begin{bmatrix} -1/6 & 1/6 & 1/3 \\ 1/6 & -1/6 & -1/3 \\ 1/3 & -1/3 & -2/3 \end{bmatrix}$$

$$= \begin{bmatrix} 5/6 & 1/6 & 1/3 \\ 1/6 & 5/6 & -1/3 \\ 1/3 & -1/3 & 7/12 \end{bmatrix}$$

The optimal value of α_2 is determined by an exact line search as follows:

$$y(\alpha_2) = 12\alpha_2^2 - 12\alpha_2 + 9/2 \qquad \frac{dy}{d\alpha_2} = 24\alpha_2 - 12 = 0 \rightarrow \alpha_2 = \tfrac{1}{2}$$

The value of $\mathbf{x}_2$ is computed by substituting for α_2 in the previous equation:

$$\mathbf{x}_2^T = (1, -1, 5/2) \qquad \nabla y(\mathbf{x}_2)^T = (3, 3, 0)$$

The computation of x_3 uses equations (6-13) and (6-14) as follows:

$$x_3 = x_2 - \alpha_3 H_2 \nabla y(x_2)$$

and

$$H_2 = H_1 + A_2 + B_2 = \begin{bmatrix} 1/16 & -1/6 & 1/6 \\ -1/6 & 29/30 & -17/30 \\ 1/6 & -17/30 & 37/60 \end{bmatrix}$$

where

$$A_2 = \begin{bmatrix} 1 \\ -1 \\ 1 \end{bmatrix} [1 \;\; -1 \;\; 1] \Bigg/ [1 \;\; -1 \;\; 1] \begin{bmatrix} 6 \\ 0 \\ 0 \end{bmatrix} = \begin{bmatrix} 1/6 & -1/6 & 1/6 \\ -1/6 & 1/6 & -1/6 \\ 1/6 & -1/6 & 1/6 \end{bmatrix}$$

$$B_2 = -\dfrac{\begin{bmatrix} 5/6 & 1/6 & 1/3 \\ 1/6 & 5/6 & -1/3 \\ 1/3 & -1/3 & 7/12 \end{bmatrix} \begin{bmatrix} 6 \\ 0 \\ 0 \end{bmatrix} [6 \;\; 0 \;\; 0] \begin{bmatrix} 5/6 & 1/6 & 1/3 \\ 1/6 & 5/6 & -1/3 \\ 1/3 & -1/3 & 7/12 \end{bmatrix}}{[6 \;\; 0 \;\; 0] \begin{bmatrix} 5/6 & 1/6 & -1/3 \\ 1/6 & 5/6 & -1/3 \\ 1/3 & -1/3 & 7/12 \end{bmatrix} \begin{bmatrix} 6 \\ 0 \\ 0 \end{bmatrix}}$$

$$= \begin{bmatrix} -5/6 & -1/6 & -1/3 \\ -1/6 & -1/30 & -1/15 \\ -1/3 & -1/15 & -2/15 \end{bmatrix}$$

$$\begin{bmatrix} x_{13} \\ x_{23} \\ x_{33} \end{bmatrix} = \begin{bmatrix} 1 \\ -1 \\ 5/2 \end{bmatrix} - \alpha_3 \begin{bmatrix} 1/6 & -1/6 & 1/6 \\ -1/6 & 29/30 & -17/30 \\ 1/6 & -17/30 & 37/30 \end{bmatrix} \begin{bmatrix} 3 \\ 3 \\ 0 \end{bmatrix}$$

$$= \begin{bmatrix} 1 \\ -1 - 12\alpha/5 \\ 5/2 + 6\alpha/5 \end{bmatrix} = \begin{bmatrix} 1 \\ -2 \\ 3 \end{bmatrix}$$

The optimal value of α_3 is determined by an exact line search as follows:

$$y(\alpha_3) = 5 + 2(1 + 12\alpha_3/5)^2 + 2(5/2 + 6\alpha_3/5)^2 - 2(1 + 12\alpha_3/5)$$
$$-2(1 + 12\alpha_3/5)(5/2 + 6\alpha_3/5) - 2(5/2 + 6\alpha_3/5) - 6(5/2 + 6\alpha_3/5)$$

Setting $dy(\alpha_3)/d\alpha_3 = 0$ and solving for α_3 gives $\alpha_3 = 5/12$ and $\mathbf{x}_3^T = (1, -2, 3)$, which is the value of the function at the minimum.

In the preceding example exact line searches were used to have the DFP algorithm proceed to the optimum. However, in optimization problems encountered in industrial practice, exact line searches are not possible, and numerical single-variable search methods must be used, ones such as golden section search or the quadratic method. However, the previously mentioned BFGS method will converge to the optimum of a convex function even when inexact line searches are used. Also, this global convergence property has not been demonstrated for other algorithms, such as the DFP algorithm according to Fletcher (4). Consequently, this may be part of the reason that the BFGS algorithm has demonstrated generally more satisfactory performance than other methods in numerical experiments, even though it is a more elaborate formula. The BFGS matrix update formula comparable to equations (6–14), (6–15), and (6–16), as given by Fletcher (4), is:

$$\mathbf{H}_{k+1} = \mathbf{H}_k - \left[\frac{\mathbf{H}_k \, \boldsymbol{\gamma}_k \, \boldsymbol{\delta}_k^T + \boldsymbol{\delta}_k \, \boldsymbol{\gamma}_k^T \, \mathbf{H}_k}{\boldsymbol{\delta}_k^T \, \boldsymbol{\gamma}_k} \right] + \left[\frac{\boldsymbol{\gamma}_k^T \, \mathbf{H}_k \, \boldsymbol{\gamma}_k}{\boldsymbol{\delta}_k^T \, \boldsymbol{\gamma}_k} \right] \left[\frac{\boldsymbol{\delta}_k \, \boldsymbol{\delta}_k^T}{\boldsymbol{\delta}_k^T \, \boldsymbol{\gamma}_k} \right] \quad (6\text{–}20)$$

where $\boldsymbol{\delta}_k = \mathbf{x}_{k+1} - \mathbf{x}_k$ and $\boldsymbol{\gamma}_k = \nabla y(\mathbf{x}_{k+1}) - \nabla y(\mathbf{x}_k)$.

This equation is used in place of equation (6–14) in the algorithm given by equation (6–13). The procedure is the same in that a search along the gradient line from starting point $\mathbf{x}_0$ is conducted initially according to equation (6–17). Then the Hessian matrix is updated using equation (6–20), and for quadratic functions the method arrives at the minimum after n iterations. The following example illustrates the procedure for the BFGS algorithm using the function of Example 6–3.

EXAMPLE 6–4 (14)

Determine the minimum of the following function using the BFGS algorithm starting at $\mathbf{x}_0 = (0, 0, 0)$:

Minimize: $5x_1^2 + 2x_2^2 + 2x_3^2 + 2x_1x_2 + 2x_2x_3 - 2x_1x_3 - 6x_3$

The first application of the algorithm is the same as Example 6-3, which is a search along the gradient line through $\mathbf{x}_0 = (0, 0, 0)$. These results were:

$$\mathbf{x}_1^T = (0, 0, 3/2) \qquad \nabla y(\mathbf{x}_1)^T = (-3, 3, 0)$$

$$\mathbf{x}_0^T = (0, 0, 0) \qquad \nabla y(\mathbf{x}_0)^T = (0, 0, -6)$$

The algorithm continues using equations (6–13) and (6–20) for $k = 1$:

$$\mathbf{x}_2 = \mathbf{x}_1 - \alpha_2 \, \mathbf{H}_1 \, \nabla y(\mathbf{x}_1)$$

or

$$\begin{bmatrix} x_{12} \\ x_{22} \\ x_{32} \end{bmatrix} = \begin{bmatrix} 0 \\ 0 \\ 3/2 \end{bmatrix} - \alpha_2 \begin{bmatrix} 1 & 0 & \tfrac{1}{2} \\ 0 & 1 & -\tfrac{1}{2} \\ \tfrac{1}{2} & -\tfrac{1}{2} & 3/4 \end{bmatrix} \begin{bmatrix} -3 \\ 3 \\ 0 \end{bmatrix} = \begin{bmatrix} 3\alpha_2 \\ -3\alpha_2 \\ 3/2 + 3\alpha_2 \end{bmatrix} = \begin{bmatrix} 1 \\ -1 \\ 5/2 \end{bmatrix}$$

where

$$\mathbf{H}_1 = \mathbf{H}_0 - \left[\frac{\mathbf{H}_0 \, \boldsymbol{\gamma}_0 \, \boldsymbol{\delta}_0{}^T + \boldsymbol{\delta}_0 \, \boldsymbol{\gamma}_0{}^T \, \mathbf{H}_0}{\boldsymbol{\delta}_0{}^T \, \boldsymbol{\gamma}_0} \right] + \left[\frac{\boldsymbol{\gamma}_0{}^T \, \mathbf{H}_0 \, \boldsymbol{\gamma}_0}{\boldsymbol{\delta}_0{}^T \, \boldsymbol{\gamma}_0} \right] \frac{\boldsymbol{\delta}_0 \, \boldsymbol{\delta}_0{}^T}{\boldsymbol{\delta}_0{}^T \, \boldsymbol{\gamma}_0}$$

$$\mathbf{H}_0 = \begin{bmatrix} 1 & 0 & 0 \\ 0 & 1 & 0 \\ 0 & 0 & 1 \end{bmatrix} \quad \boldsymbol{\delta}_0 = \mathbf{x}_1 - \mathbf{x}_0 = \begin{bmatrix} 0 \\ 0 \\ 3/2 \end{bmatrix} \quad \boldsymbol{\gamma}_0 = \nabla y(\mathbf{x}_1) - \nabla y(\mathbf{x}_0) = \begin{bmatrix} -3 \\ 3 \\ 6 \end{bmatrix}$$

$$\boldsymbol{\delta}_0{}^T \, \boldsymbol{\gamma}_0 = 9 \qquad \boldsymbol{\gamma}_0{}^T \, \mathbf{H}_0 \, \boldsymbol{\gamma}_0 = 54$$

$$\mathbf{H}_1 = \begin{bmatrix} 1 & 0 & 0 \\ 0 & 1 & 0 \\ 0 & 0 & 1 \end{bmatrix} - \begin{bmatrix} 0 & 0 & -\tfrac{1}{2} \\ 0 & 0 & \tfrac{1}{2} \\ -\tfrac{1}{2} & \tfrac{1}{2} & 2 \end{bmatrix} + \begin{bmatrix} 0 & 0 & 0 \\ 0 & 0 & 0 \\ 0 & 0 & 7/4 \end{bmatrix} = \begin{bmatrix} 1 & 0 & \tfrac{1}{2} \\ 0 & 1 & -\tfrac{1}{2} \\ \tfrac{1}{2} & -\tfrac{1}{2} & 3/4 \end{bmatrix}$$

The optimal value of α_2 is determined by an exact line search using $x_1 = 3\alpha_2$, $x_2 = -3\alpha_2$, $x_3 = \tfrac{3}{2} + 3\alpha_2$ in the function being minimized to give:

$$y = 27\alpha_2{}^2 - 18\alpha_2 + 4\tfrac{1}{2} \qquad \frac{dy}{d\alpha_2} = 54\alpha_2 - 18 = 0 \rightarrow \alpha_2 = 1/3$$

The value for $\mathbf{x}_2$ is computed by substituting for α_2 in the previous equation:

$$\mathbf{x}_2{}^T = (1, -1, 5/2) \qquad \nabla y(\mathbf{x}_2)^T = (3, 3, 0)$$

The computation of $\mathbf{x}_3$ repeats the application of the algorithm as follows:

$$\mathbf{x}_3 = \mathbf{x}_2 - \alpha_3 \, \mathbf{H}_2 \, \nabla y(\mathbf{x}_2)$$

or

$$\begin{bmatrix} x_{13} \\ x_{23} \\ x_{33} \end{bmatrix} = \begin{bmatrix} 1 \\ -1 \\ 5/2 \end{bmatrix} - \alpha_2 \begin{bmatrix} 1/6 & -1/6 & 1/6 \\ -1/6 & 13/6 & -7/6 \\ 1/6 & -7/6 & 11/12 \end{bmatrix} \begin{bmatrix} 3 \\ 3 \\ 0 \end{bmatrix} = \begin{bmatrix} 1 \\ -1 - 6\alpha_3 \\ 5/2 + 3\alpha_3 \end{bmatrix} = \begin{bmatrix} 1 \\ -2 \\ 3 \end{bmatrix}$$

where

$$\delta_1^T = (1, -1, 1) \qquad \gamma_1^T = (6, 0, 0) \qquad \delta_1^T \gamma_1 = 6 \qquad \gamma_1^T H_1 \gamma_1 = 36$$

$$H_2 = \begin{bmatrix} 1 & 0 & \frac{1}{2} \\ 0 & 1 & -\frac{1}{2} \\ \frac{1}{2} & -\frac{1}{2} & 3/4 \end{bmatrix} - \begin{bmatrix} 2 & -1 & 3/2 \\ -1 & 0 & -\frac{1}{2} \\ 3/2 & -\frac{1}{2} & 1 \end{bmatrix} + \begin{bmatrix} 7/6 & -7/6 & 7/6 \\ -7/6 & 7/6 & -7/6 \\ 7/6 & -7/6 & 7/6 \end{bmatrix}$$

$$= \begin{bmatrix} 1/6 & -1/6 & 1/6 \\ -1/6 & 13/6 & -7/6 \\ 1/6 & -7/6 & 11/12 \end{bmatrix}$$

The optimal value of α_3 is determined by an exact line search using $x_{13} = 1$, $x_{23} = -1 - 6\alpha_3$, $x_{33} = \frac{5}{2} + 3\alpha_2$ in the function being minimized to give $y(\alpha_3)$. The value of $\alpha_3 = 1/6$ is determined as previously by setting $dy(\alpha_3)/d\alpha_3 = 0$, and the optimal value of $x_3^T = (1, -2, 3)$ is computed, which is the value of the function at the minimum.

A program for the BFGS method is given in Table 6-4 at the end of this chapter. It employs the Fibonacci search program described in Chapter 5 for the line searches. This method and the program are applicable to functions that are not quadratic also. However, the property of quadratic termination to the optimum in a predetermined number of steps is applicable to quadratic functions only; and a stopping criterion has to be specified for general nonlinear functions. In this program the function to be minimized and the stopping criterion, EPS, are to be supplied by the user; and the program terminates when the magnitude of successive values of the profit function is less than the value of the stopping criterion. The solution to the problem of Example 6–4 is given to illustrate the use of the program.

Conjugate Gradient and Direction Methods: The distinguishing feature of these methods is that they have the quadratic termination property. The conjugate direction methods do not require derivative measurements, and the conjugate gradient methods require only gradient measurements. These procedures have been effective on a number of optimization problems, and they have been summarized by Fletcher (4) and others (6, 7, 8, 9, 15). The conjugate gradient and direction algorithms can locate the optimum of a quadratic function by searching only once along conjugate directions if exact line searches are used (quadratic termination), and all methods rely on the theorem given below. They differ in the way the conjugate directions are generated, and the objective was to have efficient methods for general functions (4). The two more effective of these methods will be described, Powell's method for conjugate directions and gradient partan for conjugate gradients.

The idea for these methods is based on the fact that the optimum of a function that is separable can be found by optimizing separately each component. A quadratic function can be converted into a separable function, a sum of perfect squares (15), using a linear transformation; and the optimum can be found by a single variable search on each of the n transformed independent variables. The directions from the transformations are called *conjugate directions*.

A quadratic function to be optimized can have the following form:

$$y(\mathbf{x}) = a + \mathbf{b}^T \mathbf{x} + \mathbf{x}^T \mathbf{H} \mathbf{x} \qquad (6\text{–}21)$$

Then by using the properties of a quadratic function, e.g., $\mathbf{H}$ is a positive definite, symmetric matrix, it can be shown that a set of linearly independent vectors $\mathbf{s}_1, \mathbf{s}_2, \ldots, \mathbf{s}_n$ are mutually conjugate with respect to $\mathbf{H}$ if:

$$\mathbf{s}_i^T \mathbf{H} \mathbf{s}_j = 0 \qquad (6\text{–}22)$$

Then, using this property, sets of conjugate search directions can be constructed that minimize the quadratic function, equation (6–21), as illustrated by Himmelblau (8). The theorem on which these methods rely, as given by Fletcher (4), is:

A conjugate direction method terminates for a quadratic function in at most n *exact line searches, and each* $\mathbf{x}_{i+1}$ *is the minimizer in the subspace generated by* $\mathbf{x}_i$ *and the directions* $\mathbf{s}_1, \mathbf{s}_2, \ldots, \mathbf{s}_i$ *(that is a set of points* $\{\mathbf{x} \mid \mathbf{x} = \mathbf{x}_1 + \sum_{j=1}^{i} \alpha_j \mathbf{s}_j\})$.

The proof uses the stationary point necessary conditions, equation (6–22) and the fact that mutually conjugate vectors are linearly independent (4, 9, 26, 57). However, the proof does not give insight into the means of constructing conjugate directions (4).

The notion of conjugate directions is a generalization of orthogonal directions where $\mathbf{H} = \mathbf{I}$, according to Avriel (9), and algorithms, such as Powell's method, initially search along orthogonal coordinate axes. Also, the DFP and the BFGS methods are conjugate direction methods when exact line searches are used (7).

Searching along conjugate directions can be represented by the following equation:

$$\mathbf{x} = \mathbf{x}_0 + \sum_{i=1}^{n} \alpha_i \, \mathbf{x}_i \qquad (6\text{--}23)$$

where α_i is the parameter of the line in the conjugate directions (the orthogonal coordinate axes initially in Powell's method), and $\mathbf{x}_i$ is the vector that gives the conjugate directions (a coordinate axis, e.g., $\mathbf{x}_i = (0, \ldots, 0, x_i, 0, \ldots, 0)$ in Powell's method). For a given direction of search, $\mathbf{x}_i$, the value of α_i is located to give the optimum of $y(\mathbf{x}_i)$ along the line of search. The function to be optimized can be written as:

$$y(\mathbf{x}^*) = y\left(\mathbf{x}_0 + \sum_{i=1}^{n} \alpha_i \, \mathbf{x}_i \right) \qquad (6\text{--}24)$$

Then to locate the optimum, $\mathbf{x}^*$ an exact line search is conducted on each of the α_i's individually. The optimum of $y(\mathbf{x})$ is then determined by exact line searches in each of the conjugate directions. Further details are given by Fletcher (4), Avriel (9), and Powell (57) about the theory for these methods.

The two methods most frequently associated with conjugate direction are illustrated in Figure 6-1. These are Powell's method (57) and steep ascent partan (12). In Powell's method, the conjugate directions are the orthogonal coordinate axes initially, and in steep ascent partan the conjugate directions are the gradient lines. Also, both procedures employ an acceleration step. In the following paragraphs these two methods are discussed in more detail for n independent variables and are illustrated with an example.

In Powell's algorithm (9) the procedure begins at a starting point $\mathbf{x}_0$, and each application of the algorithm consists of $(n + 2)$ successive exact line searches. The first $(n + 1)$ are along the n coordinate axes. The $(n + 2)$nd line search goes from the point obtained from the first line search through the best point (obtained at the end of the $(n + 1)$ line searches). If the function is quadratic, this will locate the optimum. If it is not, then the search is continued with one of the first n directions replaced by the $(n + 1)$th direction, and the procedure is repeated until a stopping criterion is met.

The basic procedure for an iteration, as given by Powell (57), is as follows

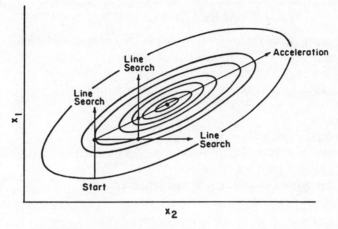

a) Powell's Method

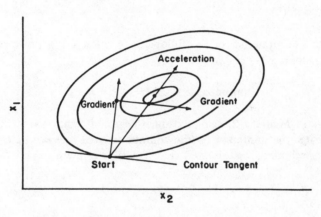

b) Steep Ascent Partan

Figure 6-1. Graphical illustration of Powell's method and steep ascent partan.

for a function of n independent variables starting at point x_I with the conjugate direction $s_1, s_2, \ldots, s_n$ chosen as the coordinate axes.

For a quadratic function the method will arrive at the minimum on completing Step 3. For a general function Steps 1–3 are repeated until a stopping criterion is satisfied. Step 0 is required to start the method by having x_0, the point beginning the iteration steps 1–3, be a minimum point on the contour tangent line s_n. The following example illustrates the above procedure for a quadratic function with two independent variables.

Powell's Method for a General Function (57)

0. Calculate α_I so that $y(\mathbf{x}_I + \alpha_I \mathbf{s}_n)$ is a minimum, and define $\mathbf{x}_0 = \mathbf{x}_I + \alpha_I \mathbf{s}_n$.
1. For $j = 1, 2, \cdots, n$:
   Calculate α_j so that $y(\mathbf{x}_{j-1} + \alpha_j \mathbf{s}_j)$ is a minimum.
   Define $\mathbf{x}_j = \mathbf{x}_{j-1} + \alpha_j \mathbf{s}_j$.
   Replace $\mathbf{s}_j$ with $\mathbf{s}_{j+1}$.
2. Replace $\mathbf{s}_n$ with $\mathbf{x}_n - \mathbf{x}_0$.
3. Choose α so that $y[\mathbf{x}_n + \alpha(\mathbf{x}_n - \mathbf{x}_0)]$ is a minimum, and replace $\mathbf{x}_0$ with $\mathbf{x}_0 + \alpha(\mathbf{x}_n - \mathbf{x}_0)$.
4. Repeat steps 1–3 until a stopping criterion is met.

EXAMPLE 6–5 (8)

Determine the minimum of the following function using Powell's method starting at point $\mathbf{x}_I = (2, 2)$.

$$\text{minimize: } y = 2x_1^2 + x_2^2 - x_1 x_2$$

As shown in Figure 6-2, the procedure begins at point $\mathbf{x}_I = (2, 2)$, and step 0 locates the minimum on the contour tangent line $\mathbf{s}_n$, $\mathbf{x}_0$, by a single variable search along coordinate axis n $(= 2)$ as follows:

Step 0. $n = 2$ $\mathbf{s}_1^T = (1, 0)$ $\mathbf{s}_2^T = (0, 1)$ $\mathbf{x}_I^T = (2, 2)$

$$\mathbf{x}_0 = \mathbf{x}_I + \alpha_I \mathbf{s}_2 \quad \text{or} \quad \begin{bmatrix} x_{1,0} \\ x_{2,0} \end{bmatrix} = \begin{bmatrix} 2 \\ 2 \end{bmatrix} + \alpha_I \begin{bmatrix} 0 \\ 1 \end{bmatrix}$$

$$y(\alpha_I) = 2(2)^2 + (2 + \alpha_I)^2 - (2)(2 + \alpha_I)$$

Using an exact line search, $\alpha_I = -1$ and $\mathbf{x}_0^T = (2, 1)$.

Step 1. $\mathbf{s}_1^T = (1, 0)$ $\mathbf{s}_2^T = (0, 1)$ $\mathbf{x}_0^T = (2, 1)$

$$j = 1 \quad \mathbf{x}_1 = \mathbf{x}_0 + \alpha_1 \mathbf{s}_1 \quad \text{or} \quad \begin{bmatrix} x_{1,1} \\ x_{2,1} \end{bmatrix} = \begin{bmatrix} 2 \\ 1 \end{bmatrix} + \alpha_I \begin{bmatrix} 1 \\ 0 \end{bmatrix}$$

$$y(\alpha_1) = 2(2 + \alpha_1)^2 + (1)^2 - (2 + \alpha_1)(1)$$

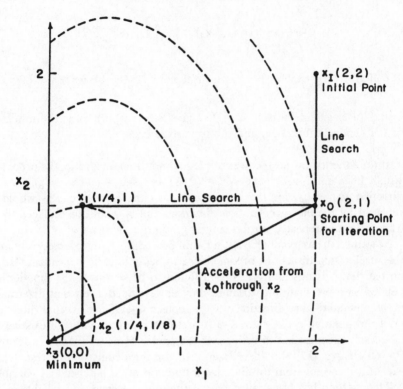

Figure 6-2.   Illustration of Powell's method for $y = 2x_1^2 + x_2^2 - x_1x_2$ from Example 6–5, after Himmelblau (8).

Using an exact line search, $\alpha_1 = -7/4$ and $x_1^T = (\frac{1}{4}, 1)$. Replace s_1 with s_2

$$j = 2 \qquad x_2 = x_1 + \alpha_2 s_2 \qquad \text{or} \begin{bmatrix} x_{1,2} \\ x_{2,2} \end{bmatrix} = \begin{bmatrix} \frac{1}{4} \\ 1 \end{bmatrix} + \alpha_2 \begin{bmatrix} 0 \\ 1 \end{bmatrix}$$

$$y(\alpha_2) = 2(\tfrac{1}{4})^2 + (1 + \alpha_2)^2 - (\tfrac{1}{4})(_1 + \alpha_2)$$

Using an exact line search, $\alpha_2 = -7/8$ and $x_2^T = (1/4, 1/8)$

Step 2. s_2 is replaced with $x_2 - x_0 = \begin{bmatrix} 1/4 \\ 1/8 \end{bmatrix} - \begin{bmatrix} 2 \\ 1 \end{bmatrix} = \begin{bmatrix} -1\frac{3}{4} \\ -7/8 \end{bmatrix}$

Step 3.   Choose α so that $y[x_2 + \alpha(x_2 - x_0)]$ is a minimum. Let

$$\mathbf{x_3} = \mathbf{x_2} + \alpha(\mathbf{x_2} - \mathbf{x_0}) = \begin{bmatrix} 1/4 \\ 1/8 \end{bmatrix} + \alpha \begin{bmatrix} -1\frac{3}{4} \\ -7/8 \end{bmatrix}$$

$$y(\alpha) = 2(1/4 - 1\tfrac{3}{4}\alpha)^2 + (1/8 - 7/8\alpha)^2 - (1/4 - 1\tfrac{3}{4}\alpha)(1/8 - 7/8\alpha)$$

Using an exact line search, $\alpha = 1/7$ and $\mathbf{x_3}^T = (0, 0)$. $\mathbf{x_3}$ is the minimum of the quadratic function, and the procedure ends.

If the function in the above example had not been quadratic, the procedure would have continued using $\mathbf{s_1}^T = (0, 1)$ and $\mathbf{s_2}^T = (-1\tfrac{3}{4}, -\tfrac{7}{8})$, i.e., the direction $(\mathbf{x_2} - \mathbf{x_0})$ for the second cycle. In the third cycle, $\mathbf{s_2}$ would be replaced by the new acceleration direction, and $\mathbf{s_1}$ would be replaced by $\mathbf{s_2}$. The cycles are repeated until a stopping criterion is met.

Powell (57) has pointed out that this procedure required modification if the acceleration directions become close to being linearly dependent. He reported that this possibility has been found to be serious if the function depended on more than five variables. Powell developed a test that determined if the new conjugate direction was to replace one of the existing directions or if the iterative cycle, steps 1–3, was to be repeated with the existing set of linearly independent directions. If the reader plans to use this procedure, Powell's paper (57) should be examined for the details of this test, which was said to be essential to minimize a function of 20 independent variables.

This method has been called one of the more efficient and reliable of the direct search methods (15). The reason is its relative simplicity and quadratic termination property. The method sectioning, which does not employ the acceleration step but just searches the coordinate axes one at a time, is not as effective and can be confounded by resolution ridges.

The conjugate gradient method gradient partan has proved to be as effective as Powell's method. It is an extension of gradient search and has the ability to locate the optimum of a function with ellipsoidal contours (quadratic termination) in a finite number of steps. The term *partan* comes from a class of search techniques that employ parallel tangents (12). These methods move in conjugate directions or, in the case of gradient partan, they move in the direction of conjugate gradients. The procedure is diagrammed in Figure 6-1, and this shows that the gradient line is perpendicular to the contour tangent. Thus, the method can begin directly from the starting point as described below.

For two variables the procedure employs two gradient searches followed by an acceleration step, as shown in Figure 6-1, for a function with elliptical contours. The acceleration line passes through the optimum. The equations for the gradient and acceleration lines for this method are:

$$\text{Gradient line: } \mathbf{x}_{k+1} = \mathbf{x}_k + \alpha \ \nabla y(\mathbf{x}_k) \qquad (6\text{–}25)$$

$$\text{Acceleration: } \mathbf{x}_{k+1} = \mathbf{x}_{k-3} + \alpha \ (\mathbf{x}_k - \mathbf{x}_{k-3}) \qquad (6\text{–}26)$$

For more than two variables the following diagram shows the sequence of gradient searches and acceleration steps required for a function with ellipsoidal contours.

Gradient Partan Algorithm for a Function with Ellipsoidal Contours

Number of Independent Variables

Start:	$\mathbf{x}_0$	2	3	4	n
Gradient:	$\mathbf{x}_0 \rightarrow \mathbf{x}_2$				
Gradient:	$\mathbf{x}_2 \rightarrow \mathbf{x}_3$	$\mathbf{x}_4 \rightarrow \mathbf{x}_5$	$\mathbf{x}_6 \rightarrow \mathbf{x}_7$	$\mathbf{x}_{2n-2} \rightarrow \mathbf{x}_{2n-1}$	
Accelerate:	$\mathbf{x}_0 \rightarrow \mathbf{x}_3 \rightarrow \mathbf{x}_4$	$\mathbf{x}_2 \rightarrow \mathbf{x}_5 \rightarrow \mathbf{x}_6$	$\mathbf{x}_4 \rightarrow \mathbf{x}_7 \rightarrow \mathbf{x}_8$	$\mathbf{x}_{2n-4} \rightarrow \mathbf{x}_{2n-1} \rightarrow \mathbf{x}_{2n}$	

To have the recursion relation shown above, it is necessary to omit a point numbered $\mathbf{x}_1$.

As shown in the above diagram for a function of n independent variables with ellipsoidal contours, a total of n gradient measurements and $(2n - 1)$ exact line searches are required to arrive at the optimum point $\mathbf{x}_{2n}$. The search begins at $\mathbf{x}_0$, and a search along the gradient line locates point $\mathbf{x}_2$. This is followed by another search along the gradient line to arrive at point $\mathbf{x}_3$. Then an acceleration step is performed from point $\mathbf{x}_0$ through $\mathbf{x}_3$ to arrive at point $\mathbf{x}_4$, the optimum of a function with elliptical contours. For n independent variables the procedure continues by repeating gradient searches and accelerations to arrive at point $\mathbf{x}_{2n}$, the optimum of a function of n independent variables having ellipsoidal contours. This procedure is illustrated in the following example for a function with three independent variables. In this case the optimum will be reached with three gradient measurements and five line searches.

EXAMPLE 6–6 (10)

Determine the minimum of the following function using gradient partan starting at the point $\mathbf{x}_0 = (2, -2, 1)$

$$y = 2x_1^2 + x_2^2 + 3x_3^2$$

Beginning with a gradient search from point x_0 to point x_2, equation (6–7) is used:

$$x = x_0 + \alpha \, \nabla y(x_0)$$

or

$$
\begin{aligned}
x_1 &= 2 + 8\alpha \\
x_2 &= -2 - 4\alpha \\
x_3 &= 1 + 6\alpha
\end{aligned}
\qquad \text{where } \nabla y =
\begin{bmatrix}
\partial y / \partial x_1 \\
\partial y / \partial x_2 \\
\partial y / \partial x_3
\end{bmatrix}
=
\begin{bmatrix}
4x_1 \\
2x_2 \\
6x_3
\end{bmatrix}
$$

Performing an exact line search along the gradient from x_0 gives:

$$y = 2(2 + 8\alpha)^2 + (-2 - 4\alpha)^2 + 3(1 + 6\alpha)^2$$

Setting $dy/d\alpha = 0$ to locate the minimum of y along the gradient line gives:

$$\frac{dy}{d\alpha} = 32(2 + 8\alpha) - 8(-2 - 4\alpha) + 36(1 + 6\alpha) = 0$$

Solving for the optimum value of α gives $\alpha^* = -0.2302$. Using α^* to compute x_2 gives $(0.1584, -1.079, -0.3810)^T$, and the gradient line at x_2 is:

$$x_1 = 0.1584 + 0.6336\alpha$$

$$x_2 = -1.079 - 2.158\alpha$$

$$x_3 = -0.3810 - 2.287\alpha$$

Performing an exact line search along the gradient gives:

$$y = 2(0.1584 + 0.6336\alpha)^2 + (-1.079 - 2.158\alpha)^2 + 3(-0.3810 - 2.287\alpha)^2$$

Setting $dy/d\alpha = 0$ and solving gives $\alpha^* = -0.2432$. Computing x_3 gives $(0.0043, -0.5543, 0.1750)^T$. Accelerating from x_0 through x_3 to locate x_4 gives:

$$x = x_0 + \alpha(x_3 - x_0)$$

or

$$x_1 = 2 - 1.996\alpha$$

$$x_2 = -2 + 1.446\alpha$$

$$x_3 = 1 - 0.8250\alpha$$

Performing a search along the acceleration line gives:

$$y = 2(2 - 1.996\alpha)^2 + (-2 + 1.446\alpha)^2 + 3(1 - 0.8250\alpha)^2$$

Setting $dy/d\alpha = 0$ and solving gives $\alpha^* = 1.1034$. Computing x_4 gives $(-0.2021, -0.4048, 0.0897)^T$.

The procedure is continued with a gradient search from x_4 to x_5 and an acceleration from x_2 through x_5 to x_6, the optimum. The following tabulates the results of these calculations and the previous ones.

		x_1	x_2	x_3	Parameter of the gradient or acceleration line
Start	x_0	2	−2	1	
Gradient					−0.2302
	x_2	0.1584	−1.079	−0.3810	
Gradient					−0.2432
	x_3	0.0043	−0.5543	0.1750	
Accelerate					1.1034
	x_4	−0.2021	−0.4048	0.0897	
Gradient					−0.2822
	x_5	0.0260	−0.1764	−0.0622	
Accelerate					1.1915
Optimum	x_6	0.0001	0.0000	−0.0001	

The parameter of the gradient line is negative showing that the procedure is moving in the direction of steep descent. The parameter of the acceleration line is greater than one, showing that the new point lies beyond the last point.

This procedure has been used successfully on numerous problems with success. However, it has been referred to as a "rich man's optimizer" by

Wilde (10). The method tends to oscillate on problems with sharp curving ridges, and numerical computation of the gradient requires more computer time and storage than some other methods. The two equations used, the gradient and acceleration lines, are simple and easy to program; and the method will find better values in each step toward the optimum.

For those interested in a detailed discussion of conjugate gradient and direction methods, the books by Fletcher (4), Gill et al. (6), Avriel (9), Himmelblau (8), Reklaitis et al. (15) and Wilde and Beightler (12) are recommended. Now, we will examine another class of methods that rely on logical algorithms to move rapidly from the starting point to one near an optimum.

Logical Methods: These procedures used algorithms based on logical concepts to find a sequence of improved values of the economic model leading to an optimum. They begin with local exploration, and then attempt to accelerate in the direction of success. Then if a failure occurs in that direction, the method repeats local exploration to find another direction of improved values of the economic model. If this fails, the algorithm's logic may then try other strategies, including a quadratic fit of the economic model (end game), to look for better values. Typically, these procedures do not require derivative measurements, and the algorithm compares the computed values of the economic model. Thus, they are sometimes called *function comparison methods.*

Two of the better known methods are pattern search (12) and the polytope or simplicial method (6). Both have been used successfully on a number of problems. Pattern search is probably the more widely used of the two procedures, and it will be discussed in more detail. The polytope method performs local explorations at the vertices of an n-dimensional generalization of an equilateral triangle and can employ an acceleration step based on these results. The details of this method and extensions are given by Gill et al. (6).

The logical algorithm of pattern search is illustrated in Figure 6-3, and it begins with short excursions from the starting point to establish a pattern of improved values of the economic model. Based on these function comparisons it accelerates in the direction established from the local explorations. If successful, the acceleration is continued. Then when a failure is encountered, i.e., a value of the economic model is less than the previous one, the pattern is said to be destroyed, and local explorations are performed to establish a new pattern of improved values of the economic model. Again, acceleration is performed in the new direction until a failure is encountered. The procedure continues in this fashion until an apparent optimum is reached. Then the step size of the local exploration is reduced, attempting to find another direction of improvement in the economic model. If this is successful, the procedure continues until another optimum is found. Reducing the step size is repeated,

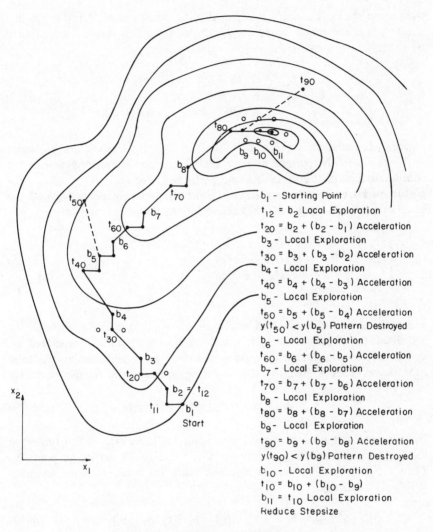

Figure 6-3. Illustration of pattern search.

and if this is unsuccessful in finding a new direction, the current point is declared a local optimum. However, a quadratic fit at the point is needed to confirm that it is an optimum rather than a saddle point.

The algorithm has two parts. One is the local exploration procedure, and the other is the acceleration step. The local explorations are performed about a base point by perturbing one variable at a time. Each time a variable is perturbed and a better value of the economic model is found, this point is used when the next variable is changed rather than returning to the original point. These are called *temporary heads,* and the first one t_{11} is computed by the following expression:

$$t_{11} = \begin{cases} \mathbf{b}_1 + \boldsymbol{\delta}_1 & \text{if } y(\mathbf{b} + \boldsymbol{\delta}_1) > y(\mathbf{b}) \\ \mathbf{b}_1 - \boldsymbol{\delta}_1 & \text{if } y(\mathbf{b} - \boldsymbol{\delta}_1) > y(\mathbf{b}) \\ \mathbf{b}_1 & \text{if } y(\mathbf{b}) > \max\,[y(\mathbf{b} + \boldsymbol{\delta}_1),\, y(\mathbf{b} - \boldsymbol{\delta}_1)] \end{cases} \tag{6-27}$$

where $\mathbf{b}_1$ is the starting point, $\boldsymbol{\delta}_1 = (\delta_1, 0, \ldots, 0)$, and the first subscript on t_{11} refers to the pattern number and the second subscript refers to the coordinate axis of the variable being perturbed. For coordinate axis x_2 the perturbations are conducted around point t_{11} to locate point t_{12}, and the equation corresponding to (6–27) above for the coordinate axis x_j is:

$$t_{1j} = \begin{cases} t_{1,j-1} + \boldsymbol{\delta}_j & \text{if } y(t_{1,j-1} + \boldsymbol{\delta}_j) > y(t_{1,j-1}) \\ t_{1,j-1} - \boldsymbol{\delta}_j & \text{if } y(t_{1,j-1} - \boldsymbol{\delta}_j) > y(t_{1,j-1}) \\ t_{1,j-1} & \text{if } y(t_{1,j-1}) > \max\,[y(t_{1,j-1} + \boldsymbol{\delta}_j),\, y(t_{1,j-1} - \boldsymbol{\delta}_j)] \end{cases} \tag{6-28}$$

When these perturbations and evaluations are performed for each of the coordinate axes, a final point $t_{1,n}$ is located. This point is designated $\mathbf{b}_2$, and an acceleration move is made in the direction established by the local exploration. This is given by the following equation and locates point t_{20}:

$$t_{20} = \mathbf{b}_1 + 2(\mathbf{b}_2 - \mathbf{b}_1) = \mathbf{b}_2 + (\mathbf{b}_2 - \mathbf{b}_1) \tag{6-29}$$

Now, point t_{20} is used as the starting point for local exploration following the same procedure using equations (6–27) and (6–28) to locate point $\mathbf{b}_3$. Then the acceleration step is repeated using the same form of equation (6–27) to locate t_{30}:

$$t_{30} = \mathbf{b}_2 + 2(\mathbf{b}_3 - \mathbf{b}_2) = \mathbf{b}_3 + (y1\mathbf{b}_3 - \mathbf{b}_2) \tag{6-30}$$

The search grows with repeated success.

At this point the two parts of the algorithm have been described in a general form. The local exploration step and the acceleration step can be readily implemented in a computer program, and one is given by Kuester and Mize (16). In addition, the following example illustrates the method on the contour diagram of a function of two independent variables shown in Figure 6-3. It shows the local exploration, acceleration, pattern destroyed and reestablished, and location of the optimum.

EXAMPLE 6–7

Locate the maximum of the function shown in Figure 6-3 using pattern search starting at the points indicated as b_1.

To begin, local explorations are performed by moving in the positive coordinate axis direction first (open circles indicate failures, and solid circle indicate successes). On the x_1 axis the largest of $y(x_1, x_2)$ is at t_{11}. Then perturbing on the x_2 axis locates the largest value of y at $t_{12} = b_2$. Effort is not wasted by evaluating y in the negative direction on the x_2 axis. Next, an acceleration is performed using equation (6–27) to locate point t_{20}. Then local exploration determines point b_3, and acceleration using equation (6–28) locates point t_{30}. Local exploration locates point b_4, and the acceleration step increases and changes directions as a result of the outcomes from the local exploration at t_{30} to reach point t_{40}. Local exploration determines point b_5, and acceleration gives point t_{50}. However, $y(t_{50}) < y(b_5)$, and the pattern is said to be destroyed. Local exploration is repeated, and b_6 is located. This sequence of local exploration is repeated determining points t_{60}, b_7, t_{70}, b_8, t_{80}, b_9, and t_{90}. However, $y(t_{90}) < y(b_9)$, and the pattern is destroyed. Local exploration is repeated to locate b_{10} and acceleration is to $t_{10,0}$. However, local exploration around $t_{10,0}$ shows that this point has the largest value of y and $t_{10,0} = b_{11}$. Then the procedure would reduce the step size to attempt to find a direction of improvement. Although this is not shown in Figure 6-3, the outcome would be that $y(b_{11})$ is still the largest value. Point b_{11} would be declared a local maximum, and a quadratic fit to the function could be performed to confirm the maximum. The pattern search steps are summarized in Figure 6-3.

Pattern search has been used successfully on a number of types of problems, and it has been found to be most effective on problems with a relatively small number of independent variables, e.g., 10 or fewer. It has the advantage of adjusting to the terrain of a function and will follow a curving ridge. However, it can be confounded by resolution ridges (12), and a quadratic fit is appropriate to avoid this weakness.

There are a number of other methods based on logical algorithms. These are discussed in some detail in the texts by Himmelblau (8), Gill et al. (6), and Reklaitis et al. (15). However, none of these are superior to the ones discussed here. Now, we will turn our attention to methods used for constrained multivariable search problems and see that the DFP and BFGS procedures are integral parts of some of these methods.

CONSTRAINED MULTIVARIABLE SEARCH METHODS

There are essentially six types of procedures to solve constrained nonlinear optimization problems. The three considered most successful are successive linear programming, successive quadratic programming, and the generalized reduce-gradient method. The other three have not proved as useful, especially on problems with a large number of variables (more than 20). These are penalty and barrier function methods, augmented Lagrangian functions, and the methods of feasible directions (or projections), which are sometimes called *methods of restricted movement.* Of these methods only successive linear programming does not require an unconstrained single or multivariable search algorithm. Also, penalty and augmented function methods have been used with successive quadratic programming. Each of these methods will be discussed in the order that they were mentioned. This will be followed by a review of studies that have evaluated the performance of the various methods.

Successive Linear Programming: This procedure was called the *method of approximate programming* (MAP) by Griffith and Stewart (18) of Shell Oil Co., who originally proposed and tested the procedure on petroleum refinery optimization. As the name implies, the method uses linear programming as a search technique. A starting point is selected, and the nonlinear economic model and constraints are linearized about this point to give a linear problem that can be solved by the Simplex Method or its extensions. The point from the linear programming solution can be used as a new point to linearize the nonlinear problem, and this can be continued until a stopping criterion is met. As shown by Reklaitis et al. (15), this procedure works without safeguards for functions that are mildly nonlinear. However, it is necessary to bound the steps taken in the iterations to ensure that the economic model improves, the values of the independent variables remain in the feasible region, and the procedure converges to the optimum. These safeguards are bounds on the independent variables specified in advance of solving the linear programming problem. The net result is that the bounds are additional constraint equations. If the bounds are set too small, the procedure will move slowly toward the optimum. If they are set too large, infeasible solutions will be generated. Consequently, logic is incorporated into computer programs to expand the bounds when they hamper rapid progress and shrink them so that the procedure may converge to a stationary point solution (1).

For successive linear programming, the general nonlinear optimization problem can be written as:

$$\text{Optimize: } y(\mathbf{x})$$

$$\begin{aligned}
\text{Subject to: } f_i(\mathbf{x}) &\leq b_i \qquad \text{for } i = 1, 2, \cdots, m \\
u_j \geq x_j &\geq 1_j \qquad \text{for } j = 1, 2, \cdots, n
\end{aligned} \qquad (6\text{-}31)$$

where upper and lower limits are shown specifically on the independent variables.

Now the economic model $y(\mathbf{x})$ and the constraints $f_i(\mathbf{x})$ can be linearized around a feasible point $\mathbf{x}_k$ to give:

$$\text{Optimize: } \sum_{j=1}^{n} c_j \, \Delta x_j = y - y(\mathbf{x}_k)$$

$$\text{(6–32)}$$

$$\text{Subject to: } \sum_{j=1}^{n} a_{ij} \, \Delta x_j \le b_i - f_i(\mathbf{x}_k) \qquad \text{for } i = 1, 2, \cdots, m$$

$$u_j - x_{jk} \ge \Delta x_j \ge 1_j - x_{jk} \qquad \text{for } j = 1, 2, \cdots, n$$

and

$$\Delta x_j = x_j - x_{jk} \qquad c_j = \frac{\partial y \, (\mathbf{x}_k)}{\partial x_j} \qquad a_{ij} = \frac{\partial f_i \, (\mathbf{x}_k)}{\partial x_j}$$

The problem is in a linear programming format in the form of equation (6–32). However, the values of Δx_j can take on either positive or negative values depending on the location of the optimum. Negative values for Δx_j are not acceptable with the Simplex Algorithm, so a change of variables was made by Griffith and Stewart (18), as follows:

$$\Delta x_j = \Delta x_j{}^+ - \Delta x_j{}^- \qquad\qquad \text{(6–33)}$$

where

$$\Delta x_j{}^+ = \begin{cases} \Delta x_j & \text{if } \Delta x_j \ge 0 \\ 0 & \text{if } \Delta x_j < 0 \end{cases}$$

$$\Delta x_j{}^- = \begin{cases} -\Delta x_j & \text{if } \Delta x_j \le 0 \\ 0 & \text{if } \Delta x_j > 0 \end{cases}$$

Substituting equation (6–33) into equation (6–32), now the linear programming problem has the form:

$$\text{Optimize: } \sum_{j=1}^{n} c_j \, \Delta x_j{}^+ - \sum_{j=1}^{n} c_j \, \Delta x_j{}^- = y - y(\mathbf{x}_k)$$

$$\text{(6–34)}$$

Subject to: $\sum\limits_{j=1}^{n} a_{ij}\,\Delta x_j^{+} - \sum\limits_{j=1}^{n} a_{ij}\,\Delta x_j^{-} \leq b_i - f_i(\mathbf{x}_k)$ for $i = 1, 2, \cdots, m$

$\Delta x_j^{+} - \Delta x_j^{-} \leq (u_j - x_{jk})$ *Control the step size*

$\Delta x_j^{+} - \Delta x_j^{-} \geq (l_j - x_{jk})$ for $j = 1, 2, \cdots, n$

The bounds on the upper and lower limits on the variables are specified by $(u_j - x_{jk})$ and $(l_j - x_{jk})$. The value of the next point for linearizing is given by $x_{jk+1} = x_{jk} + \Delta x_j^{+} - \Delta x_j^{-}$, and the procedure is started by specifying a starting point $\mathbf{x}_0 (k = 0)$.

The above equations are now a linear programming problem where the independent variables are Δx_j^{+} and Δx_j^{-}. The value of the bound u_j and l_j may affect the rate of convergence of the algorithm. The use of bounds is illustrated in the following example given by Griffith and Stewart (18).

EXAMPLE 6–8 (18)

Locate the maximum of the following constrained nonlinear optimization problem by the method of successive linear programming starting at $\mathbf{x}_0(1, 1)$, and using the bounds $(u_j - x_{jk}) = (x_{jk} - l_j) = 1$.

$$\text{Maximize:} \quad y = 2x_1 + x_2$$

$$\text{Subject to:} \quad x_1^2 + x_2^2 \leq 25$$
$$x_1^2 - x_2^2 \leq 7$$

The two constraint equations are shown in Figure 6-4 where they intersect at the maximum of the economic model, point $\mathbf{x}^*$ (4, 3).

For this problem the successive linear programming approximation is obtained using equation (6–34).

Maximize: $2\Delta x_1^{+} + \Delta x_2^{+} - 2\Delta x_1^{-} - \Delta x_2^{-} = y - (2x_{1k} + x_{2k}]$

Subject to:

$2x_{1k}\Delta x_1^{+} + 2x_{2k}\Delta x_2^{+} - 2x_{1k}\Delta x_1^{-} - 2x_{2k}\Delta x_2^{-} \leq 25 - [x_{1k}^2 + x_{2k}^2]$

$2x_{1k}\Delta x_1^{+} - 2x_{2k}\Delta x_2^{+} - 2x_{1k}\Delta x_1^{-} + 2x_{2k}\Delta x_2^{-} \leq 7 - [x_{1k}^2 - x_{2k}^2]$

$\Delta x_1^{+} \qquad\qquad - \qquad \Delta x_1^{-} \qquad\qquad\qquad \leq 1$

$\qquad\quad \Delta x_2^{+} \qquad\qquad - \qquad \Delta x_2^{-} \leq 1$

$-\Delta x_1^{+} \qquad\qquad + \qquad \Delta x_1^{-} \qquad\qquad\qquad \leq 1$

$\qquad\quad -\Delta x_2^{+} \qquad\qquad + \qquad \Delta x_2^{-} \leq 1$

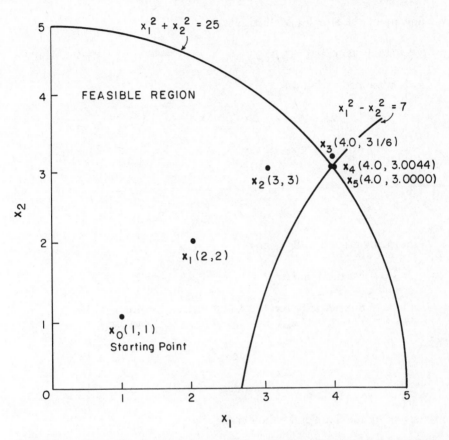

Figure 6-4.   The successive linear programming solution of Example 6–8, after Griffith and Stewart (18).

There are four variables in the above equations Δx_1^+, Δx_2^-, Δx_2^+ and Δx_2^-. Starting at point x_0 (1, 1) the above equations become:

$$\text{Maximize: } 2\Delta x_1^+ + \Delta x_2^+ - 2\Delta x_1^- - \Delta x_2^- = y - 3$$

$$\begin{aligned}
\text{Subject to: } 2\Delta x_1^+ + 2\Delta x_2^+ - 2\Delta x_1^- - 2\Delta x_2^- &\leq 23 \\
2\Delta x_1^+ - 2\Delta x_2^+ - 2\Delta x_1^- + 2\Delta x_2^- &\leq 7 \\
\Delta x_1^+ \qquad\quad - \Delta x_1^- \qquad\quad &\leq 1 \\
\Delta x_2^+ \qquad\quad - \Delta x_2^- &\leq 1 \\
-\Delta x_1^+ \qquad\quad + \Delta x_1^- \qquad\quad &\leq 1 \\
- \Delta x_2^+ \qquad\quad + \Delta x_2^- &\leq 1
\end{aligned}$$

Solving by the Simplex Method gives:

$$\Delta x_1^+ = 1 \qquad \Delta x_2^- = 0 \qquad \Delta x_2^+ = 1 \qquad \Delta x_2^- = 0$$

x_1 is computed as follows:

$$x_{1,1} = x_{1,0} + \Delta x_1^+ - \Delta x_1^- = 1 + 1 - 0 = 2$$

$$x_{2,1} = x_{2,0} + \Delta x_2^+ - \Delta x_2^- = 1 + 1 - 0 = 2$$

and

$$\mathbf{x}_1(2, 2) \qquad y(\mathbf{x}_1) = 6$$

Linearizing around $\mathbf{x}_1(2,\ 2)$ gives:

Maximize: $2\Delta x_1^+ + \Delta x_2^+ - 2\Delta x_1^- - \Delta x_2^- = y - 6$

$$
\begin{aligned}
\text{Subject to: } 4\Delta x_1^+ + 4\Delta x_2^+ - 4\Delta x_1^- - 4\Delta x_2^- &\le 17 \\
4\Delta x_1^+ - 4\Delta x_2^+ - \Delta x_1^- + 4\Delta x_2^- &\le 7 \\
\Delta x_1^+ \qquad\quad - \Delta x_1^- \qquad\quad &\le 1 \\
\Delta x_2^+ \qquad\quad - \Delta x_2^- &\le 1 \\
-\Delta x_1^+ \qquad\quad + \Delta x_1^- \qquad\quad &\le 1 \\
- \Delta x_2^+ \qquad\quad + \Delta x_2^- &\le 1
\end{aligned}
$$

Solving by the Simplex Method gives:

$$\Delta x_1^+ = 1 \qquad \Delta x_1^- = 0 \qquad \Delta x_2^+ = 1 \qquad \Delta x_2^- = 0$$

x_2 is computed as follows:

$$x_{1,2} = x_{1,1} + \Delta x_1^+ - \Delta x_1^- = 2 + 1 - 0 = 3$$

$$x_{2,2} = x_{1,2} + \Delta x_2^+ - \Delta x_2^- = 2 + 1 - 0 = 3$$

and

$$\mathbf{x}_2(3, 3) \qquad y(\mathbf{x}_2) = 9$$

Linearizing around $\mathbf{x}_2(3,\ 3)$ gives:

Maximize: $2\Delta x_1^+ + \Delta x_2^+ - 2\Delta x_1^- - \Delta x_2^- = y - 9$

Subject to:
$$6\Delta x_1^+ + 6\Delta x_2^+ - 6\Delta x_1^- - 6\Delta x_2^- \leq 7$$
$$6\Delta x_1^+ - 6\Delta x_2^+ - 6\Delta x_1^- + 6\Delta x_2^- \leq 7$$
$$\Delta x_1^+ \quad\quad - \Delta x_1^- \quad\quad \leq 1$$
$$\Delta x_2^+ \quad\quad - \Delta x_2^- \leq 1$$
$$-\Delta x_1^+ \quad\quad + \Delta x_1^- \quad\quad \leq 1$$
$$- \Delta x_2^+ \quad\quad + \Delta x_2^- \leq 1$$

Solving by the Simplex Method gives:

$$\Delta x_1^+ = 1 \qquad \Delta x_1^- = 0 \qquad \Delta x_2^+ = 1/6 \qquad \Delta x_2^- = 0$$

x_3 is computed as follows:

$$x_{1,3} = x_{1,2} + \Delta x_1^+ - \Delta x_1^- = 3 + 1 - 0 = 4$$

$$x_{2,3} = x_{2,2} + \Delta x_2^+ - \Delta x_2^- = 3 + 1/6 - 0 = 3\tfrac{1}{6}$$

and

$$x_3(4, 3\tfrac{1}{6}) \qquad y(x_3) = 11\tfrac{1}{6}$$

Linearizing around $x_3(4, 3\tfrac{1}{6})$ gives:

Maximize: $2\Delta x_1^+ + \Delta x_2^+ - 2\Delta x_1^- - \Delta x_2^- = y - 11\tfrac{1}{6}$

Subject to:
$$8\Delta x_1^+ + (19/3)\Delta x_2^+ - 8\Delta x_1^- - (19/3)\Delta x_2^- \leq -37/36$$
$$8\Delta x_1^+ - (19/3)\Delta x_2^+ - 8\Delta x_1^- + (19/3)\Delta x_2^- \leq 37/36$$
$$\Delta x_1^+ \quad\quad - \Delta x_1^- \quad\quad \leq 1$$
$$\Delta x_2^+ \quad\quad - \Delta x_2^- \leq 1$$
$$-\Delta x_1^+ \quad\quad + \Delta x_1^- \quad\quad \leq 1$$
$$- \Delta x_2^+ \quad\quad + \Delta x_2^- \leq 1$$

Solving by the Simplex Method gives:

$$\Delta x_1^+ = 0.0 \qquad \Delta x_1^- = 0.0 \qquad \Delta x_2^+ = 0.0 \qquad \Delta x_2^- = 0.1623$$

x_4 is computed as follows:

$$x_{1,4} = x_{1,3} + \Delta x_1^+ - \Delta x_1^- = 4.0 + 0.0 - 0.0 = 4.00$$

$$x_{2,4} = x_{2,3} + \Delta x_2^+ - \Delta x_2^- = 3\tfrac{1}{6} + 0.0 - 0.1623 = 3.0044$$

and

$$x_4(4.0, 3.0044) \qquad y(x_4) = 11.00$$

Linearizing around $x_4(4.0, 3.0044)$ gives:

Maximize: $2\Delta x_1^+ + \Delta x_2^+ - 2\Delta x_1^- - \Delta x_2^- = y - 11.011$

Subject to:
$$
\begin{aligned}
8.0\Delta x_1^+ + 6.0088\Delta x_2^+ &- 8.0\Delta x_1^- - 6.0088\Delta x_2^- \le -0.0264 \\
8.0\Delta x_1^+ - 6.0088\Delta x_2^+ &- 8.0\Delta x_1^- + 6.0088\Delta x_2^- \le 0.0264 \\
\Delta x_1^+ \qquad\qquad &- \Delta x_1^- \qquad\qquad \le 1 \\
\Delta x_2^+ &\qquad\qquad -\Delta x_2^- \le 1 \\
-\Delta x_1^+ \qquad\qquad &+\Delta x_1^- \qquad\qquad \le 1 \\
-\Delta x_2^+ &\qquad\qquad +\Delta x_2^- \le 1
\end{aligned}
$$

Solving the Simplex Method gives:

$$\Delta x_1^+ = 0.0 \qquad \Delta x_1^- = 0.0 \qquad \Delta x_2^+ = 0.0 \qquad \Delta x_2^- = 0.00438$$

x_5 is computed as follows:

$$x_{1,5} = x_{1,4} + \Delta x_1^+ - \Delta x_1^- = 4.0 + 0.0 - 0.0 = 4.0$$

$$x_{2,5} = x_{2,4} + \Delta x_2^+ - \Delta x_2^- = 3.0044 + 0.0 - 0.00438 = 3.0000$$

and

$$x_5 (4.0, 3.0000) \qquad y(x_5) = 11.00$$

This is the optimal solution and is the same as given by Griffith and Stewart (18).

It should be noted that point $x_3(4, 3\frac{1}{6})$ is an infeasible point and does not satisfy the first constraint equation. However, this point is sufficiently close to the optimum that the method converges to the optimum after linearizing around this point. Convergence to the optimum will not take place if bounds are not used, however.

The problem was solved without the constraints bounding the variables. Starting at point $x_0(1, 1)$ the point $x_1(8.5, 5.0)$ was found. Linearizing around $x_1(8.5, 5.0)$ and solving by the Simplex Method gave the point $x_2(0, 12.23)$. Then linearizing around $x_2(0, 12.23)$ gave a set of constraint equations that had an unbounded solution for x_3. Consequently, bounds were required on this problem to ensure convergence to a solution. Computer programs will reduce the bounds when an infeasible solution is located, and resolve the problem. This was done for the problem starting at point $x_2(3, 3)$ because point $x_3(4, 3\frac{1}{6})$ was infeasible, and the bounds were reduced by one-half each time an infeasible point was obtained. Following this procedure, the next two iterations for this problem were (3.563, 3.492) and (3.595, 3.475). Further examination showed that the method had difficulty following the first constraint to the optimum. As Himmelblau (8) points out, when constraints become active, then successive linear programming's "progress becomes quite slow." Consequently, logic is incorporated in some programs to allow the procedure to continue from an infeasible point, as was done by Griffith and Stewart in this example.

For those interested in having a successive linear programming code, Lasdon (19) reports that the most widely used and best known one, POP (Process Optimization Procedure) is available from the SHARE library (COSMIC, Bartow Hall, University of Georgia; Athens Georgia 30601). Other listings of sources of optimization codes are given by Sandgren (20) and Lasdon and Waren (22).

Large linear programming codes have been used with large simulation models in an iterative fashion to approximate the nonlinearities in these models. This approach of using linear programming successively has been successful in large plants. In most cases, this procedure has been used by companies that have many man-years of effort in the development and use of a large linear programming code for plant optimization and a corresponding amount of effort in large simulations of key process units for prediction of performance and yields. An example of this is in petroleum refining, where linear programming is used for refinery optimization. In addition, elaborate simulations and correlations have been developed for processes such as catalytic cracking, reforming, and distillation.

As discussed in Chapter 4, the results of a linear programming optimization are as accurate as the parameters in the economic model and constraint equations, c, A, and b. As shown in Figure 6-5 iterative procedures have been developed that use these programs together. The large simulation codes are used to compute the parameters used in the large linear programming code. Then the linear programming code is used to generate an optimal solution in terms of the independent variables, x, which are the process variables required by the simulation codes. This iteration procedure is continued until a stopping criterion is met. Both the linear programming code and the process simulators are very large programs, and no attempt is made to have them run at the same time. Typically, the output from the simulators is edited by a separate program to produce a data set in the form required by the linear programming code. Also, another program can be used to

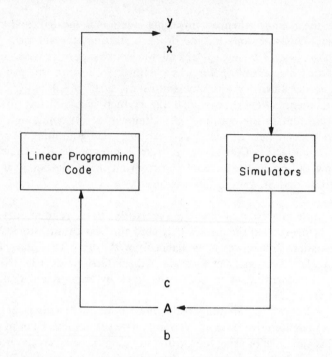

Figure 6-5. The use of process simulators with linear programming.

manipulate the output from the linear programming code into a data set for use by the simulation programs. Further descriptions of these procedures are given by Pollack and Lieder (31), for petroleum refinery optimization, and by O'Neil et al. (32), for the allocation of natural gas in large pipeline networks. SQP

Successive Quadratic Programming: Like successive linear programming, a quadratic programming problem is formed from the nonlinear programming problem and is solved iteratively until an optimum is reached. However, the iterative procedure differs from that of successive linear programming. As described by Lasdon and Waren (22), the quadratic programming solution is not accepted immediately as the next point to continue the search, but a single-variable search is performed between the old and new points to have a better and feasible point.

In quadratic programming the economic model is a quadratic function, and the constraints are all linear equations. To solve this problem the Lagrangian function is formed, and the Kuhn-Tucker conditions are applied to the Lagrangian function (23, 24, 25) to obtain a set of linear equations.

This set of linear equations can then be solved by the Simplex Method for the optimum. It turns out that artificial variables are required for part of the constraints and the slack variables can be used for the other constraints to have an initially feasible basis. Also, finding an initial basic feasible solution may be the only feasible solution (25), so the linear programming computational effort is minimal. At this point it is important to understand the solution of a quadratic programming problem, and this procedure will be described next and illustrated with an example. Then the successive quadratic programming algorithm will be described and illustrated with an example. Also, modifications of the procedure will be discussed that reduce the computational effort in numerically evaluating the Hessian matrix that must be obtained from the nonlinear programming problem.

Theoretically, using a quadratic function to approximate the nonlinear economic model of the process can be considered superior to a linear function to represent the economic model. This is part of the motivation for using quadratic programming, which can be represented by the following equations:

$$\text{Maximize: } \sum_{j=1}^{n} c_j x_j - \tfrac{1}{2} \sum_{j=1}^{n} \sum_{k=1}^{n} q_{jk} x_j x_k$$

$$(6\text{--}35)$$

$$\text{Subject to: } \sum_{j=1}^{n} a_{ij} x_j \leq b_i \qquad \text{for } i = 1, 2, \ldots, m$$

$$x_j \geq 0 \qquad \text{for } j = 1, 2, \ldots, n$$

where $q_{jk} = q_{kj}$ would be the second partial derivatives with respect to x_j and x_k of the nonlinear economic model. They would be computed numerically or analytically from the nonlinear problem given by equation (6–31). Also, c_j and a_{ij} would be computed as shown by equation (6–32) either numerically or analytically from the nonlinear problem, equation (6–31).

The quadratic programming procedure begins by adding slack variables x_{n+i} to the linear constraint equations. It will not be necessary to use x_{n+i}^2, because the problem will be solved by linear programming, and all the variables must be positive or zero. The Lagrangian function is formed as follows:

$$L(\mathbf{x}, \boldsymbol{\lambda}) = \sum_{j=1}^{n} c_j x_j - \tfrac{1}{2} \sum_{j=1}^{n} \sum_{k=1}^{n} q_{jk} x_j x_k$$

$$(6\text{--}36)$$

$$- \sum_{i=1}^{n} \lambda_i \left(\sum_{j=1}^{n} a_{ij} x_j + x_{n+i} - b_i \right)$$

Positive Lagrange multipliers are required, so a negative sign is used on the term with the constraint equations. (See equation 2–49.)

Setting the first partial derivatives of the Lagrangian function with respect to x_j and λ_i equal to zero gives the following set of $(n + m)$ linear algebraic equations:

$$c_j - \sum_{k=1}^{n} q_{jk}x_k - \sum_{i=1}^{n} a_{ij}\lambda_i \geq 0 \qquad \text{for } j = 1, 2, \ldots, n \qquad (6\text{--}38)$$

$$\sum_{j=1}^{n} a_{ij}x_j + x_{n+i} - b_i = 0 \qquad \text{for } i = 1, 2, \ldots, m \qquad (6\text{--}39)$$

The inequality form of the Kuhn-Tucker conditions equation (6–38) is used to account for $x \geq 0$. (See Hillier and Lieberman (25) and Hadley (59)). Also, the complementary slackness conditions must be satisfied, i.e., product of the slack variables x_{n+i} and the Lagrange multipliers λ_i are 0:

$$\lambda_i x_{n+i} = 0 \qquad \text{for } i = 1, 2, \ldots, m \qquad (6\text{--}40)$$

If $x_{n+i} = 0$, then the constraint is active, an equality; and $\lambda_i \neq 0$. However, if $x_{n+i} \neq 0$, then the constraint is inactive, an inequality; and $\lambda_i = 0$. For more details refer to the discussion in Chapter 2.

The equation set of (6–38) and (6–39) can be converted to a linear programming problem in the following way. Surplus variables are added to equation (6–38) as s_j, and slack variables have been added to equation (6–39) as x_{n+i}. The slack variables x_{n+i} can serve as the variables for an initially feasible basis for equations (6–39). However, artificial variables are required to have an initially feasible basis for equation (6–38). Adding artificial variables z_j with a coefficient c_j to equations (6–38) is a convenient way to start with $z_j = 1$. Also, the objective function will be to minimize the sum of the artificial variables to ensure that they will not be in the final optimal solution. As a result of these modifications, equations (6–38) and (6–39) become:

$$\text{Minimize: } \sum_{j=1}^{n} z_j \qquad (6\text{--}41)$$

$$\text{Subject to: } \sum_{k=1}^{n} q_{jk}x_k + \sum_{i=1}^{m} a_{ij}\lambda_i - s_j + c_j z_j = c_j \qquad \text{for } j = 1, 2, \cdots, n$$

$$\sum_{j=1}^{n} a_{ij}x_j + x_{n+i} = b_i \qquad \text{for } i = 1, 2, \cdots, m$$

This is now a linear programming problem that can be solved for optimal values of x and λ, the solution of the quadratic programming problem. In addition, the solution must satisfy $x \geq 0$, $\lambda \geq 0$ and $\lambda_i x_{n+i} = 0$. Consequently, the Simplex Algorithm has to be modified to avoid having both λ_i and x_{n+i} be basic variables, i.e., nonzero, to satisfy the complimentary slackness conditions (26). This may require choosing the second, best variable to enter the basis in proceeding with the Simplex Algorithm if either λ_i or x_{n+i} is in the basis and the other one is to enter.

Franklin (23) has given uniqueness and existence theorems that prove the above procedure is the solution to the quadratic programming problem and is a recommended reference for those details. At this point the method is illustrated with an example.

EXAMPLE 6–9 (25)

Using quadratic programming, determine the maximum of the following function subject to the constraints given:

$$\text{Maximize: } 5x_1 + x_2 - \tfrac{1}{2}(2x_1^2 - 2x_1x_2 - 2x_2x_1 + 2x_2^2)$$

$$\text{Subject to: } x_1 + x_2 \leq 2$$

The quadratic programming problem is constructed using equation (6–41) with $c_1 = 5$, $c_2 = 1$, $q_{11} = 2$, $q_{12} = -2$, $q_{21} = -2$, $q_{22} = 2$, $a_{11} = 1$, $a_{12} = 1$, and $b_1 = 2$.
The linear programming problem from equation (6–41) is:

$$\text{Minimize: } \quad z_1 + z_2$$

$$\text{Subject to: } \quad 2x_1 - 2x_2 + \lambda_1 - s_1 + 5z_1 = 5$$

$$-2x_1 + 2x_2 + \lambda_1 - s_2 + z_2 = 1$$

$$x_1 + x_2 + x_3 = 2$$

Eliminating z_1 and z_2 from the objective function gives the following set of equations for the application of the Simplex Method:

$1\tfrac{3}{5}x_1 - 1\tfrac{3}{5}x_2$	$-1\tfrac{1}{5}\lambda_1 + \tfrac{1}{5}s_1 + s_2$		$= C - 2$	$C = 2$
$2x_1 - 2x_2$	$+ \lambda_1 - s_1$	$+ 5z_1$	$= 5$	$z_1 = 1$
$-2x_1 + 2x_2$	$+ \lambda_1 - s_2$	$+ z_2 = 1$		$z_2 = 1$
$x_1 + x_2 + x_3$		$= 2$		$x_3 = 2$

x_2 enters the basis, z_2 leaves the basis:

$$
\begin{array}{ll}
0x_1 \qquad -\tfrac{2}{5}\lambda_1 + \tfrac{1}{5}s_1 + \tfrac{1}{5}s_2 \qquad\qquad + 4/3z_2 = C - 1\tfrac{1}{5} & C = 1\tfrac{1}{5} \\
\qquad\qquad 2\lambda_1 - \ s_1 - \ s_2 + 5z_1 + \quad z_2 = 6 & z_1 = 6/5 \\
-x_1 + x_2 \quad + \tfrac{1}{2}\lambda_1 \qquad - \tfrac{1}{2}s_2 \qquad + \ \tfrac{1}{2}z_2 = \tfrac{1}{2} & x_2 = \ \tfrac{1}{2} \\
2x_1 \quad\ + x_3 - \tfrac{1}{2}\lambda_1 \qquad + \tfrac{1}{2}s_2 \qquad - \ \tfrac{1}{2}z_2 = 1\tfrac{1}{2} & x_3 = 1\tfrac{1}{2}
\end{array}
$$

λ_1 would enter the basis, and the second constraint equation would be used for algebraic manipulations to ensure a positive right-hand side of the constraint equations, according to the Simplex Algorithm. However, this would have both λ_1 and x_3 in the basis (nonzero), and the complementary slackness conditions, $\lambda_1 x_3 = 0$, would not be satisfied. Consequently, another variable must be selected to enter the basis. This is usually the one with the next small coefficient and for this problem is x_1. Select x_1 to enter the basis, and x_3 leaves the basis:

$$
\begin{array}{ll}
\qquad -\tfrac{2}{5}\lambda_1 + \tfrac{1}{5}s_1 + \tfrac{1}{5}s_2 \qquad\qquad + \tfrac{4}{5}z_2 = C - 1\tfrac{1}{5} & C = 1\tfrac{1}{5} \\
\qquad 2\lambda_1 - \ s_1 - \ s_2 + 5z_1 + \quad z_2 = 6 & z_1 = 6/5 \\
x_2 + x_3 + \tfrac{1}{4}\lambda_1 \qquad - \tfrac{1}{4}s_2 \qquad + \tfrac{1}{4}z_2 = 1\tfrac{1}{4} & x_2 = 1\tfrac{1}{4} \\
x_1 \quad\ + x_3 - \tfrac{1}{4}\lambda_1 \qquad + \tfrac{1}{4}s_2 \qquad - \tfrac{1}{4}z_2 = \tfrac{3}{4} & x_1 = \ \tfrac{3}{4}
\end{array}
$$

λ_1 enters the basis, z_1 leaves the basis:

$$
\begin{array}{ll}
\qquad\qquad\qquad\qquad\qquad\quad z_1 + \quad\ z_2 = C - 0 & C = 0 \\
\lambda_1 - \ 1/3s_1 - \ 1/3s_2 + \ 5/3z_1 + 1/3z_2 = 3 & \lambda_1 = 3 \\
x_2 + x_3 \quad + 1/12s_1 + 1/12s_2 - 5/12z_1 - 1/6z_2 = 1/2 & x_2 = 1/2 \\
x_1 \quad\ + x_3 \quad - 1/12s_1 - 1/12s_2 + 5/12z_1 - 1/6z_2 = 3/2 & x_1 = 3/2
\end{array}
$$

The minimum has been reached. All the coefficients of the variables in the objective function are positive. Therefore, the optimal solution to this quadratic programming problem is:

$$
x_1 = 3/2 \qquad x_2 = 1/2 \qquad \lambda_1 = 3 \qquad x_4 = 0
$$

The positive Lagrange multiplier is consistent with the Kuhn-Tucker conditions, equation (2–48) since a negative sign was used in equation (6–36).

Successive quadratic programming iteratively solves a nonlinear programming problem by using a quadratic approximation to the economic model and a linear approximation to the constraint equations. As the series of quadratic programming problems is solved, these intermediate solutions generate a sequence of points that must remain in the feasible region or sufficiently close to this region to converge to the optimum. The logic used with this method is to search along the line between the new and previous point to maintain a feasible or near-feasible solution. Also, the computational effort in evaluating the Hessian matrix is significant, and quasi-Newton approximations have been used to reduce this effort. The following example illustrates successive quadratic programming for a simple problem. The discussion that follows describes modifications to the computational procedure to improve the efficiency of the method.

EXAMPLE 6–10

Solve the following problem by successive quadratic programming starting at point $x_0(0, 0)$:

$$\text{Minimize: } (x_1 - 1)^2 + (x_2 - 2)^2$$

$$\text{Subject to: } 0.104x_1^2 - 0.75x_1 + x_2 \leq 0.85$$

$$x_1 + x_2 \leq 4.0$$

The contours of the economic model and the constraint equations are shown in Figure 6-6. The nonlinear constraint equation is linearized about the point x_0, and it has the following form:

$$(0.208x_{10} - 0.75)x_1 + x_2 \leq 0.85 + 0.104x_{10}^2$$

Placing the problem in the form of equation 6–35 gives:

$$\text{Minimize: } x_1 + 4x_2 - \tfrac{1}{2}(2x_1^2 + 2x_2^2) - 5$$

$$\text{Subject to: } (0.208x_{10} - 0.75)x_1 + x_2 \leq 0.85 + 0.104x_{10}^2$$

$$x_1 + x_2 \leq 4$$

The quadratic programming problem is constructed using equation (6–41), with $c_1 = 2$, $c_2 = 4$, $q_{11} = 2$, $q_{12} = q_{21} = 0$, $q_{22} = 2$, $a_{11} = (0.208x_{10} - 0.75)$, $a_{12} = 1$, $a_{21} = 1$, $a_{22} = 1$, $b_1 = 0.85 + 0.104x_{10}$, and $b_2 = 4$:

Minimize: $z_1 + z_2$

Subject to: $2x_1 + (0.208x_{10} - 0.75)\lambda_1 + \lambda_2 - s_1 \quad + 2z_1 \qquad = 2$

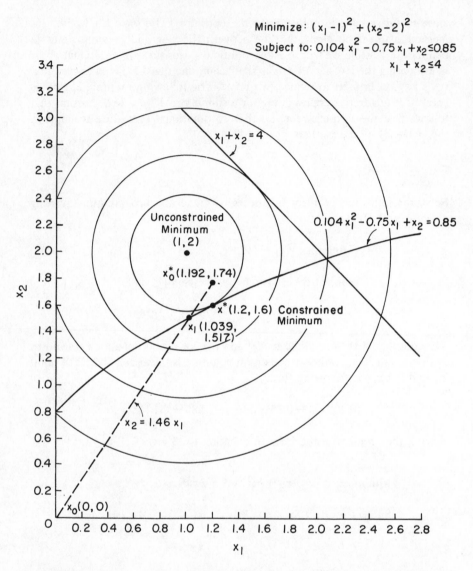

Figure 6-6. Solution of the multivariable optimization problem in Example 6–10 by successive quadratic programming.

$$2x_1 + \qquad\qquad\qquad \lambda_1 + \lambda_2 \quad -s_2 \qquad +4z_2 = 4$$

$$(0.208x_{10} - 0.75)x_1 + x_2 + x_3 \qquad\qquad\qquad = 0.85 + 0.104x_{10}{}^2$$

$$x_1 + x_2 \qquad + x_4 \qquad\qquad = 4$$

Solving the above linear programming problem by the Simplex Method with $x_0 = (0, 0)$ and ensuring that the complementary slackness conditions are met gives the following result for x_0^*:

$$x_1 = 1.192 \qquad x_2 = 1.740 \qquad \lambda_1 = 0.512$$

This point is shown on Figure 6-6, and it is outside the feasible region. Consequently, a search along the line between the starting point $x_0(0, 0)$ and $x_0^*(1.192, 1.740)$ locates feasible point $x_1(1.039, 1.517)$ on the first constraint.

The quadratic programming problem is formulated around point x_1 and solved as above. The result is $x_2(1.209, 1.608)$ with $\lambda_1 = 0.784$. Repeating the procedure by solving the quadratic programming problem at x_2 gives the value of $x_3(1.199, 1.600)$ with $\lambda_1 = 0.800$. This is sufficiently close to the optimum of the problem $x^*(1.2, 1.6)$ for the purposes of this illustration to say that a converged solution has been obtained.

The Wilson-Han-Powell method is an enhancement to successive quadratic programming where the Hessian matrix, $[q_{jk}]$, of equation (6-35) is replaced by a quasi-Newton update formula such as the BFGS algorithm in equation (6-20). Consequently, only first partial derivative information is required, and this is obtained from finite difference approximations of the Lagrangian function in equation (6-36). Also, an exact penalty function is used with the line search to adjust the step from one feasible point to the next. The theoretical basis for this algorithm is that it has a superlinear convergence rate if an exact penalty function is used with the DFP or BFGS update for the Hessian matrix of the Lagrangian function, and global convergence is obtained to a Kuhn-Tucker point when minimizing an economic model that is bounded below and contains convex functions for constraint equations. The details and proofs are given by Han (51, 52).

The problem in example 6-10 was solved with the Wilson-Han-Powell algorithm. The identity matrix was used for the Hessian matrix at the starting point $x_0(0, 0)$. The subsequent steps in the solution were $x_1(1.3803, 1.6871)$, $x_2(1.203, 1.6038)$, and $x_3(1.1988, 1.603)$, which was sufficiently close to the optimum to stop. Generally speaking, less computational effort is required with the Wilson-Han-Powell algorithm since second order partial derivatives do not have to be evaluated.

The Exxon quadratic programming code (1) uses the Wilson-Han-Powell algorithm described above, and they have added refinements to minimize the computational effort in evaluating the second partial derivatives of the Hessian matrix. This typical large quadratic programming code is described as having the following steps of basic logic. An initial starting point is selected, and the linearized constraints are constructed numerically. Then the matrix of second partial derivatives, the Hessian matrix, is evaluated either numerically or by a DFP (Davidon, Fletcher, Powell) approximation. The quadratic programming problem is solved, generating a new optimal point. Using this new point and the old point, a single-variable search is conducted for an improved, feasible solution to the nonlinear problem. This is followed by termination tests using the Kuhn-Tucker conditions, changes in step and function values, and feasibility checks. Some options included in the program include using analytical derivatives when furnished, inputting the Hessian matrix by the user or having it be a specified mutiple of the identity matrix with updating by the DFP algorithm, and having the user specify whether or not intermediate solutions are required to be feasible.

In closing this section, it should be mentioned that the Wilson-Han-Powell (WHP) method has been used successfully on computer-aided process design problems, as described by Jirapongphan et al. (42), Vanderplaats (24), and Biegler and Cuthrell (53). In some applications, the constraint equations are not converged for each step taken by the optimization algorithm, but an infeasible trajectory is followed in which the constraints are not satisfied until the optimum is reached. In the line search to adjust the step from one point to the next, an exact penalty function is used. A step length parameter is employed with the penalty function to force convergence from poor starting conditions. The size of the quadratic programming problem is reduced by substituting the linearized equality constraint equations into the quadratic economic model, leaving only the inequalities as constraints. The result can be a significant reduction in the number of the independent variables for highly constrained problems.

This technique has been included in comparisons of constrained nonlinear programming methods, which are described in a subsequent section. It has been shown to be one of the three better procedures. Now, the equally successful procedure, called the *generalized reduced gradient method,* is described.

Generalized Reduced Gradient Method: This procedure is one of a class of techniques called *reduced gradient* or *gradient projection methods* based on extending methods for linear constraints to apply to nonlinear constraints (6). They adjust the variables so the active constraints continue to be satisfied as the procedure moves from one point to another. The ideas for these algorithms were devised by Wilde and Beightler (12), using the name *constrained derivatives,* by Wolfe (29), using the name *reduced gradient method,* and extended by Abadie and Carpenter (30), using the name *generalized reduced gradient.* According to Avriel (9), if the economic model and constraints are linear, this procedure is the Simplex Method of linear programming, and if no constraints are present, it is gradient search.

The development of the procedure begins with the nonlinear optimization problem written with equality constraints. The necessary slack and surplus variables have been added as x_s or $x_s{}^2$ to any inquality constraints, and the problem is:

$$\text{Optimize: } y(x) \tag{6-42}$$

$$\text{Subject to: } f_i(\mathbf{x}) = 0 \qquad \text{for } i = 1, 2, \cdots, m$$

Again, there are m constraint equations and n independent variables with $n > m$. Also, although not specifically written above, the variables can have upper and lower limits, and the procedure as described here will ensure that all variables are positive or zero.

The idea of generalized reduced gradient is to convert the constrained problem into an unconstrained one by using direct substitution. If direct substitution were possible, it would reduce the number of independent variables to $(n - m)$ and eliminate the constraint equations. However, with nonlinear constraint equations, it is not feasible to solve the m constraint equations for m of the independent variables in terms of the remaining $(n = m)$ variables and then to substitute to these equations into the economic model. Therefore, the procedures of constrained variation and Lagrange Multipliers in the classical theory of maxima and minima are required. There, the economic model and constraint equations were expanded in a Taylor series, and only the first-order terms were retained. With these linear equations, then the constraint equations could be used to reduce the number of independent variables. This led to the Jacobian determinants of the method of constrained variation and the definition of the Lagrange Multiplier being a ratio of partial derivatives, as was shown in Chapter 2.

The development of the generalized reduced gradient method follows that of constrained variation. The case of two independent variables and one constraint equation will be used to demonstrate the concept, and then the general case will be described. Consider the following problem:

$$\text{Optimize: } y(x_1, x_2) \tag{6-43}$$

$$\text{Subject to: } f(x_1, x_2) = 0$$

Expanding the above in a Taylor series about a feasible point $\mathbf{x}_k(x_{1k}, x_{2k})$ gives:

$$y(\mathbf{x}) = y(\mathbf{x}_k) + \frac{\partial y\ (\mathbf{x}_k)}{\partial x_1}(x_1 - x_{1k}) + \frac{\partial y\ (\mathbf{x}_k)}{\partial x_2}(x_2 - x_{2k}) \tag{6-44a}$$

$$0 = f(\mathbf{x}_k) + \frac{\partial f\ (\mathbf{x}_k)}{\partial x_1}(x_1 - x_{1k}) + \frac{\partial f\ (\mathbf{x}_k)}{\partial x_2}(x_2 - x_{2k}) \tag{6-44b}$$

Substituting equation (6–44b) into equation (6–44a) to eliminate x_2 gives, after some rearrangement:

$$y(x_1) = y(\mathbf{x}_k) + \left(\frac{\partial y}{\partial x_2}(\mathbf{x}_k)\right)\left(\frac{\partial f}{\partial x_2}(\mathbf{x}_k)\right)^{-1} f(\mathbf{x}_k)$$

$$+ \left(\frac{\partial f}{\partial x_2}(\mathbf{x}_k)\right)^{-1} \left[\frac{\partial y}{\partial x_1}(\mathbf{x}_k)\frac{\partial f}{\partial x_2}(\mathbf{x}_k) - \frac{\partial y}{\partial x_1}(\mathbf{x}_k)\frac{\partial f}{\partial x_2}(\mathbf{x}_k)\right](x_1 - x_{1k}) \quad (6\text{–}45)$$

In the equation (6–45) the first two terms are known constants being evaluated at point $\mathbf{x}_k$, and the coefficient of $(x_1 - x_{1k})$ is also a known constant. Thus, to compute the stationary point for this equation, $dy_1/dx_1 = 0$; and the result is the same as for constrained variation, equation (2–18), which is the term in the brackets of equation (6–45) that is solved together with the constraint equation for the stationary point. However, the term in the bracket also can be viewed as giving the direction to move away from $\mathbf{x}_k$ to obtain improved values of the economic model and satisfy the constraint equation.

The generalized reduced gradient method uses the same approach as described for two independent variables, which is to find an improved direction for the economic model and also to satisfy the constraint equations. This leads to an expression for the reduced gradient from equation (6–42). To develop this method the independent variables are separated into basic and nonbasic ones. There are m basic variables $\mathbf{x}_b$, and $(n - m)$ nonbasic variables $\mathbf{x}_{nb}$. In theory the m constraint equations could be solved for the m basic variables in terms of the $(n - m)$ nonbasic variables, i.e.:

$$f_i(\mathbf{x}) = f_i(\mathbf{x}_b, \mathbf{x}_{nb}) = 0 \qquad \text{for } i = 1, 2, \cdots, m \qquad (6\text{–}46)$$

Indicating the solution of $\mathbf{x}_b$ in terms of $\mathbf{x}_{nb}$ from equation (6–46) gives:

$$x_{i,\, b} = \tilde{f}_i(\mathbf{x}_{nb}) \qquad \text{for } i = 1, 2, \cdots, m \qquad (6\text{–}47)$$

The names *basic* and *nonbasic* variables are from linear programming. In linear programming the basic variables are all positive, and the nonbasic variables are all zero. However in nonlinear programming, the nonbasic variables are used to compute the values of the basic variables and are manipulated to obtain the optimum of the economic model.

The economic model can be thought of as a function of the nonbasic variables only, that is, if the constraint equations (6–47) are used to eliminate the basic variables, i.e.:

$$y(\mathbf{x}) = y(\mathbf{x}_b, \mathbf{x}_{nb}) = y[\tilde{\mathbf{f}}(\mathbf{x}_{nb}), \mathbf{x}_{nb}] = Y(\mathbf{x}_{nb}) \qquad (6\text{–}48)$$

Expanding the above equation in a Taylor Series about $\mathbf{x}_k$, and including only the first-order terms, gives:

$$\sum_{j=1}^{m} \frac{\partial y}{\partial x_j}(\mathbf{x}_k) \, dx_{j,\,b} + \sum_{j=m+1}^{n} \frac{\partial y}{\partial x_j}(\mathbf{x}_k) \, dx_{j,\,nb}$$

$$= \sum_{j=m+1}^{n} \frac{\partial Y}{\partial x_j}(\mathbf{x}_k) \, dx_{j,\,nb} \qquad (6\text{-}49)$$

In matrix notation, equation (6–49) can be written as:

$$\nabla^T Y(\mathbf{x}_k) \, d\mathbf{x}_{nb} = \nabla^T y_b(\mathbf{x}_k) \, d\mathbf{x}_b + \nabla^T y_{nb}(\mathbf{x}_k) \, d\mathbf{x}_{nb} \qquad (6\text{-}50)$$

This equation is comparable to equation 6–44a).

A Taylor Series expansion of the constraint equations (6–46) gives an equation that can be substituted into equation (6–50) to eliminate the basic variables:

$$\sum_{j=1}^{m} \frac{\partial f_i}{\partial x_j}(\mathbf{x}_k) \, dx_{j,\,b} + \sum_{j=m+1}^{n} \frac{\partial f_i}{\partial x_j}(\mathbf{x}_k) \, dx_{j,\,nb} = 0$$

$$\text{for } i = 1, 2, \cdots, m \qquad (6\text{-}51)$$

or in matrix form equation (6–51) is:

$$
\begin{bmatrix}
\dfrac{\partial f_1(\mathbf{x}_k)}{\partial x_1} & .. & \dfrac{\partial f_1(\mathbf{x}_k)}{\partial x_1} \\
\vdots & & \vdots \\
\dfrac{\partial f_m(\mathbf{x}_k)}{\partial x_1} & .. & \dfrac{\partial f_m(\mathbf{x}_k)}{\partial x_m}
\end{bmatrix}
\begin{bmatrix}
dx_{lb} \\
\vdots \\
dx_{mb}
\end{bmatrix}
+
\begin{bmatrix}
\dfrac{\partial f_1}{\partial x_{m+1}}(\mathbf{x}_k) & \cdots & \dfrac{\partial f_1}{\partial x_n}(\mathbf{x}_k) \\
\vdots & & \vdots \\
\dfrac{\partial f_m}{\partial x_{m+1}}(\mathbf{x}_k) & \cdots & \dfrac{\partial f_m}{\partial x_n}(\mathbf{x}_k)
\end{bmatrix}
\begin{bmatrix}
dx_{m+1} \\
\vdots \\
dx_n
\end{bmatrix}
= 0
$$

$$(6\text{-}52)$$

The following equation defines $\mathbf{B}_b$ as the matrix of the first partial derivatives of f_i associated with the basic variables and B_{nb} as the matrix associated with the nonbasic variables, i.e.:

$$\mathbf{B}_b \, d\mathbf{x}_b + \mathbf{B}_{nb} \, d\mathbf{x}_{nb} = 0 \qquad (6\text{-}53)$$

This is a convenient form of equation (6–52) that can be used to eliminate $d\mathbf{x}_b$ from equation (6–50). Solving equation (6–53) for $d\mathbf{x}_b$ gives:

$$d\mathbf{x}_b = -\mathbf{B}_b^{-1} \mathbf{B}_{nb} \, d\mathbf{x}_{nb} \qquad (6\text{-}54)$$

Substituting equation (6–54) into equation (6–50) gives:

$$\nabla^T Y(\mathbf{x}_k) \, d\mathbf{x}_{nb} = - \nabla^T y_b (\mathbf{x}_k) \, \mathbf{B}_b^{-1} \, \mathbf{B}_{nb} \, d\mathbf{x}_{nb} + \nabla^T y_{nb} (\mathbf{x}_k) \, d\mathbf{x}_{nb} \quad (6–55)$$

Eliminating $d\mathbf{x}_{nb}$ fom equation (6–55), the equation for the reduced gradient $\nabla Y(\mathbf{x}_k)$ is obtained:

$$\nabla^T Y (\mathbf{x}_k) = \nabla^T y_{nb} (\mathbf{x}_k) - \nabla^T y_b (\mathbf{x}_k) \, \mathbf{B}_b^{-1} \, \mathbf{B}_{nb} \quad (6–57)$$

Knowing the values of the first partial derivatives of the economic model and constraint equations at a feasible point, we can compute the reduced gradient by equation (6–57). This will satisfy the economic model and the constraint equations. The generalized reduced gradient method uses the reduced gradient to locate better values of the economic model in the same way unconstrained gradient search was used, i.e.:

$$\mathbf{x}_{nb} = \mathbf{x}_{k, \, nb} + \alpha \, \nabla Y (\mathbf{x}_k) \quad (6–58)$$

where α is the parameter of the line along the reduced gradient. A line search on α is used to locate the optimum of $Y(\mathbf{x}_{nb})$ along the reduced gradient line from $\mathbf{x}_k$.

In taking trial steps as α is varied along the generalized reduced gradient line, the matrices $\mathbf{B}_b$ and $\mathbf{B}_{nb}$ must be evaluated along with the gradients $\nabla y_b (\mathbf{x}_b)$ and $\nabla y_{nb} (\mathbf{x}_k)$. This requires knowing both $\mathbf{x}_{nb}$ and $\mathbf{x}_b$ at each step. The values of $\mathbf{x}_{nb}$ are obtained from equation (6–58). However, equation (6–46) must be solved for $\mathbf{x}_b$, and frequently this must be done numerically using the Newton-Raphson method. As pointed out by Reklaitis et al. (15), most of the computational effort can be involved in using the Newton-Raphson method to evaluate feasible values of the basic variables once the nonbasic variables have been computed from equation (6–58). The Newton-Raphson algorithm in terms of the nomenclature for this procedure is given by the following equation:

$$\mathbf{x}_{i+1, \, b} = \mathbf{x}_{i, \, b} - \mathbf{B}_b^{-1} \, \mathbf{f}(\mathbf{x}_{i, \, b}, \mathbf{x}_{nb}) \quad (6–59)$$

where the values of the roots of the constraint equations (6–46) are being sought for $\mathbf{x}_b$, $\mathbf{x}_{nb}$ having been computed from equation (6–58). Thus, the derivatives computed for the generalized reduced gradient's $\mathbf{B}_b$ matrix can be used in the Newton-Raphson root-seeking procedure also.

The following example illustrates the generalized reduced gradient algorithm. It is a modification and extension of an example given by Reklaitis et al. (15).

EXAMPLE 6–11 (15)

Solve the following problem by the generalized reduced gradient method starting at point $x_0(0, 0)$. The constrained minimum is located at $(1.2, 1.6)$ as shown in Figure 6–7:

$$\text{Minimize:} \quad -2x_1 - 4x_2 + x_1^2 + x_2^2 + 5$$

$$\text{Subject to:} \quad -x_1 + 2x_2 \leq 2$$

$$x_1 + x_2 \leq 4$$

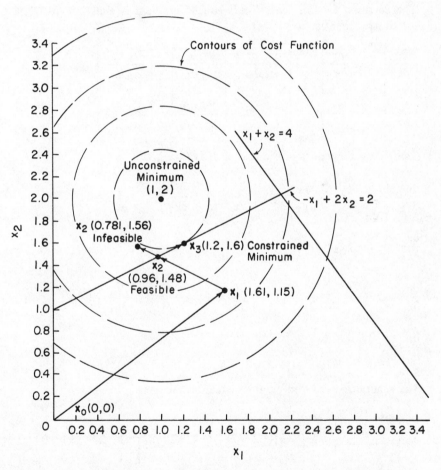

Figure 6-7. Solution of the multivariable optimization problem in Example 6–11 by the generalized reduced gradient method.

Solution: The problem is placed in the generalized reduced gradient format, equation (6–42):

$$\text{Minimize:} \quad y = -2x_1 - 4x_2 + x_1^2 + x_2^2 + 5$$

$$\text{Subject to:} \quad f_1 = -x_1 + 2x_2 + x_3 \qquad -2 = 0$$

$$f_2 = \quad x_1 + x_2 \qquad + x_4 - 4 = 0$$

where x_3 and x_4 have been added as slack variables. To begin, x_1 and x_2 are selected to be basic variables, and x_3 and x_4 to be nonbasic variables. The equation for the generalized reduced gradient is equation (6–57) and for this problem is:

$$
\begin{bmatrix} \dfrac{\partial Y}{\partial x_3} \\[2ex] \dfrac{\partial Y}{\partial x_4} \end{bmatrix}^T
=
\begin{bmatrix} \dfrac{\partial y}{\partial x_3} \\[2ex] \dfrac{\partial y}{\partial x_4} \end{bmatrix}^T
-
\begin{bmatrix} \dfrac{\partial y}{\partial x_1} & \dfrac{\partial y}{\partial x_2} \end{bmatrix}
\begin{bmatrix} \dfrac{\partial f_1}{\partial x_1} & \dfrac{\partial f_1}{\partial x_2} \\[2ex] \dfrac{\partial f_2}{\partial x_1} & \dfrac{\partial f_2}{\partial x_2} \end{bmatrix}^{-1}
\begin{bmatrix} \dfrac{\partial f_1}{\partial x_3} & \dfrac{\partial f_1}{\partial x_4} \\[2ex] \dfrac{\partial f_2}{\partial x_3} & \dfrac{\partial f_2}{\partial x_4} \end{bmatrix}
$$

Computing the values of the partial derivative gives:

$$\frac{\partial y}{\partial x_1} = -2 + 2x_1 \qquad \frac{\partial f_1}{\partial x_1} = -1 \qquad \frac{\partial f_1}{\partial x_2} = 2 \qquad \frac{\partial f_1}{\partial x_3} = 1 \qquad \frac{\partial f_1}{\partial x_4} = 0$$

$$\frac{\partial y}{\partial x_2} = -4 + 2x_2$$

$$\frac{\partial y}{\partial x_3} = 0 \qquad \frac{\partial f_2}{\partial x_1} = 1 \qquad \frac{\partial f_2}{\partial x_2} = 1 \qquad \frac{\partial f_2}{\partial x_3} = 0 \qquad \frac{\partial f_2}{\partial x_4} = 1$$

$$\frac{\partial y}{\partial x_4} = 0$$

The generalized reduced gradient equation becomes:

$$
\begin{bmatrix} \dfrac{\partial Y}{\partial x_3} \\[2ex] \dfrac{\partial Y}{\partial x_4} \end{bmatrix}^T
=
\begin{bmatrix} \dfrac{\partial y}{\partial x_3} \\[2ex] \dfrac{\partial y}{\partial x_4} \end{bmatrix}^T
- [(-2 + 2x_1)(-4 + 2x_2)]
\begin{bmatrix} -1 & 2 \\ 1 & 1 \end{bmatrix}^{-1}
\begin{bmatrix} 1 & 0 \\ 0 & 1 \end{bmatrix}
$$

where

$$\mathbf{B}_b^{-1} = \begin{bmatrix} -1 & 2 \\ 1 & 1 \end{bmatrix}^{-1} = \begin{bmatrix} -1/3 & 2/3 \\ 1/3 & 1/3 \end{bmatrix} \quad \mathbf{B}_{nb} = \begin{bmatrix} 1 & 0 \\ 0 & 1 \end{bmatrix}$$

The equation for the generalized reduced gradient through $\mathbf{x}_0$ (0, 0) is:

$$\begin{bmatrix} \dfrac{\partial Y}{\partial x_3} \\[2mm] \dfrac{\partial Y}{\partial x_4} \end{bmatrix} = \begin{bmatrix} 0 \\ 0 \end{bmatrix}^T - [-2 - 4] \begin{bmatrix} -1/3 & 2/3 \\ 1/3 & 1/3 \end{bmatrix} \begin{bmatrix} 1 & 0 \\ 0 & 1 \end{bmatrix} = \begin{bmatrix} 2/3 \\ 8/3 \end{bmatrix}$$

The generalized reduced gradient line through starting point $\mathbf{x}_0$ (0, 0, 2, 4) is given by equation (6–58) and for this example is:

$$x_3 = 2 + 2/3 \, \alpha$$

$$x_4 = 4 + 8/3 \, \alpha$$

A line search is required. The equations for x_1 and x_2 are needed in terms of x_3 and x_4 to be able to evaluate $dy/d\alpha$, because $y = y(x_1, x_2)$. Solving the constraint equations for x_1 and x_2 in terms of x_3 and x_4 gives:

$$x_2 = -1/3 \, (x_3 + x_4) + 2$$

$$x_1 = 1/3 \, (x_3 - 2x_4) + 2$$

Substituting to have x_1 and x_2 in terms of α gives:

$$x_2 = -1/3 \, (2 + 2/3 \, \alpha + 4 + 8/3 \, \alpha) + 2 = -10/9 \, \alpha$$

$$x_1 = 1/3 \, [2 + 2/3 \, \alpha - 2(4 + 8/3 \, \alpha)] + 2 = -14/9 \, \alpha$$

Substituting into y gives:

$$y = -2 \, (-14/9)\alpha - 4(-10/9)\alpha + (-14/9 \, \alpha)^2 + (-10/9 \, \alpha)^2 + 5$$

$$y = 68/9 \, \alpha + 296/81 \, \alpha^2 + 5$$

Locating the minimum along the reduced gradient line:

$$\frac{dy}{d\alpha} = \frac{68}{9} + \frac{2(296)}{81}\alpha = 0$$

$$\alpha = -153/148$$

Solving for x_1, x_2, x_3, and x_4 gives:

$$x_1 = 1.608 \qquad x_3 = 1.311$$

$$x_2 = 1.149 \qquad x_4 = 1.243$$

The location of point x_1 (1.608, 1.149, 1.311, 1.243) is shown in Figure 6-7. Also, the constraint equations are satisfied. Now, repeating the search starting at x_1 gives the following equation for the reduced gradient:

$$\begin{bmatrix} \dfrac{\partial Y}{\partial x_3} \\[2ex] \dfrac{\partial Y}{\partial x_4} \end{bmatrix}^T = \begin{bmatrix} 0 \\ 0 \end{bmatrix}^T - [[-2 + 2(1.608)], [-4 + 2(1.149)]] \begin{bmatrix} -1/3 & 2/3 \\ 1/3 & 1/3 \end{bmatrix} \begin{bmatrix} 1 & 0 \\ 0 & 1 \end{bmatrix}$$

$$\begin{bmatrix} \dfrac{\partial Y}{\partial x_3} \\[2ex] \dfrac{\partial Y}{\partial x_4} \end{bmatrix}^T = \begin{bmatrix} 0.973 \\ -0.243 \end{bmatrix}$$

The equations for x_1, x_2, x_3, and x_4, in terms of the parameter of the reduced gradient line, are now computed as:

$$x_3 = 1.311 + 0.973\alpha$$

$$x_4 = 1.243 - 0.243\alpha$$

$$x_1 = 1.61 + 0.486\alpha$$

$$x_2 = 1.149 - 0.243\alpha$$

Using the above equations, we locate the minimum along the reduced gradient line by an exact line search:

$$y = -2(1.61 + 0.486\alpha) - 4(1.149 - 0.243\alpha) + (1.61 + 0.486\alpha)^2$$
$$+ (1.149 - 0.243\alpha)^2 + 5$$

Setting $dy/d\alpha$ equal to 0 solving for α gives:

$$\alpha = -1.705$$

With this value of α, the values for x_1, x_2, x_3, and x_4 are:

$$x_1 = \quad 0.781$$

$$x_2 = \quad 1.563$$

$$x_3 = -0.348$$

$$x_4 = \quad 1.657$$

The point $x_2(0.781, 1.563, -0.348, 1.657)$ is an infeasible point, as shown in Figure 6-7. The first constraint is violated ($x_3 = -0.348$). This constraint is active, an equality; and the value of α has to be reduced to have the slack variable x_3 be equal to zero, i.e.:

$$0 = 1.311 + 0.973\alpha$$

or

$$\alpha = -1.347$$

Recalculating x_1, x_2, and x_4 for $\alpha = -1.347$ gives:

$$x_1 = 0.955$$

$$x_2 = 1.476$$

$$x_4 = 1.57$$

and the point to continue the next reduced gradient search is $x_2 = (0.955, 1.476, 0, 0.157)$.

Now $\partial f_1/\partial x_3 = 0$ in the reduced gradient equation. The reduced gradient equation at x_2 becomes:

$$\begin{bmatrix} \dfrac{\partial Y}{\partial x_3} \\[3mm] \dfrac{\partial Y}{\partial x_4} \end{bmatrix}^{T} = \begin{bmatrix} 0 \\ 0 \end{bmatrix}^{T} - [[-2 + 2(0.955)], \; [-4 + 2(1.476)]] \begin{bmatrix} -1/3 & 2/3 \\ 1/3 & 1/3 \end{bmatrix} \begin{bmatrix} 0 & 0 \\ 0 & 1 \end{bmatrix}$$

Solving gives:

$$\frac{\partial Y}{\partial x_3} = 0$$

$$\frac{\partial Y}{\partial x_4} = 0.409$$

The reduced gradient line is determined as was done previously:

$$x_4 = 1.57 + \alpha(0.409)$$

$$x_3 = 0$$

$$x_1 = 0.953 - 0.273\alpha$$

$$x_2 = 1.477 - 0.136\alpha$$

In this case the reduced gradient line search will be along the first constraint, for it is now an equality constraint ($x_3 = 0$).

Solving for the optimal value of α gives:

$$y = -2(0.953 - 0.273\alpha) - 4(1.477 - 0.136\alpha) + (0.953 - 0.273\alpha)^2 \\ + (1.477 - 0.136\alpha)^2 + 5$$

Setting $dy/d\alpha = 0$ gives $\alpha = -0.890$. Then solving for x_1, x_2, and x_4 gives:

$$x_4 = 1.57 - 0.890(0.409) = 1.20$$

$$x_1 = 0.953 - 0.273(-0.890) = 1.20$$

$$x_2 = 1.477 - 0.136(-0.890) = 1.60$$

The point x_3 (1.20, 1.60, 0, 1.20) from the reduced gradient search is the minimum of the function, as shown in Figure 6-7.

A summary of the steps is as follows:

$x_0 = (0, 0, 2, 4)$

$x_1 = (1.608, 1.149, 1.311, 1.243)$

$x_2 = (0.781, 1.563, -0.348, 1.657)$ infeasible

$x_2 = (0.955, 1.476, 0, 1.57)$ reducing α to have $x_3 = 0$

$x_3 = (1.2, 1.6, 0, 1.2)$

The point x_3 (1.20, 1.60, 0, 1.20) is the minimum of the function, as shown in Figure 6-7.

The texts by Reklaitis et al. (15), Himmelblau (8), and Avriel (9) are recommended for information about additional theoretical and computational details for this method. These include procedures to maintain feasibility, i.e., the GRG, GRGS, and GRGC versions, stopping criteria, relation to Lagrange Multipliers, treatment of bounds and inequalities, approximate Newton-Raphson computations, and use of numerical derivatives, among others.

In the first comprehensive comparison of nonlinear programming codes, which was conducted by Colville (21), the generalized reduced gradient method ranked best among 15 codes from industrial firms and universities in this country and Europe. This algorithm has been a consistently successful performer in computer programs implementing it to solve industrial problems. Lasdon (2) reported that he has a GRG code available for distribution (Professor L. S. Lasdon, School of Business Administration, University of Texas, Austin, Texas 78712), and the article by Waren and Lasdon lists several other sources of GRG codes.

Penalty, Barrier, and Augmented Lagrangian Functions: These methods convert the constrained optimization problem into an unconstrained one. The idea is to modify the economic model by adding the constraints in such a manner as to have the optimum be located and the constraints be satisfied. Several forms for the function of the constraints can be used. These create a penalty to the economic model if the constraints are not satisfied or form a barrier to force the constraints to be satisfied, as the unconstrained search method moves from the starting point to the optimum. This approach is related to the method of Lagrange Multipliers, which is a procedure that modifies the economic model with the constraint equations to have an unconstrained problem. Also, the Lagrangian function can be used with an unconstrained search technique to locate the optimum and satisfy the constraints. In addition, the augmented Lagrangian function combines a penalty function with the Lagrangian function to alleviate computational difficulties associated with boundaries formed by equality constraints when the Lagrangian function is used alone.

These penalty-function-type procedures predate the previously discussed methods and have been supplanted by them. They have proved successful on relatively small problems, but the newer techniques of successive linear and quadratic programming and generalized reduced gradient were required for larger, industrial-scale problems. However, the newer techniques have incorporated these procedures on occasions to ensure a positive definite Hessian matrix and to combine the equality constraints with the profit function, which then leaves only the inequalities as constraints. The following paragraphs will review and illustrate these methods, because they are used in optimization codes and as additions to the newer methods. More detail is given in the texts by Avriel (9), Reklaitis et al. (15), and Gill et al. (6) and in the review by Sargent (33).

The penalty function concept combines two ideas. The first one is the conversion of the constrained optimization problem into an unconstrained problem, and the second is to have this unconstrained problem's solution be one that forces the constraints to be satisfied. The constraints are added to the economic model in a way to penalize movement that does not approach the optimum of the economic model and also satisfy the constraint equations. The optimization problem can be written with equality and inequality constraints as:

Minimize: $y(\mathbf{x})$

$$\text{Subject to: } f_i(\mathbf{x}) = 0 \qquad \text{for } i = 1, 2, \cdots, h \qquad (6\text{--}60)$$

$$f_i(\mathbf{x}) \geq 0 \qquad \text{for } i = h + 1, \cdots, m$$

By combining the economic model and constraint equations, we can form a penalty function as follows:

$$P(\mathbf{x}, r) = y(\mathbf{x}) + F[r, \mathbf{f}(\mathbf{x})] \qquad (6\text{--}61)$$

where the term $F[r, \mathbf{f}(\mathbf{x})]$ is a function notation that includes the constraint equations and a penalty parameter r as variables.

Various forms of this function F have been suggested and used with various degrees of success. Some of these are given in Table 6-1. Referring to the

Table 6-1. Some Forms for the Function F used to Construct the Penalty Function (9, 15, 26, 35)

Interior penalty function forms for inequality constraints (require feasible points and also are called barrier functions), $f_i(\mathbf{x}) \geq 0$

$$r/f_i(\mathbf{x}) \qquad\qquad\qquad r/[f_i(\mathbf{x})]^2$$

$$r\,\ln[f_i(\mathbf{x})] \qquad\qquad\qquad r\,|f_i(\mathbf{x})|\text{if } f_i(\mathbf{x}) < 0, \text{ otherwise } 0$$

Exterior penalty function forms for equality constraints, $f_i(\mathbf{x}) = 0$

$$|f_i(\mathbf{x})|/r \qquad\qquad\qquad [f_i(\mathbf{x})]^2/r$$

$$[f_i(\mathbf{x})]^{2M}/r \ (M \text{ a positive integer}) \qquad\qquad [f_i(\mathbf{x})]^2/r^{1/2}$$

Exterior penalty function forms for inequality constraints (feasible points are not required)

$$r[f_i(\mathbf{x})]^2 \text{ if } f_i(\mathbf{x}) < 0, \text{ otherwise } 0$$

Constrain x_j on: $1_j \leq x_j \leq u_j$

$$r\left[\frac{2x_j - (1_j + u_j)}{u_j - 1_j}\right]^{2M} \ (M \text{ a positive integer})$$

An augmented Lagrangian function

$$M(\mathbf{x}, \lambda, r) = y(\mathbf{x}) + \sum_{i=1}^{h} \lambda_i f_i(\mathbf{x}) + r \sum_{i=h+1}^{m} [f_i(\mathbf{x})]^2$$

table, we see that these functions are of two types, interior and exterior penalty functions. The interior penalty function requires a feasible starting point, and each step toward the optimum is a feasible point. An example of an interior penalty function with an economic model subject to inequality constraints is:

$$\text{Minimize: } P(\mathbf{x}, r) = y(\mathbf{x}) = r \sum_{i=h+1}^{m} 1/[f_i(\mathbf{x})]^2 \qquad (6\text{--}62)$$

Interior penalty functions are applicable only to inequality constraints, and the term in equation (6–62) with the constraints will increase as feasible points approach the boundary with the infeasible region. Consequently, the function $P(\mathbf{x}, r)$ will appear to encounter a barrier at the boundary of the feasible region. Therefore, interior penalty functions are called *barrier functions* also. The other forms of the interior penalty function shown in Table 6-1 can be used equally well as the one used for illustration in equation (6–22).

The parameter r in equation (6–62) and Table 6-1 is used to ensure convergence to the optimum and have the constraint equation be satisfied. Initially, it has a relatively large value when the search is first initiated. Then, the search is repeated with successively smaller values of r to ensure that the penalty term goes to 0, and at the optimum $P(\mathbf{x}, r \to 0) = y(\mathbf{x})$. This procedure will be illustrated subsequently. The value of r can be selected by trial and error, and normally a satisfactory starting value will be between 0.5 and 50, according to Walsh (26). Also, Walsh (26) reported a formula to compute the value of r, which involves evaluating the Jacobian matrix of the economic model and the Jacobian and Hessian matrices of the F function at the starting point.

Exterior penalty function forms start at a feasible point, and they can continue toward the optimum, even though infeasible points are generated. An example of an exterior penalty function is:

$$\text{Minimize: } P(\mathbf{x}, r) = y(\mathbf{x}) + r^{-1/2} \sum_{i=1}^{h} [f_i(\mathbf{x})]^2 + r \sum_{i=h+1}^{m} [f_i(\mathbf{x})]^2 \qquad (6\text{–}63)$$

In this form infeasible points may be generated as the unconstrained search method moves. However, if convergence is required using the parameter r, a feasible and optimal solution will be obtained.

Exterior penalty functions used for equality constraints can be combined with interior penalty functions for inequality constraints to have what is referred to as *mixed interior-exterior penalty functions*. The one used successfully by Bracken and McCormick (36) has the form:

$$P(\mathbf{x}, r) = y(\mathbf{x}) + r^{-1/2} \sum_{i=1}^{h} [f_i(\mathbf{x})]^2 + r \sum_{i=h+1}^{m} [f_i(\mathbf{x})]^{-1} \qquad (6\text{–}64)$$

The following example will illustrate that the penalty parameter r must go to zero to arrive at the optimal solution. After this example, the results of Bracken and McCormick (36) will be summarized to illustrate the procedure of using an unconstrained search technique with a penalty function to locate the optimum of the constrained problem.

EXAMPLE 6–12 (37)

Form the exterior penalty function for the following problem using the penalty parameter r, and use the classical theory of maxima and minima to locate the minimum. The result will include the parameter r. Show that it is necessary to have r go to zero for the optimal solution of the unconstrained problem (penalty function) to be equal to the optimal solution of the original constrained problem.

$$\text{Minimize: } 2x_1^2 + 3x_2^2$$

$$\text{Subject to: } x_1 + 2x_2 = 5$$

The penalty function is:

$$P(x_1, x_2, r) = 2x_1^2 + 3x_2^2 + 1/r\,[x_1 + 2x_2 - 5]^2$$

Setting the first partial derivative with respect to x_1 and x_2 equal to 0 gives:

$$\frac{\partial P}{\partial x_1} = 4x_1 + \frac{2}{r}\,[x_1 + 2x_2 - 5] = 0$$

$$\frac{\partial P}{\partial x_2} = 6x_2 + \frac{4}{r}\,[x_1 + 2x_2 - 5] = 0$$

Solving for x_1 and x_2 gives:

$$x_1 = \frac{15}{11 + 6r} \qquad x_2 = \frac{20}{11 + 6r}$$

To have the optimal solution of the penalty function be equal to the optimal solution of constrained problem, r must be 0, i.e.:

$$x_1 = 15/11 \qquad x_2 = 20/11$$

A solution by Lagrange Multipliers will give these results.

When a search technique is used, a value of r must be selected that is sufficiently large to allow movement toward the optimum. As the optimum is approached, successively smaller values of r must be used to have the optimum of the penalty function approach the optimum of the constrained problem. Bracken and McCormick (36) have illustrated this procedure by solving the problem shown in Figure 6-8. For this problem, a mixed penalty function was selected in the form of equation (6–64).

For the unconstrained problem to represent the constrained problem and

Constrained problem:

$$\text{Minimize: } (x_1 - 2)^2 + (x_2 - 1)^2 = y$$

$$\text{Subject to: } -x_1^2/4 \ - \ x_2^2 = 1 \ \geq 0$$

$$x_1 \ \ - \ 2x_2 + 1 \ = 0$$

Unconstrained mixed penalty function problem:

$$\text{Minimize: } (x_1 - 2)^2 + (x_2 - 1)^2 + r[-x_1^2/4 - x_2^2 + 1]^{-1} \\ + r^{-1/2}[x_1 - 2x_2 + 1]^2$$

Optimal solution using SUMT program:

r	x_1	x_2	y
1.0	0.7489	0.5485	1.7691
4.0×10^{-2}	0.8177	0.8323	1.4258
1.6×10^{-3}	0.8224	0.8954	1.3976
6.4×10^{-5}	0.8228	0.9082	1.3942
2.56×10^{-6}	0.8229	0.9113	1.3935
1.024×10^{-7}	0.8229	0.9113	1.3935
4.096×10^{-9}	0.8229	0.9113	1.3935

Starting point for $r = 1.0$ was $\mathbf{x}_0(2, 2)$

Analytical solution $\mathbf{x}^*$ $[(-1 + \sqrt{7})/2 = 0.8229,$
$(1 + \sqrt{7})/4 = 0.9114]$ and $y(\mathbf{x}^*) = 1.3935$.

Figure 6-8. The use of a penalty function to converge to the optimum of a constrained problem by Bracken and McCormick (36).

have the same solution at the optimum, i.e., $P(\mathbf{x}^*, r) = y(\mathbf{x}^*)$, the following conditions must be satisfied:

$$\lim_{r \to 0} \left\{ r \sum_{i=1}^{h} [f_i(\mathbf{x})]^{-1} \right\} = 0 \tag{6--64}$$

$$f_i(\mathbf{x}) = 0$$

$$\lim_{r \to 0} \left\{ r^{-1/2} \sum_{i=h+1}^{m} [f_i(\mathbf{x})]^2 \right\} = 0 \qquad (6\text{-}65)$$

$$f_i(\mathbf{x}) \geq 0$$

along with constraints being satisfied.

The computational effort required to meet the above requirements is illustrated by the problem given in Figure 6-8. The search technique SUMT began at starting point $\mathbf{x}_0(2, 2)$ and arrived at the apparent optimum (0.7489, 0.5485) with a value of $r = 1.0$. The search technique was started again at point (0.7489, 0.5495) using a value for r of 4.0×10^{-2} to arrive at the apparent optimum (0.8177, 0.8323) as shown in the table in Figure 6-8. This procedure was repeated continually, reducing the value for r until an acceptable result was obtained for x_1 and x_2. In this case, the values from one optimal solution to the next agreed to within four significant figures. At this point, the value of r had decreased to 4.096×10^{-9}, practically zero for the problem.

In summary, significant computational effort is required to ensure that the solution of the penalty function problem approaches the solution to the constrained problem. For the illustration, the optimization problem was solved seven times as r went from 1.0 to 4.096×10^{-9} to have a converged solution of the unconstrained problem to the constrained one. This is typical of what is to be expected when penalty functions are used.

The conventional penalty function method obtains the optimal solution only at the limit of a series of solutions of unconstrained problems (33). Consequently, exact penalty functions have been proposed that would give the optimal solution in one application of the unconstrained algorithm. Several exact penalty functions have been constructed (33), but their use has been limited, because they contain absolute values that are not differentiable.

A procedure corresponding to the penalty function method has used the Lagrangian function. The Lagrangian function is formed as indicated below, where the slack and surplus variables have been used for the inequality constraints:

$$L(\mathbf{x}, \boldsymbol{\lambda}) = y(\mathbf{x}) + \sum_{i=1}^{m} \lambda_i f_i(\mathbf{x}) \qquad (6\text{-}66)$$

In this situation an initial estimate is made for the Lagrange Multipliers, and the unconstrained problem given by equation (6–66) is solved for an apparent optimum, $\mathbf{x}$. However, this value of $\mathbf{x}$ usually does not satisfy the constraints, and the estimated values of the Lagrange Multipliers are adjusted to give a new unconstrained problem, which is solved again for the apparent optimum. This procedure is repeated until the optimum is located and the constraints are satisfied. Methods have been developed to estimate the Lagrange Multipliers (33) for this procedure. The following simple example illustrates this idea of having to resolve the unconstrained optimization problem with various values of the Lagrange Multipliers until the constraints are satisfied.

EXAMPLE 6–13

Form the Lagrangian function for the following constrained problem and solve it by analytical methods for values of the Lagrange Multiplier of $-1/2$, -1.0, and -2.0. Compare these results with the analytical solution of $x_1 = x_2 = \sqrt{2}/2$ and $\lambda = -\sqrt{2}/2$:

$$\text{Maximize: } y = x_1 + x_2$$

$$\text{Subject to: } f = x_1^2 + x_2^2 - 1 = 0$$

The Lagrangian function is:

$$L(x_1, x_2, \lambda) = x_1 + x_2 + \lambda(x_1^2 + x_2^2 - 1)$$

When $\lambda = -1$, the Lagrangian function becomes:

$$L(x_1, x_2) = x_1 + x_2 + (x_1^2 + x_2^2 - 1)$$

Solving by analytical methods gives $x_1 = \frac{1}{2}$, $x_2 = \frac{1}{2}$, and using these values in the constraint gives:

$$f = (\tfrac{1}{2})^2 + (\tfrac{1}{2})^2 - 1 = -\tfrac{1}{2} \neq 0$$

The other values are determined in a similar fashion, and the following table summarizes the results:

λ	x_1	x_2	f
$-1/2$	1	1	1
$-\sqrt{2}/2$	$\sqrt{2}/2$	$\sqrt{2}/2$	0
-1	$1/2$	$1/2$	$-1/2$
-2	$1/4$	$1/4$	$-7/8$

The value of the Lagrange Multiplier goes from -1 to $-1/2$ as the value of f goes from -1–2 to 1 with the value of $f = 0$ (constraint satisfied) at $\lambda = -\sqrt{2}/2$.

Using the Lagrangian function is similar to using the penalty function in converting a constrained problem into an unconstrained one in the sense that the problem has to be resolved until the unconstrained problem has converged to the solution of the constrained one. There appears to be a disadvantage to using the Lagrangian function, because a set of Lagrange Multipliers (one for each constraint) has to be adjusted while only one penalty parameter is required. However, it turns out that there are difficulties in implementing penalty functions, including discontinuities on the boundaries of the feasible region (11), the Hessian matrix of the penalty function can become ill-conditioned (9) and the distortion of contours as r grows smaller (15). Also, it has been found that using the Lagrangian function alone has been relatively unsuccessful especially for large problems (8), except when the constraints are linear (38).

Combining penalty functions and Lagrange Multipliers has proved more successful, and this technique is called the *augmented Lagrangian method,* or the method of multipliers (6, 9, 15), and the relation between the penalty parameter and the Lagrange Multipliers has been reported (9, 28). The augmented Lagrangian function can be written as follows (11):

$$M(\mathbf{x},\lambda,r) = y(\mathbf{x}) + \sum_{i=1}^{h} \lambda_i f_i(\mathbf{x}) + r \sum_{i=h+1}^{m} [f_i(\mathbf{x})]^2 \qquad (6\text{--}67)$$

and an updated algorithm has been obtained for the Lagrange multipliers (11):

$$\lambda_{i,k+1} = \lambda_{i,k} - r f_i(\mathbf{x}_k) \qquad (6\text{--}68)$$

Avriel (11) gave an example of the use of this procedure for a simple problem. There have been difficulties associated with this method in the choice of the penalty parameter r. As discussed by Gill et al. (6), too small a value can lead to an unbounded number of unconstrained searches having to be performed, in addition to a possible ill-conditioned Hessian matrix of the Lagrangian function. As will be seen in the section on comparison of techniques, these methods have not performed as well as successive linear and quadratic programming and the generalized reduced gradient method.

Other Multivariable Constrained Search Methods: Other methods for constrained multivariable problems fall into a class referred to as *feasible* *directions, projection methods,* or *methods of restricted movement.* Also, there are random search procedures, cutting plane methods, and feasible region elimination techniques. The concepts associated with each of these procedures will be described and references given for sources of more information. These techniques have founded limited application, and the reasons for this will be described.

The restricted movement methods are described in some detail by Avriel (9, 11) and others (6, 8, 15, 27). According to Reklaitis et al. (15), even though there are similarities between these projection methods and reduced gradient techniques, the latter are preferred because sparse-matrix methods can be used, but the former methods are said to have "sparsity-destroying matrix products." Consequently, the details of these methods are available in the previously cited references, and only an illustration from McMillan (27) will be given to show some of the concepts involved.

A simple problem is shown in Figure 6-9, where the starting point is in the feasible region at point x_0 (8, 2). There are three constraints that bound the feasible region, and the unconstrained maximum lies outside the region. This gradient-projection method begins by a single-variable search along the gradient line to locate a maximum. The maximum along the line will be found where a constraint is encountered at point x_1 (6.6, 3.6). The gradient line at point x_1 points into the infeasible region. Therefore to continue to move toward the optimum, the gradient line is projected on the constraint,

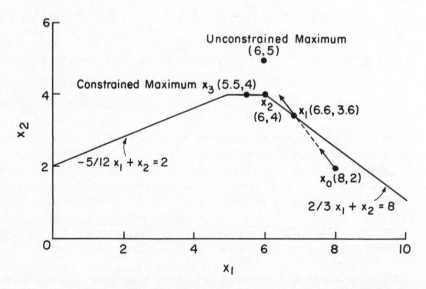

Figure 6-9. Illustration of the gradient-projection method, after McMillan (27).

and the search proceeds in this projected-gradient direction along the constraint. The constraint is linear, and a single-variable search for the maximum locates point x_2 (6, 4), which is the intersection with another constraint. The gradient line at x_2 (6, 4) points into the infeasible region, so it is projected on the constraint, in this case $x_2 = 4$, and the single-variable search for the maxima continues. The search arrives at point x_3 (5.5, 4), which is the constrained maximum.

In summary, the procedure began with an unconstrained search method, gradient search, until a constraint was encountered. The unconstrained search line was projected on the constraints to be able to stay in the feasible region, and it moved until the maximum was located. Other unconstrained search methods could have been used rather than gradient search, such as the BFGS method. Also, had the constraints been curved, the search method would not follow the constraint; and a hemstitching pattern would have developed as the search method attempted to follow the active nonlinear constraint. This is illustrated in Figure 6-10 and is one of the problems encountered with this method, as discussed by Avriel (9).

In the cutting plane method (15, 28), the nonlinear optimization problem

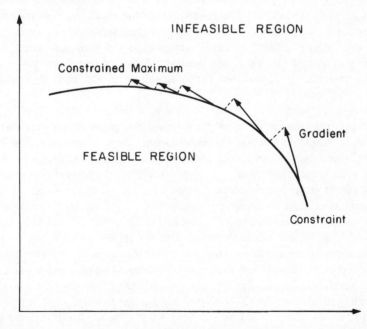

Figure 6-10. Hemstitching pattern developed by restricted movement methods following an active constraint, after Avriel (9).

is formulated as follows. Beginning with the nonlinear optimization problem as:

$$\text{Minimize: } y(\mathbf{x})$$

$$\text{Subject to: } f_i(\mathbf{x}) \geq 0 \quad \text{for } i = 1, 2, \cdots, m \tag{6–69}$$

The problem is converted to the following one:

$$\text{Minimize: } x_0$$

$$\text{Subject to: } f_i(\mathbf{x}) \geq 0 \tag{6–70}$$

$$x_0 - y(\mathbf{x}) \geq 0$$

which gives a linear economic model. Then if a starting point is selected that violates only one of the constraints, this constraint can be linearized, and the resulting problem can be solved by linear programming. At the new point the most violated constraint is added and linearized to find the third point in the search. The procedure continues adding constraints until the optimum is reached and the constraints are satisfied. However, a number of computational difficulties have been encountered with this procedure, according to Avriel (9), but it has been attractive because convergence to the global optimum is guaranteed if the economic model and constraints are convex functions.

In random search the feasible region is divided into a grid where each nodal point is considered to be the location of a point to compute the value of the economic model, i.e., an experiement. Then if an exhaustive search is performed by calculating the value of the economic model at each point in the grid, these experiments could be ranked from the one with the maximum value of the economic model to the one with the minimum value. However, a specified number of these experiments could be selected randomly and the value of the economic model evaluated at the points. It would be possible to make a statement about the point with the largest value of the economic model being in a certain best fraction of all the experiments with a specific probability. For example, if there were 1000 nodal points, and if one experiment were placed randomly in these points, the probability of choosing one in the top 10% would be $100/1000 = 0.1$. Also, the probability of not choosing one in the top 10% would be $1 - 0.1 = 0.9$. (Probability is defined as the relative frequency of occurrences of an event.)

If two experiments were placed randomly in the grid on the feasible region, the probability of not finding one in the top 10% would be $(0.9)^2 = 0.81$, and the probability of one of these two being in the top 10% is $1 - 0.81 = 0.19$. Continuing, after n trials the formula is:

$$p(0.1) = 1 - (0.9)^n \qquad (6\text{–}71)$$

For $n = 16$, the probability of finding one of these 16 experiments to be in the best fraction of 0.1 would be $p(0.1) = 0.80$. For $n = 44$, $p(0.1) = 0.99$, which is almost a certainty.

The generalization of this procedure, Wilde (10), is given by the following equation:

$$p(f) = 1 - (1 - f)^n \qquad (6\text{–}72)$$

In this equation $p(f)$ is the probability of finding at least one nodal point in the best fraction, f, having placed n experiments randomly in the feasible region. Several values of n have been computed by Wilde (10) having specified f and $p(f)$. These are given in Table 6-2. Equation (6–72) was used in the following form for these calculations:

$$n = ln\ [1 - p(f)]/ln\ (1 - f) \qquad (6\text{–}73)$$

Referring to the table, 16 experiments would be required to have at least one in the top 10% with a probability of 0.80 from a total of 1000 experiments. To have at least one value of the economic model in the top 0.5% with a probability of 0.99, 919 experiments of the total of 1000 would have to be measured, i.e., the economic model would have to be evaluated at almost

Table 6-2. The Number of Experiments, n, Required to Have at Least One in the Best Fraction, f, with a Probability, $p(f)$, Having a Total of 1000 Possible Experiments, after Wilde (10).

f	$P(f)$			
	0.80	0.90	0.95	0.99
0.1	16	22	29	44
0.01	161	230	299	459
0.005	322	460	598	919

all the nodal points. Also, it should be noted that the values for n reported in the table have been rounded off, e.g., 919 is $918.72 \cdots$ computed from equation (6–73). If there had been 100 experiments, 92 would have been required for at least 1 in the top 0.5% with a probability of 0.99.

The number of nodal points is somewhat independent of the number of variables in the economic model. Also, the results are independent of the number of local maxima or minima. These two facts are considered to be the important advantages of random search. This has led to adaptive random search where a random search is conducted on part of the feasible region. Then another section of the feasible region is selected that contains the largest value of the economic model to repeat the placing of another set of random measurements. This converts random search into a search technique, and it has been called *adaptive random search* by Gaddy and coworkers (40, 41)

In their most recent in a series of papers using this technique, Martin and Gaddy (41) have described the optimization of a maleic anhydrate process. They showed again that their adaptive randomly directed search method efficiently optimized the types of problems described as large, heavily constrained, and often containing mixed integer variables.

The feasible region elimination techniques are an extension of the ideas associated with the interval elimination, single-variable search methods. These are described in some detail by Wilde and Beightler (12), and two techniques are contour tangent elimination and multivariable dichotomous elimination. The first method is applicable only to functions that are strongly unimodal, and the second procedure requires that functions be rectangularity unimodal, which is more restrictive than strongly unimodal.

A strongly unimodal function has a strictly rising path from any point in the feasible region to the optimum. Consequently, a function with a curving ridge would not be strongly unimodal. An example of a strongly unimodal function is given in Figure 6-11. The line from point A to the maximum illustrates a strictly rising path.

The multivariable elimination technique is illustrated in Figure 6-11 for two independent variables. First, a starting point, x_0, in the feasible region is selected, and a contour tangent line is determined. The area below the contour tangent can be eliminated, for it does not contain the optimum, and the procedure continues by placing another experiment in the area that contains the optimum, e.g., point x_1. Measuring the contour tangent at x_1, an additional region can be eliminated. In this case it will be above the contour tangent line, and the region that contains the maximum is reduced. Again, another measurement is placed in the remaining area that contains the optimum, e.g., x_3, and the contour tangent is determined. Eliminating the area to the left of this contour tangent, now the region that contains

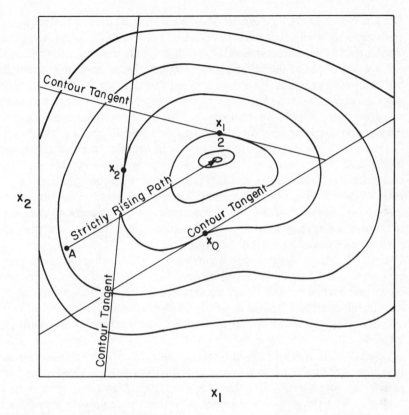

Figure 6-11. Illustration of the method of contour tangents, after Wilde and Beight-ler (12).

the optimum has been reduced to the triangular area bounded by the three contour tangents, as shown in Figure 6-11. The procedure continues in this fashion until the region that contains the optimum has been reduced to a satisfactory size. The details of the computational procedure are given by Wilde and Beightler (12), and the method has had limited use because of the restrictive requirement of being applicable only to strongly unimodal functions.

There are a number of other methods that could have been mentioned, all of which have had some degree of success in optimizing industrial problems, and these are described in the references at the end of this chapter. Many of these methods are modifications and/or combinations of the procedures that have been discussed. The next section will compare the performance of constrained multivariable procedures.

Comparison of Constrained Multivariable Search Methods: The evaluation of the effectiveness of constrained multivariable optimization procedures depends on several interrelated things. These are the optimization theory, the algorithm or the combination of algorithms to implement the theory, the computer program and programming language used for computations with the algorithms, the computer to run the program, and the optimization problems being solved. In comparing constrained optimization procedures, usually the same optimization problems are solved, and comparisons are based on measurements of computer time or the number of times the economic model and constraints are evaluated to come within a certain fraction of the optimum. If different computers are used to solve the optimization problems, then a timing program, such as a matrix inversion, is run on each machine to give a point of comparison among the computers. Consequently, if there is a superior optimization algorithm, the other factors that affect performance have made it difficult to detect.

There is debate about which algorithms and/or computer codes are the better ones, and Lasdon (3) recommended having available several computer codes that incorporate the more successful methods. A judgment about the ones to have can be obtained from the following reviews of industrial experience reporting the use of optimization procedures on process and plant problems.

In an Exxon study by Simon and Azma (1), 15 industrial optimization problems were solved using four established optimization codes, and their results are summarized in Table 6-3. The 15 problems had from 5 to 250 variables, and there were a number of active constraints at the optimum, ranging for each size problem from 50 to 95% of the number of variables. Two of the four optimization codes, ECO and SLP, were developed by Exxon. The ECO program used successive quadratic programming with many of the features described previously for the Wilson-Han-Powell algorithm, including a Davidon-Fletcher-Powell update for the Hessian matrix. The SLP program used successive linear programming as described previously with enhancements to speed convergence and circumvent problems with infeasibilities. The GRG2 program used the generalized reduced gradient method, and this program was developed by Lasdon (3). The MINOS program used a projected augmented Lagrangian algorithm combined with the generalized reduced gradient algorithm, and this program was developed by Murtagh and Saunders (43). The problems were run on Exxon's IBM 3033 computer, and the key results extracted from the article are given in Table 6-3. These include the average and range of the number of function calls and the average CPU time used. The optimization applications were complex simulations, and numerical differentiation was required. Consequently, the number of times that the economic model and constraints were evaluated (function calls) was viewed as the primary indicator of performance. CPU times were said to be a guide to performance and were not available for SLP optimizations. Also, termination criteria were used in the various convergence tests of the programs to have the value of the economic model be within the two tolerances of 0.001 and 0.0001.

In reviewing the results in Table 6-3, SLP and MINOS solved all the test problems. It was reported by Simon and Azma (1) that the performance of SLP was better on more tightly constrained problems. Also, they reported that MINOS had impressively fast run times from the use of sparse matrix computational features. The GRG2 code solved all the 5- and 20-variable

Table 6-3. Comparison of ECO, GRG2, MINOS, and SLP from the Exxon Evaluation Using 15 Optimization Problems from Simon and Azma (1).

OPTIMIZATION PROBLEMS NUMBER OF VARIABLES (PROBLEMS)	AVERAGE OF FUNCTION CALLS (RANGE) CPU SECONDS			
	ECO	GRG2	MINOS	SLP
Convergence tolerance of 0.0001				
5 variables (7)	32(23–47)	87(33–203)	33(15–49)	73(44–94)
	0.17	0.14	0.28	NR*
20 variables (12)	43(29–67)	537(475–672)	166(46–263)	181(111–261)
	5.0	3.0	0.95	NR
100 variables (2)	51(50 & 52)	445 (1 problem)	48(46 & 50)	69(57–80)
linear constraints	42.0	332.0	1.8	NR
100 variables (4)	Failed	2005(445 & 5225)	145(NR)	103(NR)
nonlinear constraints		(2 problems only)		
		983.0	2.8	NR
250 variables (4)	Not run	Not run	881(747–1073)	131(105–181)
			25.0	NR
Convergence tolerance of 0.001				
5 variables (7)	16(12–24)	73(25–174)	23(15–29)	22(12–34)
	0.1	0.1	0.2	NR
20 variables (12)	29(18–57)	486(311–647)	145(44–252)	131(62–229)
	3.7	2.5	0.8	NR
100 variables (2)	25(21 & 28)	397(1 problem)	47(46 & 48)	19(14–24)
linear constraints	25.0	289.0	1.8	NR
100 variables (4)	Failed	1682(606 & 2758)	162(82–208)	47(20–76)
nonlinear constraints		(2 problems only)		
		44.60	2.7	NR
250 variables (4)	Not run	Not run	841(714–1062)	83(47–175)
			24.0	NR

* NR, not reported.

problems and three of the six 100-variable problems. This code required the greatest number of function calls compared with the others. The ECO code solved all the 5- and 20-variable problems, the two 100-variable, linearly constrained problems, and one of the 100-variable, nonlinearly constrained problems. It was reported that nonlinear constraints caused numerical difficulties for the ECO code, because it did not contain special error checking and matrix inversion features of the other codes.

This study has shown that to solve large industrial problems these three optimization algorithms must be supplemented with other features associated with numerical differentiation and sparse matrix manipulations. In the following review of other comparison studies of optimization codes, these three procedures are found to be superior to others, and the relative merits of these methods have been tabulated by Lasdon and Warren (22). Successive linear programming (SLP) is said to be easy to implement, widely used in practice, rapidly convergent when the optimum is at a vertex, and able to handle very large problems, furthermore; it does not attempt to satisfy equalities at each iteration, may converge slowly on problems with nonvertex optimum, and will violate nonlinear constraints until convergence is reached. Successive quadratic programming (SQP) is said to require fewest function and gradient evaluations of the three methods; it does not attempt to satisfy equalities at each iteration, will violate nonlinear constraints until convergence is reached, is harder to implement than SLP, and requires a good quadratic programming solver. Generalized reduced gradient (GRG) is said to be probably the most robust and versatile, being able to employ existing process simulators using the Newton-Raphson method, but is the hardest to implement and needs to satisfy equality constraints at each step of the algorithm.

In a dissertation by Sandgren (20) on the utility of nonlinear programming algorithms, 35 optimization algorithms were collected from university and industry sources, of which 29 used penalty functions, 4 used generalized reduced gradient (GRG), and 2 used successive linear programming (SLP). Thirty test problems were selected from a variety of applications and sources that had from 2 to 48 variables and 4 to 75 constraints. Computations were performed on Purdue University's CDC 6500 computer in double precision, and all gradients were calculated using a forward difference approximation. Solution times were measured, and a rating procedure was used to rank the programs. The results showed that the four codes using the GRG algorithm and one code using SLP solved 50% of the test problems using 25% or less of the computer time averaged for all the programs. This study established fairly conclusively that GRG and SLP algorithms are superior to penalty function methods.

In a study by Schittkowski reported by Reklaitis et al. (15) 22 optimization programs and 180 test problems were evaluated. The optimization program included 11 SLP, 3 GRG, 4 SQP, and 4 penalty function codes; and nine criteria were used and weighted to rank the programs. The ranking of the algorithm classes were in the order of SQP, GRG, SLP, and penalty functions last. Also, it was emphasized that these tests showed that code reliability is more a function of the programming of the algorithm than the algorithm itself.

In probably the first comprehensive study of nonlinear constrained optimization procedures, Colville (21) organized participants from 15 industrial firms and universities and had them test eight industrial problems with their 30 optimization codes. He grouped the methods into five categories and developed a scoring procedure. This involved using a timing program for matrix inversion, because the results were obtained from a number of different computers. The highest score was received by the GRG method. Himmelblau (8) extended these results and ran some of Colville's and other problems on the same computer. Again, the GRG code was the best performer. However, Palacios-Gomez et al. (47) have shown that their improved version of SLP based on industrial computational experience was comparable to or better than GRG2 and MINOS on Himmelblau's and other test problems.

In a recent article, the successive quadratic programming and generalized reduced gradient algorithms have been used with large computer simulations and flowsheeting programs for optimal design. Biegler and Hughes (44, 49) showed that successive quadratic programming was effective for optimization of a propylene chlorination process simulation. Also, the previously mentioned study of Jirapongpham et al. (42) demonstrated that the WHP algorithm was effective for process flowsheeting optimization. Also, Locke and Westerberg (45, 46) used an advanced quadratic programming algorithm with an equation-oriented process flowsheeting program with success. In addition, Chen and Stadtherr (48) reported enhancements of the WHP method that were effective on several chemical process optimization problems. Moreover, Biegler and Cuthrell (53) showed the Armijo line search to be one of several improvements to successive quadratic programming. Finally, Drud (58) has developed a GRG program CONOPT, which uses the industry standard MPS input format for large static and dynamic problems at the World Bank.

In summary, the three methods of choice for optimization of industrial-scale problems are successive linear and quadratic programming and the generalized reduced gradient method. The available programs that use these procedures are elaborate and use a combination of techniques for efficient computer computations. Sources of programs using these methods are given by Waren and Lasdon (2), Reklaitis et al. (15), and Gill et al. (6). Waren and Lasdon (2) list the desirable features of nonlinear programming software, which can be used as a guide for selection of codes. It is advisable to have several proven optimization codes available to solve industrial-scale problems. Unfortunately, it is not envisioned that one code will be available in the near future that is effective on almost all large problems, such as those for linear programming like MPSX. However, progress is being made in that direction, e.g., Drud's work (59), and the current literature should be the first source in looking for optimization programs because of the improvements in computer and optimization algorithms.

STOCHASTIC APPROXIMATION PROCEDURES

All the procedures described up to now have been for deterministic processes, and they can be confounded by random error. There are search techniques that converge to an optimum in the face of random error, and some of these will be discussed briefly following the approach of Wilde (10), who gives more details about these methods. Random (e.g., experimental) error clouds the preception of what is happening and greatly hampers the search for the optimum. Stochastic approximation procedures deal with random error as noise superimposed on a deterministic process. Therefore, convergence to the optimum must be considered first, and then efficiency can be evaluated. The works of Dvoretzky, Kiefer, and Wolfowitz in this area have been summarized in an excellent manner by Wilde (10). Consequently, only the most important of these techniques will be described. This is the Kiefer-Wolfowitz stochastic approximation procedure, and it is applicable for n independent variables.

With noise present, a search technique is forced to creep to prevent being confounded by random error. However, for unimodal functions, it can be shown that stochastic approximation procedures converge to the optimum in the mean square and with probability 1.

The Kiefer-Wolfowitz algorithm is given by the following equation. Beginning at a starting point x_0, the method proceeds according to this equation:

$$
\begin{bmatrix} x_{1,\,k+1} \\ x_{2,\,k+1} \\ \vdots \\ x_{n,\,k+1} \end{bmatrix} = \begin{bmatrix} x_{1,\,k} \\ x_{2,\,k} \\ \vdots \\ x_{n,\,k} \end{bmatrix} + \frac{a_k}{c_k} \begin{bmatrix} y(x_{1,\,k}+c_k,\,x_{2,\,k},\,\cdots,x_{n,\,k}) - y(x_{1,\,k}-c_k,\,x_{2,\,k},\,\cdots,x_{n,\,k}) \\ y(x_{1,\,k},\,x_{2,\,k}+c_k,\,\cdots,\,x_{n,\,k}) - y(x_{1,\,k},\,x_2-c_k,\,k,\,\cdots,x_{n,\,k}) \\ \vdots \\ y(x_{1,\,k},\,x_{2,\,k},\,\cdots,x_{n,\,k}+c_k) - y(x_{1,\,k},\,x_{2,\,k},\,\cdots,\,x_{n,\,k}-c_k) \end{bmatrix}
$$

For convergence, the parameters a_k and c_k must satisfy the following criteria:

$$\lim_{k \to \infty} a_k = 0$$

$$\lim_{k \to \infty} c_k = 0$$

$$\sum_{k=1}^{\infty} a_k = \infty \tag{6-75}$$

$$\sum_{k=1}^{\infty} (a_k/c_k)^2 < \infty$$

The following example illustrates the use of the Kiefer-Wolfowitz procedure.

EXAMPLE 6–13

Develop the procedure to obtain the minimum of a function of the form $[Ax_1 (x_1 - x_1^*)^2 + Bx_2(x_2 - x_2^*)^2]$, which is affected by experimental error. The value of the minimum is somewhere on the interval $1 \le x_1^* \le 3$, $1 \le x_2^* \le 3$. Starting with the midpoint of the interval, give the equations for the second, third, and last of 20 trials.

Solution: $a_k = 1/k$, $c_k = 1k^{1/4}$ satisfies the criterion of the equation (6–75).

For $x_2 = (x_{1, 2}, x_{2, 2})$, $k = 1$:

$$\begin{bmatrix} x_{1, 2} \\ x_{2, 2} \end{bmatrix} = \begin{bmatrix} 2 \\ 2 \end{bmatrix} + \begin{bmatrix} y(3, 2) - y(1, 2) \\ y(2, 3) - y(2, 1) \end{bmatrix}$$

For $x_3 = (x_{1, 3}, x_{2, 3})$, $k = 2$:

$$\begin{bmatrix} x_{1, 3} \\ x_{2, 3} \end{bmatrix} = \begin{bmatrix} x_{1, 2} \\ x_{2, 2} \end{bmatrix} + \frac{1}{2^{3/4}} \begin{bmatrix} y(x_{1, 2} + 2^{-1/4}, x_{2, 2}) - y(x_{1, 2} - 2^{-1/4}, x_{2, 2}) \\ y(x_{1, 2}, x_{2, 2} + 2^{-1/4}) - y(x_{1, 2}, x_{2, 2} - 2^{-1/4}) \end{bmatrix}$$

For $x_{20} = (x_{1, 20}, x_{2, 20})$, $k = 19$:

$$\begin{bmatrix} x_{1, 20} \\ x_{2, 20} \end{bmatrix} = \begin{bmatrix} x_{1, 19} \\ x_{2, 19} \end{bmatrix} + \frac{1}{19^{3/4}} \begin{bmatrix} y(x_{1, 19} + 19^{-1/4}, x_{2, 19}) - y(x_{1, 19} - 19^{-1/4}, x_{2, 19}) \\ y(x_{1, 19}, x_{2, 19} + 19^{-1/4}) - y(x_{1, 19}, x_{2, 19} - 19^{-1/4}) \end{bmatrix}$$

There are variations of the above procedure, such as using only the sign of the approximation to the derivatives. This can be used effectively when there is difficulty with convergence that is being caused by the shape of the curve on either side of the optimum. Also, a forward difference approximation can be used in evaluating the derivative, rather than the central difference form, but convergence is not as rapid.

CLOSURE

In this chapter the important algorithms for optimizing a nonlinear economic model with nonlinear constraints have been described, and their performance has been reviewed. This required presenting methods for unconstrained problems first and outlining the strategy required to move from a starting point to a point near an optimum. It was not possible to discuss each of the many algorithms that have been proposed and employed as unconstrained multivariable search techniques, but the references at the end of the chapter will lead to comprehensive descriptions of those procedures. The texts by Avriel (9), Fletcher (4,5), Gill et al. (6), Himmelblau (8), McCormick (7), and Reklaitis et al. (15) are particularly recommended for this purpose. However, the more successful algorithms were described for both unconstrained and constrained optimization problems. It is recommended that the BFGS algorithm be used for unconstrained problems and a FORTRAN program for this procedure (Table 6-4) has been included at the end of the chapter. For constrained problems, the three methods that have been more successful in comparison studies on industrial problems are successive linear and quadratic programming (SLP and SQP) and generalized reduced gradient (GRG). Advanced computation techniques for numerical derivatives and sparse matrix manipulations are required to have efficient codes, and sources to contact for these types of programs were referenced.

In addition to deterministic optimization methods, stochastic approximation procedures were described briefly, based on material from Wilde's book (10). These methods are designed to locate the optimum in the face of experimental error, even though their movement is slowed to avoid being confounded.

This area of optimization is probably the most rapidly growing part of the subject. The growth of computers and applied mathematical techniques for large systems of equations promises to continue to allow significant developments to take place.

Table 6-4.   FORTRAN Program with Sample Input and Output for BFGS Search of an Unconstrained Nonlinear Function

```
C       PROGRAM BFGS
C
C
C-------------------------------------------------------------------
C
C       NOTATION :
C
C       NTERM  : NO. OF INDEPENDENT VARIABLES IN THE COST FUNCTION
C
C       X      : INDEPENDENT VARIABLES
C
C       EPS    : STOPPING CRITERION ON COST FUNCTION
C
C       ITER   : LOOP COUNTER
C
C       HESS   : HESSIAN MATRIX
C
C       K      : PARAMETER OF THE LINE SEARCHED
C
C-------------------------------------------------------------------
C
        INTEGER ITER
        DOUBLE PRECISION TOLER, FUNCT, FIBON,
     1  HESS(20,20), GRAD(20), GRAD1(20), GAMMA(20), DELTA(20),
     2  HG(20), K, ERR, ERROLD, EPS, GPHG, DPG, X(20), S(20)
C
        COMMON X, S, NTERM
C
        ITER= 0
        K   = 0
C-------------------------------------------------------------------
C
C       READ AND ECHO INPUT DATA
C
C-------------------------------------------------------------------
C
        READ(5,*) NTERM, EPS
        READ(5,*) ( X(I), I=1,NTERM)
        WRITE(6,600) NTERM, EPS,( X(I), I=1,NTERM)
  600   FORMAT(/,5X,'INPUT DATA :  ',
     &          /,5X,'NO. OF INDEPENDENT VARIABLES, NTERM = ',I4,
     &          /,5X,'STOPPING CRITERION, EPS         = ',F9.4,
     &          /,5X,'STARTING POINTS, X              = ',10(1X,F6.2))
        WRITE(6,601)
  601   FORMAT(/,5X,'RESULTS    :',
     &          /,5X,'ITERATION',2X,'COST FUNCTION',6X,'VALUES OF X',12X,'
     &K',/)
```

Table 6-4. Continued

```
C------------------------------------------------------------------
C
C     BFGS SEARCH
C
C------------------------------------------------------------------
C
      ERR= FUNCT( X )
      CALL PRINT( ITER, NTERM, ERR, X, K)
      CALL SLOPE( GRAD, ERR )
C------------------------------------------------------------------
C
C     FORM THE IDENTITY MATRIX
C
C------------------------------------------------------------------
C
      DO 40 I=1, NTERM
         DO 40 J=1, NTERM
            IF (I.NE.J) HESS(I,J)= 0.0
            IF (I.EQ.J) HESS(I,J)= 1.0
  40  CONTINUE
  30  CONTINUE
C
      ERROLD= ERR
      ITER= ITER + 1
C------------------------------------------------------------------
C
C     S(I) = HESSIAN*GRADIENT
C
C------------------------------------------------------------------
C
      DO 50 I=1, NTERM
         S(I)= 0.0
         DO 50 J=1, NTERM
            S(I)= S(I) + HESS(I,J) * GRAD(J)
  50        CONTINUE
C------------------------------------------------------------------
C
C     K = ALPHA IN EQN.6-17
C
C------------------------------------------------------------------
C
      K= FIBON( DUMMY )
C------------------------------------------------------------------
C
C     DETERMINE NEXT X VALUE WITH EQN.6-17
C
C     DELTA = ALPHA*HESSIAN*GRADIENT, IN EQN. 6-17
C
C------------------------------------------------------------------
C
```

Table 6-4. Continued

```
        DO 60 I=1, NTERM
           DELTA(I)= K * S(I)
           X(I)= X(I) - DELTA(I)
  60       CONTINUE
        ERR= FUNCT(X)
        CALL SLOPE( GRAD1, ERR )
C-----------------------------------------------------------------
C
C       DETERMINE NEW BFGS MATRIX WITH EQN.6-20
C
C-----------------------------------------------------------------
C
        DPG=0.0
        DO 70 I=1, NTERM
           GAMMA(I)= GRAD1(I) - GRAD(I)
           DPG= DPG + GAMMA(I) * DELTA(I)
  70       CONTINUE
        DO 80 I=1, NTERM
           GRAD(I)= GRAD1(I)
  80       CONTINUE
        GPHG= 0.0
        DO 90 I=1, NTERM
           HG(I)= 0.0
           DO 90 J=1,NTERM
              HG(I)= HG(I) + HESS(I,J) * GAMMA(J)
              GPHG= GPHG+ HESS(I,J) * GAMMA(I) * GAMMA(J)
  90       CONTINUE
        DO 100 I=1, NTERM
           DO 100 J=1, NTERM
              HESS(I,J)= HESS(I,J) - (HG(I) * DELTA(J) /DPG)
       $                  - (DELTA(I) * HG(J) / DPG)
       $                  + (1 + (GPHG / DPG)) * (DELTA(I)
       $                  * DELTA(J) / DPG)
 100       CONTINUE
        TOLER = DABS(ERR-ERROLD)
        IF (TOLER .GE. EPS) CALL PRINT( ITER, NTERM, ERR, X, K)
        IF (TOLER .GE. EPS) GO TO 30
        STOP
        END
C-----------------------------------------------------------------
C
C       COMPUTATION OF PARTIAL DERIVATIVES
C
C-----------------------------------------------------------------
C
        SUBROUTINE SLOPE( DERIV, E )
        DOUBLE PRECISION DERIV(20), E, DELTA, TEMPX, Y, X(20),S(20), FUNCT
        COMMON X, S, NTERM
C
        DO 30 I=1, NTERM
           DELTA= 1.0E-04
```

Table 6-4.   Continued

```
            TEMPX= X(I)
            X(I)= X(I) + DELTA
            Y= FUNCT( X )
            DERIV(I)= (Y - E)/DELTA
            X(I)= TEMPX
   30       CONTINUE
         RETURN
         END
C-------------------------------------------------------------------
C
C     PRINT RESULTS
C
C-------------------------------------------------------------------
C
         SUBROUTINE PRINT( I, N, VAL, X, K)
         DOUBLE PRECISION X(20), VAL, K
         WRITE(6,600) I,VAL,(X(J),J=1,N), K
  600    FORMAT(7X,I3,6X,F10.3,4X,10(1X,F7.3))
         RETURN
         END
C-------------------------------------------------------------------
C
C     FIBONNACCI SEARCH FUNCTION
C
C-------------------------------------------------------------------
C
C     LBOUND : LOWER BOUND
C
C     HBOUND : UPPER BOUND
C
C     INTER  : INITIAL INTERVAL
C
C     FINTER : FINAL INTERVAL
C
C     RATIO  : RATIO OF INITIAL AND FINAL INTERVALS
C
C     DELTA  : DISPLACEMENT OF AN EXPERIMENT FROM THE BOUNDARY,
C
C              EQN.5-44, INITIALLY
C
C     FIBO   : FIBONNACCI NUMBERS
C
C     FACT   : FIBO(N+1)/FIBO(N-1)
C
C-------------------------------------------------------------------
C
         DOUBLE PRECISION FUNCTION FIBON( DUMMY )
C
C
```

Table 6-4. Continued

```
      DOUBLE PRECISION RATIO, FIBO(50),
    1 LBOUND, HBOUND, INTER, FINTER, DELTA, TESTLB,
    2 TESTHB, TLBV, THBV, TEST, FACT, TLB
      INTEGER EXPCNT, EXPNO, FLAG
      LBOUND = 0.0
      TEST   = 1.0
      HBOUND = 1.0
      FINTER = 0.00001
      FACT   = 1.618034
C-----------------------------------------------------------------------
C
C     DETERMINE THE INTERVALS OF THE FIBONNACCI SEARCH
C
C-----------------------------------------------------------------------
C
   10 CONTINUE
      TLBV = F( TEST )
      THBV = F( HBOUND )
      IF (TLBV.GT.THBV) GO TO 20
         TLB = TEST
         TEST= HBOUND
         HBOUND= HBOUND * FACT
         GO TO 10
   20 CONTINUE
C-----------------------------------------------------------------------
C
C     DETERMINE BOUNDS AND DELTA FOR FIBONNACCI SEARCH
C
C-----------------------------------------------------------------------
C
      IF(TEST .NE. 1.) LBOUND = TLB
      INTER= HBOUND - LBOUND
      DELTA = TEST - LBOUND
      TESTLB= TEST
      TESTHB= HBOUND - DELTA
      IF (TESTLB .LT. TESTHB) GOTO 38
      TLB = TESTLB
      TESTLB = TESTHB
      TESTHB = TLB
      DELTA  = TESTLB - LBOUND
      TESTHB = HBOUND - DELTA
   38 CONTINUE
      INTER  = HBOUND - LBOUND
      RATIO  = INTER/FINTER
C-----------------------------------------------------------------------
C
C     DETERMINE THE NUMBER OF EXPERIMENTS REQUIRED TO HAVE
C
C     FINTER = 0.00001
C
C-----------------------------------------------------------------------
```

Table 6-4.   Continued

```
C
      FIBO(1) = 1
      FIBO(2) = 1
      DO 39 I = 3,50
         FIBO(I) = FIBO(I-1) + FIBO(I-2)
         IF (FIBO(I) .LT. RATIO) EXPNO = I + 1
  39     CONTINUE
C-------------------------------------------------------------
C
C     START CLOSED BOUND FIBONNACCI SEARCH
C
C-------------------------------------------------------------
C
      DO 40 EXPCNT=1, EXPNO
      TLBV= F(TESTLB)
      THBV= F(TESTHB)
      IF (TLBV.GE.THBV) GO TO 30
         LBOUND= TESTLB
         INTER= HBOUND - LBOUND
         DELTA= INTER - DELTA
         TESTLB= TESTHB
         TESTHB= HBOUND - DELTA
         FLAG = 1
         GO TO 40
  30     CONTINUE
         HBOUND= TESTHB
         INTER= HBOUND - LBOUND
         DELTA= INTER - DELTA
         TESTHB= TESTLB
         TESTLB= LBOUND + DELTA
         FLAG = 0
  40     CONTINUE
      IF (FLAG .EQ. 1) FIBON = TESTLB
      IF (FLAG .EQ. 0) FIBON = TESTHB
      RETURN
      END
C-------------------------------------------------------------
C
C     FUNCTION EVALUATION FOR FIBONNACCI SEARCH
C
C-------------------------------------------------------------
C
      DOUBLE PRECISION FUNCTION F( K )
      DOUBLE PRECISION K, TEST(20), X(20), S(20)
      COMMON X, S, NTERM
      DO 10 I=1, NTERM
         TEST(I)= X(I) - K * S(I)
  10     CONTINUE
      F= -FUNCT( TEST )
      RETURN
      END
```

Table 6-4. Continued

```
C------------------------------------------------------------------
C
C      CALCULATION OF COST FUNCTION
C
C------------------------------------------------------------------
C
       DOUBLE PRECISION FUNCTION FUNCT(X)
       DOUBLE PRECISION X(20)
       FUNCT=5.0*X(1)*X(1)+2.0*X(2)*X(2)+2.0*X(3)*X(3)
     &       +2.0*X(1)*X(2)+2.0*X(2)*X(3)
     &       -2.0*X(3)*X(1) -6.0*X(3)
       RETURN
       END
```

```
*******************************************************************
       INPUT DATA :
       NO. OF INDEPENDENT VARIABLES, NTERM =    3
       STOPPING CRITERION, EPS             =    0.0001
       STARTING POINTS, X                  =    0.00    0.00    0.00
```

RESULTS :					
ITERATION	COST FUNCTION	VALUES OF X			K
0	0.000	0.000	0.000	0.000	0.000
1	-4.500	0.000	0.000	1.501	0.250
2	-7.500	1.000	-1.000	2.502	0.333
3	-9.000	1.000	-2.002	3.003	0.167

NORMAL TERMINATION OF THE BFGS PROGRAM

Program Description:

This program uses the Broyden, Fletcher, Goldfarb, and Shanno (BFGS) algorithm to minimize an unconstrained multivariable function having as many as 20 variables. The program consists of a main program, two subroutines, and three functions.

The three functions are as follows. The function FUNCT is the equation for the cost function to be minimized. The function F uses FUNCT for value of the cost function in the line search. The function FIBON uses the values of F in an open-ended Fibonacci line search. The two subroutines are SLOPE, which evaluates the partial derivatives using a forward difference approximation, and PRINT, which prints the results of the computations.

The input data are the number of independent variables, starting point for the search, and the stopping criterion, EPS. The program will terminate when the difference between the cost function values of two successive iterations is less than or equal to EPS, the stopping criteria.

The results are the iteration number, the values of the independent variables, and the cost function. Shown with the program are the input and output for the problem in Example 6–4.

The main program begins with an echo of the input data. Then it proceeds from iteration zero, the starting point, to use the BFGS algorithm to generate successive points until the stopping criterion is met. Initially, the Hessian matrix **G** is the identity matrix, and the gradient is computed using a forward difference approximation to the partial derivatives using subroutine SLOPE. The Fibonacci search function, FIBON, is used to locate the minimum along the gradient line from x_0 to x_1. Then the stopping criterion is checked, and the Hessian matrix **G** is updated. The value of the function is stored in ERROLD for future comparisons. The search direction to the next point is calculated and stored in the vector **S**. The value of the parameter of the line in the search direction, K, is calculated using FIBON to locate the next point. The value of the function at the new point is calculated and stored in ERR. The values of the iteration counter, the function at the new point, and the new point are printed using PRINT. The values of the gradient at the current point are computed and stored in the vector GRAD. The Hessian matrix **G** is updated, and the program returns to repeat the calculation until the error criterion is met.

To solve other problems, supply the equation to be minimized in the function FUNCT. It is used only by the procedure FIBON. If more than 20 variables are needed, then the CONST SIZE should be changed to the required number. No other modifications are needed. If this program is to be run in an 8-bit microcomputer, the real variables must be declared double precision to prevent underflow. Otherwise a division by zero will occur.

REFERENCES

1. Simon, J. D., and H. M. Azma, "Exxon Experience with Large Scale Linear and Nonlinear Programming Applications," *Computers and Chemical Engineering,* 7(5):605 (1983).
2. Waren, A. D., and L. S. Lasdon, "The Status of Nonlinear Programming Software," *Operations Research,* 27(3):431 (May–June 1979).
3. Lasdon, L. S., "A Survey of Nonlinear Programming Algorithms and Software," *Foundations of Computer-Aided Chemical Process Design,* Vol. 1, American Institute of Chemical Engineers, New York p. 185 (1981).
4. Fletcher, R., *Practical Methods of Optimization, Vol. I, Unconstrained Optimization,* John Wiley & Sons, Inc., New York (1981).
5. Fletcher, R., *Practical Methods of Optimization, Vol. II, Constrained Optimization,* John Wiley & Sons, Inc., New York (1981).
6. Gill, P. E., E. Murray, and M. H. Wright, *Practical Optimization,* Academic Press, New York (1981).

7. McCormick, G. P., *Nonlinear Programming: Theory, Algorithms and Applications,* John Wiley & Sons, Inc., New York (1983).
8. Himmelblau, D. M., *Applied Nonlinear Programming,* McGraw-Hill Book Co., New York (1972).
9. Avriel, M., *Nonlinear Programming: Methods and Analysis,* Prentice-Hall, Inc., Englewood Cliffs, N.J. (1976).
10. Wilde, D. J., *Optimum Seeking Methods,* Prentice-Hall, Inc., Englewood Cliffs, N.J. (1964).
11. Avriel, M., "Nonlinear Programming," Chapter 11 in *Mathematical Programming for Operations Researchers and Computer Scientists,* Ed. A. G. Holtzman, Marcel Dekker, Inc., New York (1981).
12. Wilde, D. J., and C. S. Beightler, *Foundations of Optimization,* Prentice-Hall, Inc., Englewood Cliffs, N.J. (1967).
13. Fletcher, R., op. cit., p. 57. Vol. I.
14. Churchhouse, R. F., *Handbook of Applicable Mathematics, Vol. III, Numerical Methods,* John Wiley & Sons, Inc., New York (1981).
15. Reklaitis, G. V., A. Ravindran, and K. M. Ragsdell, *Engineering Optimization, Methods and Applications,* John Wiley & Sons, Inc., New York (1983).
16. Kuester, J. L., and J. H. Mize, *Optimization Techniques with Fortran,* McGraw-Hill Book Co., New York (1973).
17. Smith, C. L., R. W. Pike, and P. W. Murrill, *Formulation and Optimization of Mathematical Models,* International Textbook Company, Scranton, PA (1970).
18. Griffith, R. E., and R. A. Stewart, "A Nonlinear Programming Technique for the Optimization of Continous Processing Systems," *Management Science,* 7:379 (1961).
19. Lasdon, L. S., op. cit., p. 202.
20. Sandgren, E., "The Utility of Nonlinear Programming Algorithms," Ph.D. dissertation, Purdue University, West Lafayette, Ind. (1977).
21. Colville, A. R., *A Comparative Study of Nonlinear Programming Codes,* IBM New York Scientific Center Report No. 320-2949, IBM Corp., New York Scientific Center, 410 East 62nd Street, New York, N.Y. 10021 (June 1968).
22. Lasdon, L. S., and A. D. Waren, "Large Scale Nonlinear Programming," *Computers and Chemical Engineering,* 7(5):595 (1983).
23. Franklin, J., *Methods of Mathematical Economies, Linear and Nonlinear Programming, Fixed Point Theorems,* Springer-Verlag, Inc., New York (1980).
24. Vanderplaats, G. N., *Numerical Optimization Techniques for Engineering Design with Applications,* McGraw-Hill Book Co., New York (1984).
25. Hillier, F. S., and G. J. Lieberman, *Operations Research,* 3rd Ed., Holden-Day, Inc., San Francisco (1980).
26. Walsh, G. R., *Methods of Optimization,* John Wiley & Sons, Inc., New York (1975).
27. McMillan, Claude, Jr., *Mathematical Programming: An Introduction to the Design and Application of Optimal Decision Machines,* John Wiley & Sons, Inc., New York (1970).
28. Gottfried, B. S., and J. Weisman, *Introduction to Optimization Theory,* Prentice-Hall, Inc., Englewood Cliffs, N.J. (1973).
29. Wolfe, P., "Methods of Nonlinear Programming," in *Recent Advances in Mathematical Programming,* Ed. R. L. Graves and P. Wolfe, McGraw-Hill Book Co., New York (1963).
30. Abadie, J., and J. Carpentier, "Generalization of the Wolfe Reduced Gradient Method to the Case of Nonlinear Constraints," in *Optimization,* Ed. R. Fletcher, Academic Press, London (1969).
31. Pollack, A. W., and W. D. Lieder, "Linking Process Simulators to a Refinery Linear Programming Model," in *Computer Applications to Chemical Engineering,* Ed. R. G. Squires and

G. V. Reklaitis, ACS Symposium Series No. 124, American Chemical Society, Washington, D.C. (1980).

32. O'Neil, R. P., M. A. Williard, B. Wilkins, and R. W. Pike, "A Mathematical Programming Model for Natural Gas Allocation," *Operations Research,* 27(5):857–873 (Sept./Oct. 1979).

33. Sargent, R. W. H., "A Review of Optimization Methods for Nonlinear Problems," in *Computer Applications to Chemical Engineering,* Ed. R. G. Squires and G. V. Reklaitis, ACS Symposium Series No. 124, American Chemical Society, Washington, D.C. (1980).

34. Cooper, L., and D. Steinberg, *Introduction to Methods of Optimization,* W. B. Saunders Co., Philadelphia (1970).

35. Adby, P. R., and M. A. H. Dempster, *Introduction to Optimization Methods,* John Wiley & Sons, Inc., New York (1974).

36. Bracken, J., and G. P. McCormick, *Selected Applications of Nonlinear Programming,* John Wiley & Sons, Inc., New York, pp. 16 ff (1968).

37. Ray, W. H., and J. Szekely, *Process Optimization with Applications in Metallurgy and Chemical Engineering,* John Wiley & Sons, Inc., New York (1973).

38. April, G. C., and R. W. Pike, "Modeling Complex Chemical Reaction Systems," *Industrial and Engineering Chemistry, Process Design and Development,* 13(1):1 (January 1974).

39. Fletcher, R., "Methods Related to Lagrangian Functions," *Numerical Methods for Constrained Optimization,* Ed. P. E. Gill and W. Murray, Academic Press, New York (1974).

40. Doering, F. J., and J. L. Gaddy, "Optimization of the Sulfuric Acid Process with a Flowsheet Simulator," *Computers and Chemical Engineering,* 4:113 (1980).

41. Martin, D. L., and J. L. Gaddy, "Modeling the Maleic Anhydrate Process," Summer National Meeting, American Institute of Chemical Engineers, Anaheim (May 20–24, 1984).

42. Jirapongphan, S., J. F. Boston, H. I. Britt, and L. B. Evans, "A Nonlinear Simultaneous Modular Algorithm for Process Flowsheeting Optimization," American Institute of Chemical Engineers Annual Meeting, Chicago (November 1980).

43. Murtagh, B. A., and M. A. Saunders, *MINOS 5.0 Users Guide,* Technical Report SOL 83-20, Systems Optimization Laboratory, Department of Operations Research, Stanford University (December 1983).

44. Beigler, L. T., and R. R. Hughes, "Process Optimization: A Comparative Case Study," *Computers and Chemical Engineering,* 7(5):645 (1983).

45. Locke, M. H., and A. W. Westerberg, "The ASCEND-II System—A Flowsheeting Application of a Successive Quadratic Programming Methodology," *Computers and Chemical Engineering,* 7(5):615 (1983).

46. Locke, M. H., A. W. Westerberg, and R. H. Edahl, "Improved Successive Quadratic Programming Optimization Algorithm for Engineering Design Problems," *AIChE Journal,* 29(5):871 (September, 1983).

47. Palacios-Gomez, F., L. Lasdon, and M. Engquist, "Nonlinear Optimization by Successive Linear Programming," *Management Science,* 28(5):871 (September 1983).

48. Chen, H. S., and M. A. Stadtherr, "Enhancements of the Han-Powell Method for Successive Quadratic Programming," *Computers and Chemical Engineering,* Vol. 8 No. 314 p. 229 (1984).

49. Biegler, L. T., and R. R. Hughes, "Infeasible Path Optimization with Sequential Modular Simulators," *AIChE Journal,* 28(6):994 (November 1982).

50. Bertsekas, D. P., *Constrained Optimization and Lagrange Multiplier Methods,* Academic Press, New York (1982).

51. Han, S. P., "A Globally Convergent Method for Nonlinear Programming," *Journal of Optimization Theory and Applications,* 22(3):297 (July 1977).

52. Han, S. P., "Superlinearly Convergent Variable Metric Algorithms for General Nonlinear

Programming Problems," *Mathematical Programming,* 11:263, Noth-Holland Publishing Co. (1976).

53. Biegler, L. T., and J. E. Cuthrell, "Improved Infeasible Path Optimization for Sequential Modular Simulators—II: The Optimization Algorithm," *Computer and Chemical Engineering,* 9(3):257 (1985).

54. Haftka, R. T., and M. P. Kamat, *Elements of Structural Optimization,* Martinus Nijhoff Publisher, Dordrecht, The Netherlands (1985).

55. Dennis, J. E., and R. B. Schnable, *Numerical Methods for Unconstrained Optimization and Nonlinear Equations,* Prentice-Hall, Inc., Englewood Cliffs, N.J. (1983).

56. Bazaraa, M. S., and C. M. Shetty, *Nonlinear Programming: Theory and Algorithms,* John Wiley & Sons, Inc., New York (1979).

57. Powell, M. J. D., "An Efficient Method for Finding the Minimum of a Function of Several Variables without Calculating Derivatives," *The Computer Journal,* 7:155 (1964).

58. Drud, A. "CONOPT: A GRG Code for Large Sparse Dynamic Nonlinear Optimization Problems," *Mathematical Programming,* 31:153 (1985).

59. Hadley, G. H. *Nonlinear and Dynamic Programming,* Addison-Wesley Publishing Co., Inc., Reading, MA (1964).

PROBLEMS

6-1.[10] A Fibonacci search can be used to find the point on a line in space where a function is maximum. For the two points $(1, -1, 0, 2)$ and $(-5, -1, 3, 1)$, use a Fibonacci search, assuming perfect resolution and unimodality.

a. Give the coordinates of the points where the first two experiments would be placed, assuming a total of five measurements will be used.

b. What is the final interval of uncertainty on the coordinate axis x_1?

6-2.[10] In the following table eight values of y are given, and y is a function of four independent variables.

x_1	x_1	x_3	x_4	y
0	1	-1	3	5
1	1	-1	3	7
2	1	-1	3	9
-1	2	-1	3	2
0	-1	-1	3	7
0	1	1	3	7
0	1	-1	2	5
0	2	0	3	5

a. Determine the line of steep ascent passing through the point $(0, 1, -1, 3)$.

b. Determine the contour tangent hyperplane passing through (0, 1, −1, 3).

6–3.[17] Use the method of gradient partan to find the minimum of the following function starting at (2, 1, 3)

$$y = x_1^2 + 3x_2^2 + 5x_3^2$$

6–4. For the following function, draw contours on a graph for values of y of 20.0, 40.0, 60.0, and 80.0 in the region $0 \leq x_1 \leq 10$ and $0 \leq x_2 \leq 10$.

$$y = x_1 x_2$$

Starting at point x_0 (4, 4), apply pattern search to move toward maximum and employ a step size $\delta(\frac{1}{2}, \frac{1}{2})$. Make local explorations and accelerations (pattern moves) to obtain the points through b_5.

6–5. In Figure 6-12 a contour map is given for a function with a maximum located in the upper center. For the four multivariable search techniques, gradient search, sectioning, gradient partan, and pattern search, sketch (precisely) the path these algorithms would take, beginning at the indicated starting point and going toward the maximum. For pattern search make the step size equal to one-half of the width of the grid. The pattern search step size can be cut in half for the search to continue, if necessary. This will be the resolution limit, however. In addition, make brief comments about the effectiveness of these four techniques as applied to this function.

6–6. On the contour map given in Figure 6–13, sketch (precisely) the path of gradient partan, Powell's method, and pattern search beginning at the starting point shown. For pattern search, have the step size initially equal to the grid shown on the contour map and reduce the step size by one-half to have the search continue. Reduce the step size by one-half again if necessary to have pattern search continue. Give a brief discussion of the performance of these methods on this function.

6–7. Newton's method is obtained from the Taylor Series expansion for $y(x)$, truncating the terms that are third-order and higher, equation (6–8). Then equation (6–12) is obtained from the quadratic approximation, where x is the location of the minimum of the quadratic approximation. Discuss the iterative procedure that would be used to move to an optimum. To ensure convergence to a minimum (maximum), the value of $dy(\alpha)/d\alpha$ always must be negative (positive),

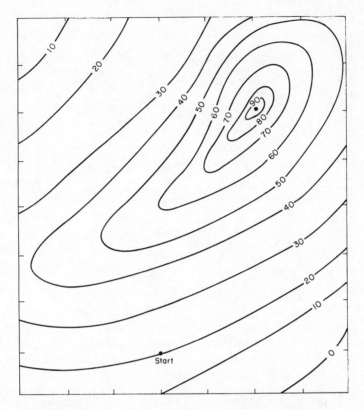

Figure 6-12. Contour map of a function with a maximum located in the upper center for Problem 6–5.

where α is the parameter of the line between points $\mathbf{x}_k$ and $\mathbf{x}_{k+1}$ obtained from successive applications of the algorithm.

$$\mathbf{x} = \mathbf{x}_k + \alpha(\mathbf{x}_{k+1} - \mathbf{x}_k)$$

Explain why this restriction is required for convergence to a local minimum (maximum).

6–8. Search for the minimum of the following function using gradient search starting at point $\mathbf{x}_0$ (1, 1, 1):

$$y = x_1{}^2 + x_2{}^2 + x_3{}^2$$

6–9. Develop and use a simplified version of Newton's method (quadratic fit) to search for the minimum of the function given in Problem 6–

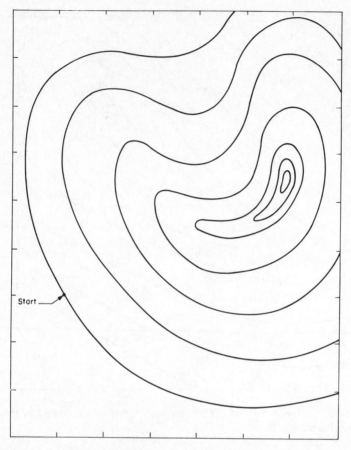

Figure 6-13. Contour map of a function with a curving ridge for Problem 6–6.

8 starting at the same point. Give the Taylor Series expansion for three independent variables truncating third- and higher order terms, neglecting iteracting (mixed partial derivative) terms for simplicity. Differentiate the truncated Taylor Series equation with respect to x_1, x_2, and x_3 to compute the optimum of the quadratic approximation, x_1^*, x_2^*, and x_3^*. Then apply these results to minimize the function of the problem. Compare the effort required for one iteration of the linear algorithm in Problem 6–8 to one iteration of the quadratic algorithm.

6–10. In Problem 7–7 a simplified alkylation process with three identical reactors in series is described. The profit function for each reactor can be represented by an equation with elliptical contours, and the catalyst degradation function can be represented by a linear equation.

a. If the optimum of the profit function for an individual reactor is at $F = 10$ and $C = 95$, derive the profit function to be maximized and the constraint equations to be satisfied for the process. The profit function for one reactor is given by the following equation:

$$y = 150 - 6(F - 10)^2 - 24(C - 95)^2$$

The constraint equations have the form $y = mx + b$, and the parameters m and b can be determined from Figure 7-31.

b. Form the penalty function for the above problem and discuss how this form will maximize the profit function and satisfy the constraint equations when a search technique is used to find the optimum.

6-11. Solve the following optimization problem by successive linear programming starting at x_0 (0, ½) using limits of (1, 1). Reduce the limits by one-half if infeasible points are encountered:

Minimize: $(x_1 - 2)^2 + (x_2 - 1)^2$

Subject to: $(-1/4) x_1 - x_2^2 + 1 \geq 0$

$x_1 - 2x_2 + 1 \geq 0$

6-12. Solve the following optimization problem by successive linear programming starting at point x_0 (1, 1) using limits of (1, 1). Reduce the limits by one-half if infeasible points are encountered:

Maximize: $4x_1 + x_2$

Subject to: $x_1^2 + 2x_2^2 \leq 20.25$

$x_1^2 - x_2^2 \leq 8.25$

6-13. Solve the following optimization problem by successive linear programming starting at point x_0 (1, 1) using limits of (1, 1). Reduce the limits by one-half if infeasible points are encountered:

Minimize: $y = 2x_1^2 + 2x_1x_2 + x_2^2 - 20x_1 - 14x_2$

Subject to: $x_1^2 + x_2^2 \leq 25$

$x_1^2 - x_2^2 \leq 7$

6–14.[26] Solve the following problem by successive linear programming starting at point (2, 1) using limits of (½, ½). Reduce the limits by one-half if infeasible points are encountered:

$$\text{Maximize: } 2x_1^2 - x_1x_2 + 3x_2^2$$

$$\text{Subject to: } 3x_1 + 4x_2 \le 12$$

$$x_1^2 - x_2^2 \ge 1$$

6–15.[34] Solve the following problem by successive linear programming starting at point x_0 (1, 1) using limits of (2, 2). Reduce the limits by one-half if infeasible points are encountered:

$$\text{Maximize: } 3x_1^2 + 2x_2^2$$

$$\text{Subject to: } x_1^2 + x_2^2 \le 25$$

$$9x_1 - x_2^2 \le 27$$

6–16. The following multivariable optimization problem is shown in Figure 6-7.

$$\text{Minimize: } -2x_1 - 4x_2 + x_1^2 + x_2^2 + 5$$

$$\text{Subject to: } -x_1 + 2x_2 \le 2$$

$$x_1 + x_2 \le 4$$

a. Give the successive linear programming algorithm for this problem in the form of equations (6–34). The upper and lower bounds are the same and are equal to 1.0.
b. For starting point $x_0 = (0, 0)$, apply the algorithm from part (a) to search for the optimum by successive linear programming.

6–17. Solve Problem 6–16 by quadratic programming.

6–18.[26] Solve the following problem by quadratic programming:

$$\text{Maximize: } -2x_1^2 - x_2^2 + 4x_1 + 6x_2$$

$$\text{Subject to: } x_1 + 3x_2 \le 3$$

6–19.[27] Solve the following problem by quadratic programming:

$$\text{Maximize: } 6x_1 - 2x_1^2 + 2x_1x_2 - 2x_2^2$$

$$\text{Subject to: } x_1 + x_2 \leq 2$$

6-20.[28] Solve the following problem by quadratic programming:

$$\text{Maximize: } 9x_2 + x_1^2$$

$$\text{Subject to: } x_1 + 2x_2 = 10$$

6-21. Solve the following problem by quadratic programming:

$$\text{Minimize: } 2x_1^2 + 2x_1x_2 + x_2^2 - 20x_1 - 14x_2$$

$$\text{Subject to: } x_1 + 3x_2 \leq 5$$

$$2x_1 - x_2 \leq 4$$

6-22. Solve the following problem by the generalized reduced gradient method starting at the feasible point x_0 (1, 1, 19) to find the optimum located at x^* (4, 3, 0). Use the optimum point to determine the appropriate value of the parameter of the reduced gradient line for one line search to arrive at the optimum:

$$\text{Maximize: } 3x_1^2 + 2x_2^2 - x_3$$

$$\text{Subject to: } x_1^2 + x_2^2 = 25$$

$$9x_1 - x_2^2 + x_3 = 27$$

6-23.[11] Solve the following problem by the generalized reduced gradient method. Start at the point $x_0 = (2, 1, 3, 1)$, and have x_1 and x_4 be the basic or dependent variables and x_2 and x_3 the nonbasic or independent variables:

$$\text{Minimize: } x_1^2 + 4x_2^2$$

$$\text{Subject to: } x_1 + 2x_2 - x_3 = 1$$

$$-x_1 + x_2 + x_4 = 0$$

6-24. Solve the following problem by the generalized reduced gradient method starting at point x_0 (2, 4, 5). Show that the value of the parameters of the reduced gradient line $\alpha_1 = -1/20$ locates the minimum of the economic model and satisfies the constraints:

$$\text{Minimize: } 4x_1 - x_2^2 + x_3^2 - 12$$

$$\text{Subject to: } -x_1^2 - x_2^2 \qquad + 20 = 0$$

$$x_1 \qquad + x_3 - 7 = 0$$

6-25.[17] Find the minimum of the following function starting at the point x_0 (1, 1, 1). However, this time experimental error is involved, and the Kiefer-Wolfowitz procedure must be used, employing $a_k = 1/k$ and $c_k = 1/k^{1/4}$ with $k = 1, 2, \cdots, 10$. Simulate experimental error by flipping a coin and adding (subtracting) 0.1 from y if the coin turn up heads (tails):

$$y = x_1^2 + 3x_2^2 + 5x_2^2$$

7
DYNAMIC PROGRAMMING

INTRODUCTION

This optimization procedure was developed at the same organization where Danzig developed linear programming, the RAND Corporation, a U.S. Air Force-sponsored "think tank." The research was in response to the need in the early 1950s, the *Sputnik* era, for a solution to the optimum missile-trajectory problem, which required extensions to the calculus of variations. Two parallel efforts, one in this country by Richard Bellman and another in Russia by L. S. Pontryagin, led to similar but different solutions to the problem.

The name, *dynamic programming,* was selected by Richard Bellman for this optimization method that he devised and described in a series of papers and the books *Dynamic Programming* (1) and *Applied Dynamic Programming* (2). It is thought that the selection of the name bore no direct relation to the method, which was not the situation for linear and geometric programming.

There are continuous and discrete versions of this optimization method. The continuous version is used for solutions to the trajectory problem where a continuous function is required, and the discrete version is used when a problem can be described in a series of stages. Most engineering applications use the discrete version of dynamic programming, and it will be the subject of this chapter.

One of the first books on the method that elaborated on engineering applications was by Roberts (3) in 1964. It was a comprehensive treatment of the subject at the time and dealt with numerous applications, including optimal allocation problems, the relation to optimal process control, the calculus of variations, and continuous dynamic and stochastic dynamic programming. It is still a valuable reference.

The efforts of Mitten, Nemhauser, Aris, and Wilde led to the extension of dynamic programming for systems that involved loops and branches. Aris (4) had published results of research on the application of dynamic programming to the optimal design of chemical reactors, and Mitten and Nemhauser (5) had described a procedure to apply the method to a chemical process that involved a branched system. Professor Wilde (6) of Stanford University was conducting research on dynamic programming at this time and had the opportunity to discuss the method with both Aris and Nemhauser within a short time. This led to a collaboration that produced a landmark paper extending the theory of dynamic programming from serial processes to ones with loops and branches (7). In a subsequent publication, Wilde (8) developed the concept of functional diagrams to represent the functional equations of dynamic programming and a systematic method of converting a process flow diagram to a dynamic programming functional diagram. These results have become the standard way of analyzing processes for dynamic programming optimization and will serve as the foundation for this chapter.

Dynamic programming converts a large, complicated optimization problem into a series of interconnected smaller ones, each containing only a few variables. The result is a series of partial optimizations requiring a reduced effort to find the optimum, even though some of the variables may have to be enumerated throughout their range. Also, the previously discussed single and multivariable search methods are applicable to each of the partial optimization steps. Then, the dynamic programming algorithm can be applied to find the optimum of the entire process by using the connected partial optimizations of the smaller problems.

As with the other optimization methods, dynamic programming has a unique nomenclature. To introduce this nomenclature, we will begin to discuss the subject with a simple network problem. This will illustrate the concept of stages and partial optimization at a stage by decision variables. Also, it will show the use of state variables to link the stages and serve as the path for the dynamic programming algorithm to complete the optimization of the entire process. This will be followed by a process example where the network is replaced by graphical representations of the economic model (return function) and constraint equations (transition functions) to illustrate the additional complications introduced by continuous functions. Then the dynamic programming algorithm is given and discussed for N-stage serial systems and extended to ones that involve loops and branches. Following this, Wilde's rules are given and illustrated to convert a process flow diagram to a dynamic programming functional diagram. Also, the optimal allocation of resources and the use of time rather than a process unit as a stage are described and illustrated. The latter is the application of dynamic programming to the optimal equipment replacement problem.

It is necessary to begin with the definition of dynamic programming nomenclature. An individual process unit or a unit of time can be represented as a stage, the black box of Chapter 5. A stage is shown diagrammatically in Figure 7-1 and represents the economic model of the unit. The economic model is called a return function $R_i(s_i, d_i)$ and gives the measure of profit or cost for the stage. This economic model depends on the independent variables at the stage. These are decision and state variables. Decision variables,

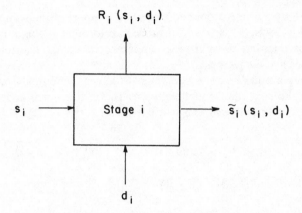

Figure 7-1. Diagrammatic representation of a dynamic programming stage.

d_i, are ones that can be manipulated independently. State variables, s_i, are ones that are inputs to the stage from an adjacent stage. Consequently, they cannot be manipulated independently. The stage will have outputs, $\tilde{s}_i$, that are inputs to adjacent stages. Input state variables to a stage could represent the flow rate of feed from an upstream unit, and output state variables could represent products from the stage that go to a downstream unit for further refining.

There are transition functions, $\tilde{s}_i = T_i(s_i, d_i)$, at each stage; and these equations could represent material and energy balances at the stage, i.e., the conversion of raw materials to products. Recall in linear programming that transition functions were represented by the volumetric yields. The stage shown in Figure 7-1 represents the transition functions also.

Stages can be connected, and a simple serial process is shown in Figure 7-2 with three stages. The diagram illustrates incident identities, the equations

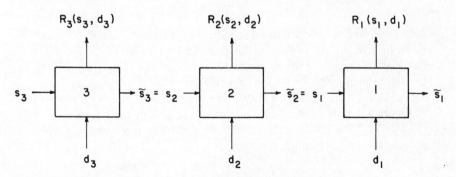

Figure 7-2. A simple, three-stage serial process.

that relate the outputs from one stage to the inputs of the subsequent stage, e.g., $\tilde{s}_2 = s_1$. Also, it is standard procedure to number stages from right to left rather than left to right in dynamic programming. The reason for this will be given subsequently.

The diagram in Figure 7-2 represents the economic model or the return function, the constraint equations or transition functions, and the incident identities. These functions can be written as:

$$\text{Optimize: } R_1(s_1, d_1) + R_2(s_2, d_2) + R_3(s_3, d_3) \tag{7-1}$$

$$\text{Subject to: } \tilde{s}_1 = T_1(s_1, d_1) \tag{7-2a}$$

$$\tilde{s}_2 = T_2(s_2, d_2) \tag{7-2b}$$

$$\tilde{s}_3 = T_3(s_3, d_3) \tag{7-2c}$$

$$\tilde{s}_2 = s_1, \ \tilde{s}_3 = s_2 \tag{7-3}$$

There are four independent variables, d_1, d_2, d_3, and s_3. These are to be determined to optimize the sum of the returns R_1, R_2, and R_3. Also any bounds specified on $\tilde{s}_3 = s_2$, $\tilde{s}_2 = s_1$, and $\tilde{s}_1$ would have to be satisfied.

With dynamic programming three partial optimizations are performed, one at each stage; and then this information is used to locate the optimum for the entire process. The following equation gives the dynamic programming algorithm for the first stage in terms of maximizing the profit given by the return function:

$$f_1(s_1) = \max_{d_1} [R_1(s_1, d_1)] \tag{7-4}$$

It is necessary to exhaustively list individual values of s_1 and to search on d_1 to determine $f_1(s_1)$. This is illustrated in Figure 7-3 where the values of $f_1(s_1)$ are along the line of maximum values of $R_1(s_1, d_1)$ as determined by the optimal value of d_1 for selected values of s_1. The values of $f_1(s_1)$ are tabulated and stored for future use, and equation (7-4) is represented in Figure 7-4 as the functional diagram for stage 1 of the process.

At stage 2 the optimal information at stage 1 is used, and the dynamic programming algorithm at this stage is:

$$f_2(s_2) = \max_{d_2} [R_2(s_2, d_2) + f_1(s_1)] \tag{7-5}$$

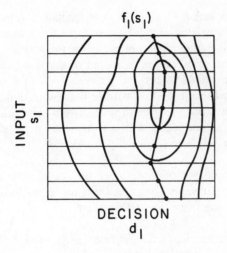

$f_1(s_1)$

INPUT s_1

The points represent the optimal decision, d_1, for each input s_1 to maximize the return function, $R_1(s_1, d_1)$.

DECISION d_1

Figure 7-3. Contours of a return function, $R_1(s_1, d_1)$.

Again, it is necessary to exhaustively list individual values of s_2 and to search on d_2 to obtain the maximum of the sum of the return at stage 2 and the optimal return at stage 1, $f_1(s_1)$. The appropriate values of $f_1(s_1)$ are determined using incident identity and transition function $s_1 = \tilde{s}_2 = T_2(s_2, d_2)$. Thus, the optimal values of $f_2(s_2)$ can be determined and stored for future use.

At the third and final stage, the optimal information $f_2(s_2)$ from stage 2 is used, and the dynamic programming algorithm at this stage is:

$$f_3(s_3) = \max_{d_3} [R_3(s_3, d_3) + f_2(s_2)] \qquad (7\text{--}6)$$

At this point either the value of s_3 is known or it is an independent variable. If s_3 is a known constant value, it is necessary only to determine the value of d_3 that maximizes $f_3(s_3)$ in equation (7–6) for that value of s_3. An exhaus-

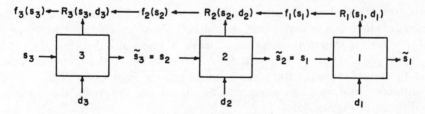

Figure 7-4. A functional diagram for a three-serial process.

tive listing of values of s_3 is not required. If s_3 is an independent variable, it is necessary to conduct a two-variable search to determine the maximum value of $f_3(s_3, d_3)$. This determines the maximum profit for the system, and the optimal values of the decision variables are extracted from the tabulated partial optimizations from the previous stages.

Before giving a simple network example to illustrate the use of dynamic programming, we will give the dynamic programming algorithm in its general form. Bellman (1) devised this method along with a statement for the algorithm in what he called the "Principle of Optimality," which is:

An optimal policy has the property that whatever the initial state and initial decision, the remaining decisions must constitute an optimal policy with regard to the state resulting from the first decision.

This principle was stated mathematically as the dynamic programming algorithm to maximize a serial process with i stages as:

$$f_i(s_i) = \max_{d_i} \ [R_i(s_i, d_i) + f_{i-1}(s_{i-1})] \qquad (7\text{--}7)$$

In the algorithm $R_i(s_i, d_i)$ is the return from stage i with inputs s_i and d_i and output s_{i-1}; $f_{i-1}(s_{1-1})$ is the maximum return for stages 1 through $i-1$ as a function of input s_{i-1}; and $f_i(s_i)$ is the maximum return for stages 1 through i as a function of s_i.

A dynamic programming analysis begins with the last section of a system and ends with the first section. The last section of a serial system has an output that does not affect another unit of the system. Therefore, it is convenient to number the stages beginning with the last section and ending with the first section. The following simple network example illustrates the concepts of stages, state and decision variables, and the applications of the dynamic programming algorithm.

EXAMPLE 7–1

A tank truck of an expensive product manufactured in San Francisco is to be delivered to any major port on the East Coast for shipment to Europe. The cost for shipment across the Atlantic is essentially the same from the major ports on the East coast. It is desired to select the optimum route (lowest road mileage) from San Francisco to the East Coast. The relative distances between cities along possible routes are shown on the network diagram in Figure 7-5.

To solve the problem one essentially works backward. Beginning at cities

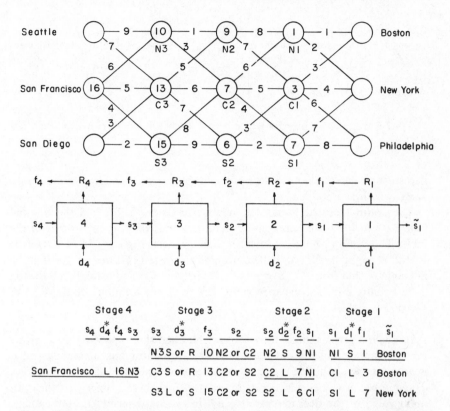

Figure 7-5. Dynamic programming solution of network problem of Example 7-1.

N1, C1, and S1, one places the minimum distance to the East Coast in the circle, and this distance, f_1, along with the optimal decision, is recorded in the table. For example, if the optimal route led to the central city (C1), the optimal decision, d_1^*, would be to drive to Boston (L-left, not S-straight or R-right), which is closer than New York or Philadelphia. For each value of the state variable, the optimal decision, d_1^*, is tabulated at stage 1 according to equation (7-4). At stage 2 for each state variable (city N2, C2, S2) the minimum distance from that city to the East Coast is determined by the dynamic programming algorithm, equation (7-5). The optimal return is the minimum of the sum of the distance from a city in row 2 (N2, C2, or S2) to those in row 1, R_2, and the minimum distance from the cities in row 1 to the East Coast f_1. The minimum total distance is placed in the circle and recorded in the table at stage 2 along with the optimal decision (L, S, or R). This procedure is repeated for the third stage of the process. At the fourth stage the state variable has only one value, San Francisco; and it is

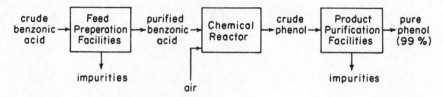

Figure 7-6. Simplified process flow diagram for the phenol from benzoic acid process.

necessary to determine only the optimal decision corresponding to San Francisco, which is N3.

The optimal return (minimum relative distance) is 16, and the optimal policy is shown as the underlined input-output sequence back through the table. The optimal policy is: start at San Francisco, go left to N3, straight to N2, straight to N1, and then straight to Boston. However, the route is not unique, for from N3 a right to C2, left to N1, and straight to Boston is an equally minimal distance route. There is not a unique optimal set of decision variables.

In this network example the state variables had three specific values. However, in most problems the state variables are continuous functions, and it is necessary to subdivide the state variables into a number of discrete values. The number of values selected determines the number of times that the optimum value of the decision variable d_i^* has to be determined at the stage. The choice of the number of values of the state variable determines the computational effort required at the stage. Also, this choice determines the grid of values on s_i available when the dynamic programming algorithm is used to determine the optimal decisions, d_i^*. Interpolation is required to determine the optimal values of the state and decision variables coming back through the table. The following example illustrates these additional complications for a simplified process with continuous transition and return functions given graphically.

EXAMPLE 7-2

A simplified process for the production of phenol employes crude benzoic acid as a feed and is shown in the flow diagram in Figure 7-6. Separation facilities (absorption and distillation) purify the benzoic acid, which is sent to a chemical reactor where it is oxidized to phenol. The impure phenol is sent to separation facilities (evaporation and distillation) where pure (99%) phenol is produced. The economic and process models for each of the three

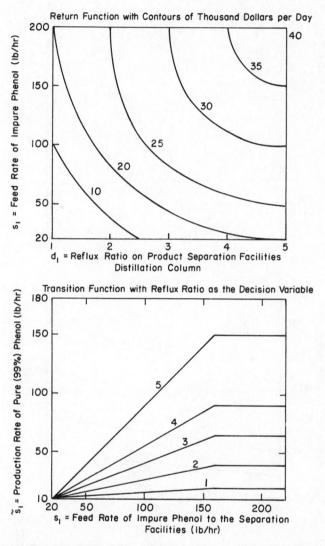

Figure 7-7. Economic model (return function) and process model (transition function) for the product purification facilities.

steps in the process are shown graphically in Figures 7-7, 7-8, and 7-9. These give the return functions and transition functions for each dynamic programming stage. The contours shown on the figures for the return function are profits, if positive, and operating costs, if negative.

To obtain the optimum by dynamic programming, each step in the process

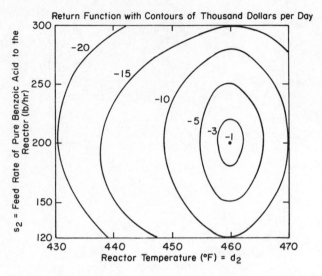

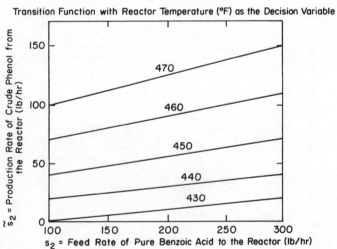

Figure 7-8. Economic model (return function) and process model (transition function) for the chemical reactor.

is made a dynamic programming stage. The state and decision variables are given on the diagrams shown in Figures 7-7, 7-8, and 7-9. The tables at each stage can be developed using the information in these figures for the dynamic programming optimization. This is illustrated in Table 7-1, and for stage 1 the optimal decision for the maximum profit is to use the largest

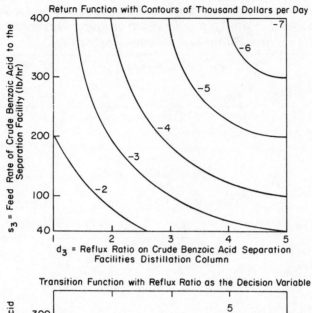

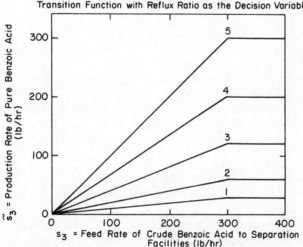

Figure 7-9. Economic model (return function) and process model (transition function) for the feed preparation facilities.

value of the reflux ratio, $d_1 = 5$. The set of values for the state variable, s_1, were selected to be separated by 50 units. This was an arbitrary decision at this point, but it seemed reasonable to permit linear interpolation between the values of the state variables when the dynamic programming algorithm is applied.

Table 7-1. Illustrating the Computation of the State and Decision Variables for the Dynamic Programming Optimization of the Simplified Phenol Process.

STAGE 1		$f_1(s_1) = \max\limits_{d_1} [R_1(s_1, d_1)]$		
s_1	d_1		R_1	$\tilde{s}_1$
200	5		40	150
150	5		35	140
100	5		30	90
50	5		25	40
20	5		20	10

STAGE 2		$f_2(s_2) = \max\limits_{d_2} [R_2(s_2, d_2) + f_1(s_1)]$			
s_2	d_2	$\tilde{s}_2 = s_1$	R_2	f_1	$R_2 + f_1$
300	470	150	-17	35	$\underline{18} = f_2$
	460	110	-15	31	16
	450	70	-17	27	10
	440	40	-21	23	2

STAGE 3		$f_3(s_3) = \max\limits_{d_3} [R_3(s_3, d_3) + f_2(s_2)]$			
s_3	d_3	$\tilde{s}_3 = s_2$	R_3	f_2	$R_3 + f_2$
400	5	300	-7	18	11
	4	200	-6	28	$\underline{22} = f_3$
	3	120	-5	17.5	12.5
	2	60	-4	8.75	4.75

This information developed for stage 1 is recorded in Figure 7-10, which gives the dynamic programming functional diagram for the process programming stage.

The dynamic programming algorithm is given in Table 7-1 for the second stage, and it is necessary to exhaustively list values of the state variable s_2 and to determine the optimum value of the decision variable. Again a spacing of 50 units is selected for the values of the state variables beginning at the upper limit of 300. For this value of $s_2 = 300$ a range of values for d_2 are listed in Table 7-1, and the corresponding values of $\tilde{s}_2 = s_1$, R_2, and f_1 are determined from Figures 7-8 and 7-10. Computing $(R_2 + f_1)$ the optimal value of the decision d_2 is determined that gives the largest value of $(R_2 + f_1)$. This is shown in Table 7-1 as $d_2 = 470$ and $(R_2 + f_1) = 18$, and this determines $f_2(300) = 18$ by the application of the dynamic programming algorithm.

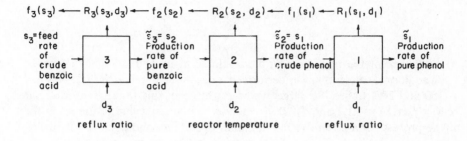

Stage 3				Stage 2				Stage 1			
s_3	d_3^*	f_3	$\tilde{s}_3$	s_2	d_2^*	f_2	$\tilde{s}_2$	s_1	d_1^*	f_1	$\tilde{s}_1$
400	4	22	200	300	470	18	150	200	5	40	150
300	4	22.5	200	250	460	25	100	150	5	35	140
250	4.4	22.7	200	200	460	28	90	100	5	30	90
200	5	23	200	150	460	23	80	(90	5	29	80)
180	5	21.2	180	120	460	17.5	75	50	5	25	40
150	5	20	150					20	5	20	10
100	5	10	100								

Figure 7-10. Dynamic programming functional diagram and optimal results for the simplified phenol process.

Other values of $f_2(s_2)$ are computed in the same way, and then results are listed in Figure 7-10 at stage 2. It should be noted at this point that an exhaustive search is being done on d_2 to determine the optimal value. This is being done for illustrative purposes and is convenient with the process data in a graphical form. However, in an industrial problem the transition and return functions could be considerably more complicated, and the search effort to determine the optimal value of the decision variables could be significantly reduced by using one of the previously described single or multivariable search methods.

Using the dynamic programming algorithm at stage 3 shown in Table 7-1, we obtain the optimal results for the state and decision variables, tabulated in Figure 7-10. The calculation procedure used to locate the optimal value of d_3 for $s_3 = 400$ is shown in Table 7-1, and this involved the same procedure used at stage 2. However, industrial problems would have significantly more complicated transitions and return functions, and a two-variable search would be used to locate the best values of s_3 and d_3 that maximized $f_3(s_3, d_3)$. In this case the dynamic programming algorithm would be:

$$f_3 = \max_{\substack{d_3 \\ s_3}} [R_3(s_3, d_3) + f_2(s_2)]$$

At this point the maximum profit would seem to be $f_3 = 23.0$. However, an additional calculation was performed for $s_3 = 180$ to refine the grid between 150 and 200, to see if a larger value might be in this range. It turned out that $f_3(180) = 21.2$ and $f_3(200)$ remained the largest value of the profit for the process. Consequently, the optimum operating conditions can be determined as shown in Figure 7-10, and it is necessary to interpolate for the values of d_1 and $\tilde{s}_1$ at stage 1. However, the grid of values for s_1 is satisfactory to permit linear interpolation for d_1 and $\tilde{s}_1$ within the accuracy known for those variables from the economic and process models.

Now we are ready to extend our discussion to a system with N dynamic programming stages. This follows in the next section for serial processes, and these results are extended for the cases with loops and branches. Then we will turn to the problem of relating units of an industrial process to dynamic programming stages.

VARIABLES, TRANSFORMS, AND STAGES

Although it was adequate in the preceding problem, usually the process flow diagram will have to be modified to obtain the dynamic programming functional diagram, because information flow rather than material flow must be evaluated. Functional equations and the corresponding functional diagrams of the stages of the system are developed to describe this information flow using the process flow diagram. It will be necessary to broaden the description of a stage to have more than one state and decision variable. Also, when loops and branches are involved, the outputs from one stage may be the inputs to more than one stage.

Figure 7-11 shows a dynamic programming stage that has more than one state and one decision variable. The transition and return functions are given in the figure for this stage, also. As shown, there are two output state variables that are determined by the two transition functions. These transition functions have six independent variables: three state and three decision variables. The dynamic programming algorithm is given in the figure and shows that a three-variable search is required to determine the optimal values of the decision variables. Also, the three state variables have to be exhaustively listed to develop the tabular information for the partial optimization at the stage. It turns out that three is the limit for the number of state variables at a stage because of the computational effort required to obtain optimal decisions for the exhaustive list of values of the state variables.

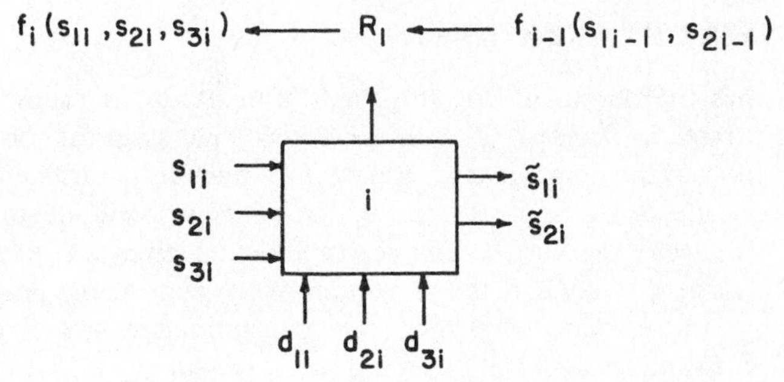

$$f_i(s_{1i},s_{2i},s_{3i}) \longleftarrow R_i \longleftarrow f_{i-1}(s_{1i-1},s_{2i-1})$$

Transition Functions

$$\tilde{s}_{1i} = T_{1i}(s_{1i}, s_{2i}, s_{3i}, d_{1i}, d_{2i}, d_{3i})$$
$$\tilde{s}_{2i} = T_{2i}(s_{1i}, s_{2i}, s_{3i}, d_{1i}, d_{2i}, d_{3i})$$

Incident Identities

$$\tilde{s}_{1i} = s_{1i-1}$$
$$\tilde{s}_{2i} = s_{2i-1}$$

Return Function

$$R_i = R_i(s_{1i}, s_{2i}, s_{3i}, d_{1i}, d_{2i}, d_{3i})$$

Dynamic Programming Alogorithm

$$f_i(s_{1i},s_{2i},s_{3i}) = \max_{\substack{d_{1i} \\ d_{2i} \\ d_{3i}}} \left[R_i(s_{1i},s_{2i},s_{3i},d_{1i},d_{2i},d_{3i}) + f_{i-1}(s_{1i-1},s_{2i-1}) \right]$$

Figure 7-11. Dynamic programming stage with more than one state and decision variable.

The incident identities are not shown in this figure. These are the equations that give the relations among the outputs from a stage and the inputs to adjacent stages. Here $\tilde{s}_{1i}$ and $\tilde{s}_{2i}$ could both be inputs to stage $i - 1$, or they could be inputs to two stages, which would be the case for a diverging branch. The discussion follows for the serial optimization problem where the outputs from one stage are inputs to the following stage. Then this is expanded to include loops and branches.

SERIAL SYSTEM OPTIMIZATION (7)

A serial system has the output of one stage as the input to the following stage. This is illustrated in Figure 7-12, with one decision per stage for convenience. The functional equations given in Figure 7-12 include the transition functions, incident identities, and return function. The incident identities give the relation between the stages. The return function gives a measure of the profit or cost at a stage, and the maximum of the sum of the profits from each stage is to be found by determining the optimal values of the decision variables. Examples 7–1 and 7–2 were serial systems.

Serial system optimization problems are of four types: initial value, final

FUNCTIONAL DIAGRAM

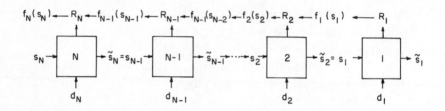

FUNCTIONAL EQUATIONS

Dynamic Programming Algorithm

$$f_i(s_i) = \max_{d_i} \left[R_i(s_i, d_i) + f_{i-1}(s_{i-1}) \right] \quad \text{for } i = 1, 2, \ldots, N$$

Transition Equations

$$\tilde{s}_i = T_i(s_i, d_i) \qquad\qquad \text{for } i = 1, 2, \cdots, N$$

Return Functions

$$R_i = R_i(s_i, d_i) \qquad\qquad \text{for } i = 1, 2, \cdots, N$$

Incident Identities

$$\tilde{s}_i = s_{i-1} \qquad\qquad \text{for } i = 1, 2, \cdots, N$$

Figure 7-12. Functional diagram and functional equations for a serial process.

value, two-point boundary value, and cyclic problems. In an initial value problem s_N is a known constant, in a final value problem $\tilde{s}_1$ is a known constant, and in a two-point boundary value problem both s_N and $\tilde{s}_1$ are known. In a cyclic problem $s_N = \tilde{s}_1$, and the best value has to be determined that maximizes $f_N(s_N)$.

Initial Value Problem: The dynamic programming algorithm for the ith stage of the initial value problem is the same as given in Figure 7-12.

$$f_i(s_i) = \max_{d_i} \; [R_i(s_i, d_i) + f_{i-1}(s_{i-1})] \qquad (7\text{-}7)$$

The optimal return at stage i, f_i, is only a function of s_i, the state variables at stage i. The incident identity and transition function are used to show this result:

$$s_{i-1} = \tilde{s}_i = T_i(s_i, d_i) \qquad (7\text{-}8)$$

Substituting the above equation into equation (7–7) gives:

$$f_i(s_i) = \max_{d_i} \; \{R_i(s_i, d_i) + f_{i-1}[T_i(s_i, d_i)]\} \qquad (7\text{-}9)$$

which shows that f_i is a function of s_i, optimizing out d_i.

This algorithm, equation (7–9), applies from stage 2 to stage $N - 1$. At stage 1 the dynamic programming algorithm is:

$$f_1(s_1) = \max_{d_1} R_1(s_1, d_1) \qquad (7\text{-}10)$$

This is the only algorithm that does not contain the optimal return from a preceding stage.

At the last stage, stage N, the dynamic programming algorithm is:

$$f_N(s_N) = \max_{d_N} \; (R_N(s_N, d_N) + f_{N-1}[T_N(s_N, d_N)]) \qquad (7\text{-}11)$$

If the value of s_N is a known constant, the maximum return is $f_N(s_N)$, and an exhaustive tabulation of s_N is not required. The problem is referred to as an N-decision, no-state optimization problem. However, if s_N is not a constant and can be manipulated like a decision variable to maximize f_N, the dynamic programming algorithm at stage N is:

$$f_N = \max_{\substack{d_N \\ s_N}} \left[R_N(s_N, d_N) + f_{N-1}(s_{N-1}) \right] \qquad (7\text{--}12)$$

This is a no-state, two-decision partial optimization at stage N. Consequently, it is referred to as an $(N + 1)$ decision, no-state optimization problem, and there are $N + 1$ independent variables. The set of values for the decision variables, d_i, and state variables, s_N, that maximize the return function is called the *optimal policy*. N partial optimizations have been required to obtain an optimal return and optimal policy for the system.

Final Value Problem: For this situation the output from the first stage, $\tilde{s}_1$, is a known constant. There are two approaches to solve this problem, called *state inversion* and *decision inversion*.

State inversion means to transform the final value problem into an initial value problem by obtaining the N inverse transition functions, i.e., solve the transition functions for s_i in terms of $\tilde{s}_i$ as indicated below:

$$s_i = \tilde{T}_1(\tilde{s}_i, d_i) \qquad \text{for } i = 1, 2, \cdots, N \qquad (7\text{--}13)$$

This results in reversing the arrows in Figure 7-12, as shown in Figure 7-13(a). Renumbering the stages makes the problem into an initial value one. The problem has $(N - 1)$ one-state, one-decision and one no-state, one-decision partial optimizations.

In some cases inverting the transition functions is not possible, and the technique of decision inversion is employed. Here the roles of d_1 and s_1 are interchanged. The stage one transition function is:

$$\tilde{s}_1 = T_1(s_1, d_1) = \text{constant} \qquad (7\text{--}14)$$

This equation can be put in the form:

$$d_1 = \tilde{T}_1(s_1, \tilde{s}_1) \qquad (7\text{--}15)$$

and d_1 is uniquely determined by specifying s_1, for $\tilde{s}_1$ is a constant for this case. Stage 1 is decisionless and is combined with stage 2. This is shown diagrammatically in Figure 7-13(b) with the arrow reversed on d_1, indicating that it is no longer a decision, and the arrow crossed on $\tilde{s}_1$, indicating that it is a constant.

The functional equation for the combined stages 1 and 2 is now:

$$f_2(s_2) = \max_{d_2} \left[R_2(s_2, d_2) + R_1(s_1, d_1) \right] \qquad (7\text{--}16)$$

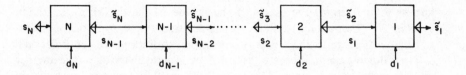

a. State Inversion

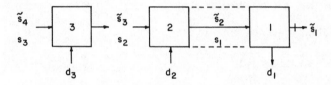

b. Decision Inversion

Figure 7-13. Functional diagrams for state and decision inversion for a final value serial problem.

which can be combined with equation (7–15) and

$$s_1 = \tilde{s}_2 = T_2(s_2, d_2) \tag{7–17}$$

to obtain the following equation:

$$f_2(s_2) = \max_{d_2} \{(R_2(s_2, d_2) + R_1[T_2(s_2, d_2), \tilde{T}_1[T_2(s_2, d_2), \tilde{s}_1]]\}$$

or

$$f_2(s_2) = \max_{d_2} [R_2(s_2, d_2) + R_1(s_2, d_2)] \tag{7–18}$$

These manipulations show that combining stages 1 and 2 gives one new stage. This new stage requires a one-state, one-decision partial optimization. The final form of the functional diagram for decision inversion is shown in Figure 7-13(b).

After decision inversion is performed, the usual serial problem procedure applies to the rest of the stages in the problem. The overall optimization involves $N-1$ total stages with $N-2$ one-decision, one-state partial optimizations, and at stage N there is a two-decision, no-state partial optimization.

The following example illustrates the effect on state inversion by the number of state variables at a stage. There are three cases to consider, as shown in the example.

EXAMPLE 7–3

In state inversion three cases may occur at a stage. These are: the stage has the same number of input state variables as outputs, the stage has more input state variable than outputs or the stage has fewer input state variables than outputs. Assuming the transition functions can be inverted, obtain the transition functions from state inversion for these cases with three state variables and one decision variable per stage.

a. State variable inputs are equal to the outputs.

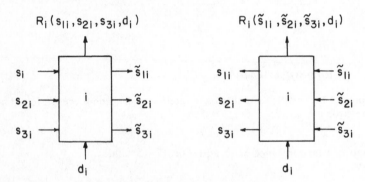

In this case state inversion has the input and output variables interchanged.

b. State variable inputs are more than outputs.

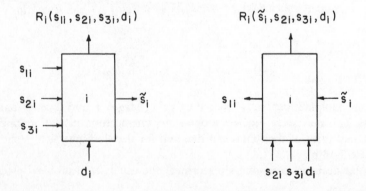

In this case there is only one transition function, and for state inversion it is written as:

$$s_{1i} = \hat{T}_i(\tilde{s}_i, s_{2i}, s_{3i}, d_i)$$

The state variables s_{2i} and s_{3i} become decision variables along with d_i. State inversion for this case has a significant advantage for the dynamic programming optimization by converting state variables to decision variables.

c. State variable outputs are more than inputs.

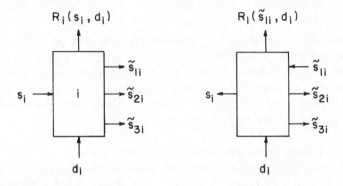

In this case there are three transition functions, but only one is inverted, as shown below:

$$\tilde{s}_{1i} = T_{1i}(s_i, d_i) \qquad s_i = \hat{T}_{1i}(\tilde{s}_{1i}, d_i)$$

$$\tilde{s}_{2i} = T_{2i}(s_i\, d_i) \qquad \tilde{s}_{2i} = \hat{T}_{2i}(\tilde{s}_{1i}, d_i)$$

$$\tilde{s}_{3i} = T_{3i}(s_i, d_i) \qquad \tilde{s}_{3i} = \hat{T}_{3i}(\tilde{s}_{1i}, d_i)$$

The remaining two transition functions become equations that calculate output $\tilde{s}_{2i}$ and $\tilde{s}_{3i}$ from values of $\tilde{s}_{1i}$ and d_i.

Two-Point Boundary Value Problem: This type of problem arises when both the initial and final values of the state variables $\tilde{s}_1$ and s_N are specified. The problem requires decision inversion, because state inversion still would give a two-point, boundary value problem. Decision inversion is performed condensing stages 1 and 2, as was shown in Figure 7-13(b). Then the partial optimization proceeds as in an initial value problem. The dynamic programming algorithm for the combined stage 1 and 2 is the same as equation (7–18). This is a one-state, one-decision optimization at stage 1–2, because $\tilde{s}_1$ is a specified constant.

The optimization continues in the usual fashion, the dynamic programming algorithm at stage 3 being:

$$f_3(s_3) = \max_{d_3} \{R_3(s_3, d_3) + f_2[T_3(d_3, s_3)]\} \tag{7–19}$$

At stage N, the dynamic programming algorithm is:

$$f_N(s_N) = \max_{d_N} \{R_N(s_N, d_N) + f_{N-1}(s_{N-1})\} \tag{7–20}$$

This is a no-state, one-decision partial optimization, because s_N is a constant.

To solve the two-point, boundary value problem, first a decision inversion is performed and followed by the partial optimizations for an initial value problem. This involves $N-2$ one-state, one-decision and one no-state, one-decision partial optimizations. Two-point, boundary value problems always require decision inversion.

Cyclic System Optimization: The cyclic system is a special case of the two-point boundary value problem where $s_N = \tilde{s}_1$, and the functional diagram is shown in Figure 7-14. The method to solve this problem is to select a value of $\tilde{s}_1 = s_N = C$ and proceed to determine the optimum return as a two-point boundary value problem. The dynamic programming algorithm at stage N is:

$$f_N(C) = \max_{d_N} [R_N(C, d_N) + f_{N-1}(s_{N-1})] \tag{7–21}$$

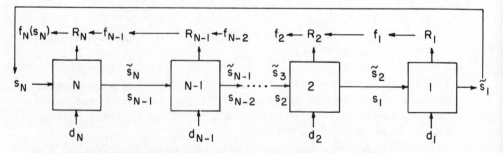

Figure 7-14. Functional diagram for an N stage cyclic system.

Then a single-variable search is performed by varying C until the maximum return $f_N(C)$ is located. A Fibonacci or golden section search can be used effectively on the cut state values of $s_N = \tilde{s}_1 = C$ to locate the best value that maximizes $f_N(C)$. Fixing the value of a state variable is referred to as *cutting the state* and is indicated on a functional diagram by two slashes on the arrow of the state variable. The following example illustrates the procedure for cyclic optimization.

EXAMPLE 7–4

In the dynamic programming optimization of the contact process for sulfuric acid discussed later in the chapter, the final functional diagram consisted of five stages with recycle loop with two state variables.

In this problem it is necessary to cut the state of both variables in the recycle loop. The problem is to show that this will have stages 1 and 2 combined with stage 3 to give a three-stage cyclic optimization problem.

The dynamic programming algorithm and transition functions at stage 1 are:

$$f_1(s_1) = \max_{d_1} [R_1(s_1, d_1)] \qquad \tilde{s}_{11} = T_{11}(s_1, d_1)$$

$$\tilde{s}_{21} = T_{21}(s_1, d_1)$$

Cutting the state on the recycle loop gives:

$$\tilde{s}_{11} = s_{15} = \text{constant}$$

$$\tilde{s}_{21} = s_{25} = \text{constant}$$

Performing decision inversion using the transition functions converts $\tilde{s}_{11}$ and $\tilde{s}_{21}$ from fixed outputs to inputs. Solving the transition function for s_1 and d_1 in terms of $\tilde{s}_{11}$ and $\tilde{s}_{21}$ gives:

$$s_1 = \hat{T}_{11}(\tilde{s}_{11}, \tilde{s}_{21}) \qquad d_1 = \hat{T}_{21}(\tilde{s}_{11}, s_{21})$$

Consequently both s_1 and d_1 are computed by these transition functions if $\tilde{s}_{11}$ and $\tilde{s}_{21}$ are specified. This means that $f_1(s_1)$ is specified also.

$$f_1(s_1) = R_1(\tilde{s}_{11}, \tilde{s}_{21})$$

There is no partial optimization at stage 1, and the output from stage 2 is fixed also, for $\tilde{s}_2 = s_1$. The dynamic programming algorithm and transition function at stage 2 are:

$$f_2(s_2) = \max_{d_2} [R_2(d_2, s_2) + f_1(s_1)] \qquad \tilde{s}_2 = T_2(s_2, d_2) = s_1$$

There is no decision at stage 2, because the fixed output $\tilde{s}_2$ will convert decision d_2 into a computed output by decision inversion, i.e., $d_2 = \hat{T}_2(\tilde{s}_2, s_2)$ where $\tilde{s}_2 = s_1 = \hat{T}_{11}(\tilde{s}_{11}, \tilde{s}_{21})$. There is no partial optimization at stage 2, as shown by the following equation, for $R_2(s_2, d_2) = R_2(s_2, \tilde{s}_{11}, \tilde{s}_{21})$:

$$f_2(s_2) = R_2(s_2, \tilde{s}_{11}, \tilde{s}_{21}) + R_1(\tilde{s}_{11}, \tilde{s}_{21})$$

The dynamic programming algorithm and transition function at stage 3 is:

$$f_3(s_3) = \max_{d_3} [R_3(s_3, d_3) + f_2(s_2)] \qquad \tilde{s}_3 = T_3(s_3, d_3) = s_2$$

This is a one-state, one-decision partial optimization, and the functional diagram for the combined stages 1, 2, and 3 is shown below:

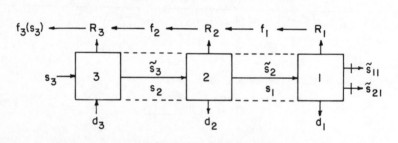

The dynamic programming algorithm and transition function for stage 4 give a one-state, one-decision partial optimization by the following:

$$f_4(s_4) = \max_{d_4} [R_4(s_4, d_4) + f_3(s_3)] \qquad \tilde{s}_4 = T_4(s_4, d_4) = s_3$$

The dynamic programming algorithm and transition functions for stage 5 give a no-state, one-decision partial optimization by the following:

$$f_5(s_{15}, s_{25}) = \max_{d_5} [R_5(s_{15}, s_{25}, d_5) + f_4(s_4)] \qquad \tilde{s}_5 = T_5(s_{15}, s_{25}, d_5) = s_4$$

To locate the best value of $s_{15} = \tilde{s}_{11}$ and $s_{25} = \tilde{s}_{21}$ a two-variable search can be performed that maximizes $f_5(s_{15}, s_{25})$. However, as we will see subsequently, this is a borderline problem for dynamic programming. One should consider optimizing the problem using a multivariable search on the five decision variables directly, rather than having to perform the decision inversion and two-variable search.

BRANCHED SYSTEMS

Branched systems can have either converging or diverging branches. A feedforward loop (by-pass) is a special case of a diverging branch, and a feedback loop (recycle) is a special case of a converging branch. The discussion will begin with diverging branches, which is the simpler of the two cases to describe, but not necessarily to optimize.

Diverging Branches: The functional diagram of a diverging branch is given in Figure 7-15. The branch consists of stages $1'$ through m', and these stages have the following transition functions, incident identities and return function:

Transition functions: $\tilde{s}_i' = T_i'(s_i', d_i')$ (7–22)

Incident identities: $\tilde{s}_i' = s_{i-1}'$ (7–23)

Return functions: $R_i' = R_i'(s_i', d_i')$ for $i' = 1', 2', \cdots, m'$ (7–24)

The maximum return for the diverging branch is:

$$f_m'(s_m') = \max_{d_1', d_2' \ldots, d_m'} \left(\sum_{1'}^{m'} R_i' [d_i', s_m'] \right) \tag{7–25}$$

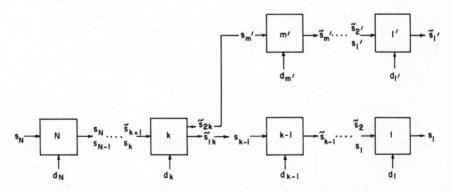

Figure 7-15. Functional diagram of a diverging branch system.

To find the return $f'_m(s'_m)$ requires the solution of an initial value serial problem, which is "easily" done. If the final value of the diverging branch is specified, decision inversion is performed, and stage $1'$ is combined with stage $2'$. Then one-stage, one-decision partial optimizations are continued to stage m'.

To connect the branch to the main system at stage k, the following transition functions, incident identities, and dynamic programming algorithm are used:

Transition functions:
$$\tilde{s}_{1k} = T_{1k}(s_k, d_k) = s_{k-1} \qquad (7\text{--}26)$$

$$\tilde{s}_{2k} = T_{2k}(s_k, d_k) = s'_m \qquad (7\text{--}27)$$

Incident identities:
$$\tilde{s}_{1k} = s_{k-1}, \ \tilde{s}_{2k} = s'_m \qquad (7\text{--}28)$$

Dynamic programming algorithm:

$$f_k(s_k) = \max_{d_k} \ [R_k(s_k, d_k) + f'_m(s'_m) + f_{k-1}(s_{k-1})] \qquad (7\text{--}29)$$

This can be combined with the transition functions to give an algorithm in d_k and s_k only:

$$f_k(s_k) = \max_{d_k} \ \{R_k(s_k, d_k) + f'_m \ [T_{2k}(s_k, d_k)] + f_{k-1} \ [T_{1k}(s_k, d_k)]\} \qquad (7\text{--}30)$$

This equation shows that there is a one-state, one-decision partial optimization at stage k. It is referred to as *absorption of a diverging branch*. The partial optimization can then proceed to stage N to complete the solution.

A special case of a diverging branch is a feed-forward loop, schematically in Figure 7-16. The approach is to convert this structure into a diverging branch and solve it as described previously. The loop enters at stage j, and the transition and return functions for this stage are:

$$\tilde{s}_j = T_j(s_{1j}, s_{2j}, d_j) \qquad (7\text{--}31)$$

$$R_j = R_j(s_{1j}, s_{2j}, d_j) \qquad (7\text{--}32)$$

At this point a value of $s_{2j} = \tilde{s}'_1$ is selected (cut state), and the feed-forward loop is converted into a diverging branch having a fixed output. At stage j the dynamic programming algorithm is:

$$f_j(s_{1j}) = \max_{d_j} \ \{R_j[s_{1j}, s_{2j}, d_j] + f_{j-1}[T_j(s_{1j}, s_{2j}, d_j)]\} \qquad (7\text{--}33)$$

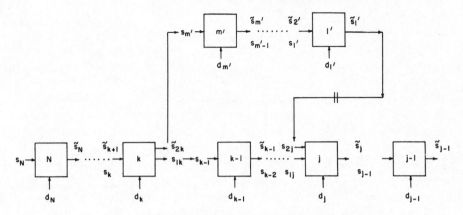

Figure 7-16. Functional diagram of a feed-forward loop.

This is a one-state, one-decision partial optimization at stage j, because s_{2j} is fixed. The value of f_{j-1} is available from partial optimizations from stage 1 to stage $j-1$.

The partial optimizations can now proceed to stage k along the main section and along the loop. When it arrives at stage k, the dynamic programming algorithm is:

$$f_k(s_k) = \max_{\substack{d_k \\ s_{2j}}} [R_k(s_k, d_k) + f_{k-1}(s_{k-1}) + f'_m(s'_m)] \qquad (7\text{--}34)$$

where $f_k(s_k)$ is determined for the best value of d_k and a cut state value of s_{2j}, i.e., a value for s_{2j} is picked that will be used as the first point of a single-variable search. Then, it is necessary to return to stage j to select a new value of s_{2j} and repeat the partial optimizations to obtain a new set of $f_k(s_k)$. These are compared with the previous set for best values. This procedure is continued using a single-variable search to locate the best value of $s_{2j} = \tilde{s}_1$. This best value is the one that gives the maximum values of $f_k(s_k)$. The partial optimizations can then proceed to stage N to complete the solution.

Converging Branches: The functional diagram for a converging branch system is given in Figure 7-17. The branch consists of stages $1'$ through m'. One approach to optimize this system is to perform state inversion on the branch, and this will convert the system to one with a diverging branch. Unfortunately, this may be difficult to accomplish.

There is another approach that is slightly more complicated to describe,

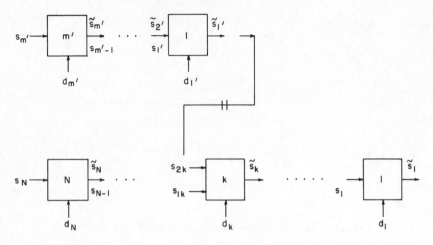

Figure 7-17. Functional diagram of converging branch system.

but is easier to implement. First the dynamic programming algorithm at stage k can be written as:

$$f_k(s_{1k}) = \max_{\substack{d_k \\ s_{2k}}} \; [R_k(s_{1k}, s_{2k}, d_k) + f_{k-1}(s_{k-1}) + f'_m(s'_m)] \qquad (7\text{--}35)$$

It includes the optimal return from the converging branch $f'_m(s'_m)$. This algorithm treats s_{2k} as a decision variable. A two-variable search on d_k and s_{2k} is used to maximize the right-hand side of the equation.

The maximum return from the branch is obtained by cutting the state between the branch and stage k where $s_{2k} = \tilde{s}'_1$. Then the branch becomes a final value problem, if s'_m is a decision variable, or a two-point boundary value problem, if s'_m is fixed, and the previously described procedures are applicable. Once the optimal value of $f_k(s_{1k})$ is determined, then the partial optimizations are continued forward as a serial problem to stage N.

A special case of a converging branch is a feed-back loop, shown in Figure 7-18, and the loop consists of stages $1'$ through m'. It turns out that the feed-back loop will be converted to a converging branch during the partial optimization along the main branch. Conducting partial optimizations from stage 1 to stage i, the dynamic programming algorithm at stage i is:

$$f_i(s_i) = \max_{d_i} \; [R_i(s_i, d_i) + f_{i-1}(s_{i-1})] \qquad (7\text{--}36)$$

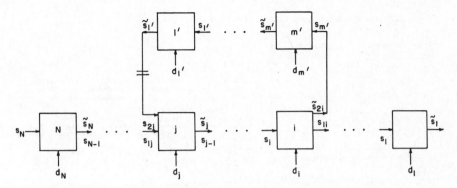

Figure 7-18.   Functional diagram for a feed-back loop.

and the transition functions for this stage are:

$$\tilde{s}_{2i} = T_{2i}(s_i, d_i) \tag{7-37}$$

$$\tilde{s}_{1i} = T_{1i}(s_i, d_i) \tag{7-38}$$

At stage i, the output $\tilde{s}_{2i}$ is uniquely determined by the input s_i and decision d_i. Because $\tilde{s}_{2i} = s'_m$, this specifies the end of the feed-back loop and converts it to a converging branch.

Proceeding with the partial optimization to stage j, the dynamic programming algorithm at this stage is the same as for the converging branch, equation (7-35). Using the transition function:

$$s_{j-1} = T_j(s_{1j}, s_{2j}, d_j) \tag{7-39}$$

then the dynamic programming algorithm equation (7-35), becomes:

$$f_j(s_{1j}) = \max_{\substack{d_j \\ s_{2j}}} \{R_j(s_{1j}, s_{2j}, d_j) + f_{j-1}[T_j(s_{1j}, s_{2j}, d_j)] + f'_m(s'_m)\} \tag{7-40}$$

The values of $f'_m(s'_m)$, the optimal return from the feed-back loop, are determined by treating $s_{2j} = s'_m$ as a decision variable. The feed-back loop is a two-point boundary value problem, for s'_m is fixed, and $\tilde{s}_1 = s_{2j}$ is found to maximize $f_j(s_{1j})$. A one-state, two-decision partial optimization is required at stage j.

The following example illustrates some of the methods that have been described. It was developed by Prof. D. J. Wilde (6) for his optimization class at Stanford University.

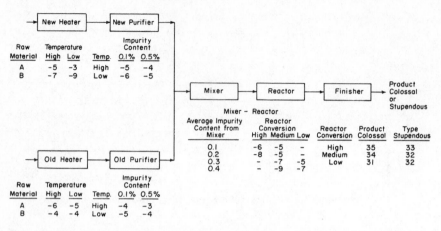

New Heater → New Purifier

Raw Material	Temperature High	Low	Temp.	Impurity Content 0.1%	0.5%
A	-5	-3	High	-5	-4
B	-7	-9	Low	-6	-5

Mixer → Reactor → Finisher → Product Colossal or Stupendous

Mixer - Reactor

Average Impurity Content from Mixer	Reactor Conversion High	Medium	Low	Reactor Conversion	Product Colossal	Type Stupendous
0.1	-6	-5	–	High	35	33
0.2	-8	-5	–	Medium	34	32
0.3	–	-7	-5	Low	31	32
0.4	–	-9	-7			

Old Heater → Old Purifier

Raw Material	Temperature High	Low	Temp.	Impurity Content 0.1%	0.5%
A	-6	-5	High	-4	-3
B	-4	-4	Low	-5	-4

Figure 7-19. Flow diagram of a manufacturing process to produce product types colossal and stupendous with operating cost and sales prices tabulated.

EXAMPLE 7–5

A manufacturing process is arranged as shown in Figure 7-19 along with the operating conditions and costs for each unit. Raw material, which comes in two variations, A and B, is successively heated and purified before it is sent to a reactor where it undergoes transformation into impure products. The impure products are cleaned up in a "finisher," and the final products are sold. A new heating-purifying train has just been built, and it is operated in parallel with the old one. The new unit processes the same amount of material as the old unit, which is then mixed and pumped to the reactor. The impurity content is averaged in the mixer. After the reaction and finishing steps, two grades of product can be marketed, "colossal" and "stupendous." We wish to find the maximum profit and the corresponding optimum policy for the plant operations. It is not necessary for the old and new heating-purifying train to use the same raw material.

The problem involves a converging branch with a choice of raw materials for input values on the branch and on the main system. The functional diagram for the branch and main system is shown in Figure 7-20. At stage 1, the optimal decisions are shown for various values of the state variable using the dynamic programming algorithm. At stage 2 the dynamic programming algorithm is:

$$f_2(s_{12}) = \max_{\substack{d_2 \\ s_{22}}} [R_2(s_{12}, s_{22}, d_2) + f_1(s_1) + f_{4'}(s_{22}, s_{4'})]$$

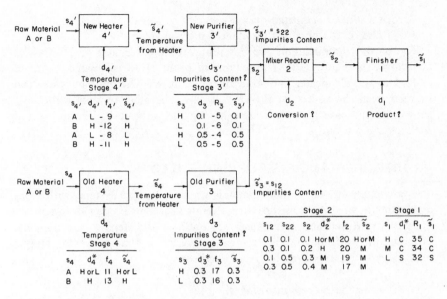

Figure 7-20. Functional diagram and the optimal policy for the manufacturing process operations.

A two-variable search is required to locate the best values of s_{22} on the branch and d_2^* at stage 2 that maximize the return from stage, R_2, the main system, f_1, and the branch, $f_{4'}$, for various values of the state variable s_{12}. Decision inversion is required for the branch, and these results are shown at stages 3' and 4' for cut state values of 0.1% and 0.5%. The minimum cost to operate the branch is -9 for an impurities content of 0.1% and -8 for 0.5%. The information is now available to complete the partial optimization at stage 2. To illustrate this procedure, consider the case of $s_{12} = 0.3\%$ impurities content and a cut state value of $s_{22} = 0.1\%$ and values of the decision variable, d_2, equal to high, medium, and low.

$$\text{Decision variable, } d_2$$

	High	Medium	Low
R_2	-8	-5	—
f_1	35	34	—
$f_{4'}$	$\underline{-9}$	$\underline{-9}$	$\underline{-9}$

$$f_2(s_{12} = 0.3, s_{22} = 0.1) = \max [\quad 18 \qquad 20 \qquad -] = 20$$

This procedure is repeated over a range of values of s_{12} searching on s_{22} and d_2. The results obtained for stage 2 are shown in Figure 7-20.

The partial optimizations are continued to stages 3 and 4. The results are shown in Figure 7-20. The maximum profit of 13 is obtained using B as feed to the old heater and A to the new heater. The optimal policy can be read from the values on Figure 7-20. Also, another optimal solution is shown for the case of both heaters having the same feed. This is A, and the maximum profit is 11 for this case.

PROCEDURES AND SIMPLIFYING RULES

The previous methods to apply dynamic programming to systems with loops and branches were developed by Aris, Nemhauser, and Wilde (7). In a previous article, Mitten and Nemhauser (5) outlined the steps to use dynamic programming. Although this procedure should be almost obvious at this point, it is worth repeating for reenforcement:

1. Separate the process into stages.
2. Formulate the return and transition functions for each stage of the process.
3. For each stage select the inputs, decisions, and outputs to have as few state variables per stage as possible.
4. Apply the dynamic programming algorithm to find the optimal return from the process and the optimal decisions at each stage.

Based on the results of the article with Aris and Nemhauser, Wilde (8) formulated several rules for simplifying a system to make a dynamic programming optimization plan more efficient. These are as follows:

Rule 1. Irrelevant Stages

If a stage has no return and if its outputs are not inputs to other stages of the system, then the stage and its decisions may be eliminated.

It is not necessary to consider a stage that does not affect the return function. An example could be a waste treatment step at the end of the process where the cost of operation is equal to the sales of product recovered, i.e., break-even.

Rule 2. Stage Combination

If a stage has as many or more output state variables as it has input state variables, then elimination of the output state variables by combination with the adjacent stage should be considered.

Because an exhaustive search is required on the state variables, an overall savings of effort is obtained when state variables are eliminated, even at the expense of obtaining more decision variables. Multivariable search techniques can be applied to decision variables. This leads to the following corollary.

Corollary 2. Decisionless Stages

Any decisionless stage should be combined with an adjacent stage. Choose the one that eliminates the most state variables.

Rule 3. Fixed Output Constraints

Any fixed output should be transformed into an input by inverting either the state or decision variables. This transforms a final-value problem into an initial-value problem.

Applying this rule reduces the number of state and decision variables. For a final-value problem, decision inversion transforms a decision into an output that is completely specified by the input state variable.

Rule 4. Small Loops

Any loop with fewer than four decision variables should be optimized with respect to all decision variables simultaneously.

If this rule is applied to cyclic optimizations for a system with three decision variables, one of these is eliminated by cutting the state. Then decision inversion is performed, and stages 1 and 2 are combined. Thus, a one-state, one-decision partial optimization is performed at stage 1-2, and a no-state, one-decision partial optimization is performed at stage 3. This procedure is repeated, searching on $s_3 = \tilde{s}_1$ for the maximum return. Advising against going through this procedure, Wilde suggests that it is easier to perform a three-variable search on the decision variables.

Rule 5. Cut State Location

Cut states should be input state variables to multiple input stages.

This rule converts loops into diverging branches, which are easier to optimize than converging branches. Further, a single-variable search can be performed on the state variable.

APPLICATION TO THE CONTACT PROCESS—A CASE STUDY (9)

At this point we have dealt with the theory of dynamic programming and simple examples to illustrate the use of the theory. Now, we will describe an application to an industrial process done by Lowry (9).

In applying dynamic programming to the contact process for sulfuric acid manufacture, Lowry (9) demonstrated the capability of this procedure to optimize an established industrial process. The details of this work are given by Lowry (9), and they include the detailed process description, material and energy balance equations, and the related chemical equilibrium calculations with transport and thermodynamic properties. This study will be summarized with a brief description of the process and an analysis of the logic required to convert the process flow diagram into the dynamic programming functional diagram. Also a summary of the results obtained by the optimization will be presented.

Brief Description of the Process: The contact process produces 98% sulfuric acid as a primary product and process steam as a secondary product, as shown in the process flow diagram given in Figure 7-21. Both products are usually consumed in adjacent plants. For this study the sulfur feed rate was set at 10,000 pounds per hour, which corresponds to a standard industrial-size plant. The sulfur is burned to form sulfur dioxide with air that has been dried with 98% sulfuric acid. The reaction is exothermic and goes to completion. Excess air is supplied to provide sufficient oxygen to react the sulfur dioxide to sulfur trioxide in the two converters.

In the oxidation of sulfur dioxide to sulfur trioxide, the reaction rate increases with temperature, and the equilibrium conversion decreases with temperature. Therefore, two converters are used, and the first converter is operated in a higher temperature range to take advantage of the increased rate of reaction. The second converter is operated in a lower temperature range to obtain an increased conversion. The temperature to each concerter is controlled by a waste heat boiler that produces process steam.

The hot gas from the burner enters waste heat boiler 1, and steam is produced by cooling the gas that enters converter A. Partial oxidation of sulfur dioxide to sulfur trioxide takes place in the converter, which has a vanadium catalyst. Due to the exothermic reaction, the temperature of the gas increases in the converter. Then the gas enters waste heat boiler 2, and

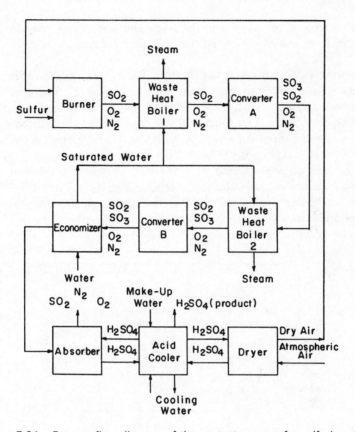

Figure 7-21. Process flow diagram of the contact process for sulfuric acid.

additional steam is produced. From the boiler the gas flows to converter B to have essentially all the sulfur dioxide converted to sulfur trioxide. From the converter the gas goes to the economizer where energy is recovered by heating water to its saturation temperature for use in the two waste-heat boilers. Also, the gas is cooled to the temperature required for the absorber.

In the absorber the sulfur trioxide is converted to sulfuric acid in a packed tower by contacting the gas with 98% sulfuric acid. The other gases in this stream, mainly nitrogen with some oxygen and a trace of sulfur dioxide, are vented to the atmosphere.

In the acid cooler make-up water is added to hold the concentration at 98%, because there is not enough moisture in the air to supply all the water required. Heat of reaction in the absorber and heat of dilution in the dryer raise the temperature of the acid, and the acid cooler includes a heat exchanger used to remove the heat from the acid. The acid cooler provides the acid for the dryer and absorber and the 98% acid product for sale.

Dynamic Programming Analysis: The dynamic programming analysis begins with each unit in the process being a stage in the functional diagram, as shown in Figure 7-22. The rules from the previous section now can be used to develop the final functional diagram. In Figure 7-22 there are nine stages, and the input state variable s_9 is the fixed flow rate of sulfur to the burner of 10,000 pounds per hour. There is an output at stage 2, s_{12}, which is flow rate of product acid from the acid cooler. The decision variables are d_4, the flow rate of water to the economizer; d_2, the flow rate of cooling water to the acid cooler; and d_1, the atmospheric air flow rate to the dryer. There are two other decision variables, d_6 and d_8, which are the flow rates

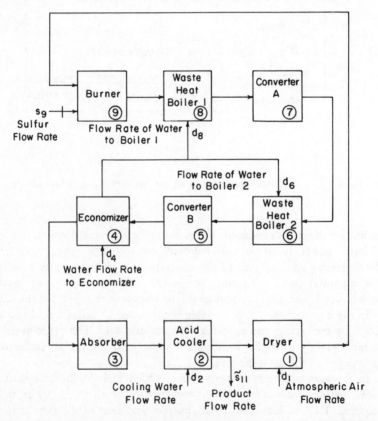

Figure 7-22. Initial, nine-stage functional diagram for the contact process.

of water to the two waste heat boilers. However, their sum must equal d_4, the flow rate of water to the economizer. Also, there are two recycle streams. One is from the economizer to the waste heat boilers, and the other is from the dryer to the burner.

The following paragraphs will describe one way of simplifying the functional diagram to one that has one state and decision variable per stage. This was obtained after a number of trials. Converting the process flow diagram to the dynamic programming functional diagram is the most difficult step in the optimization procedure. Selecting a variable to be either state or decision is somewhat arbitrary as is the way stages are combined. Many combinations have to be tried, and a final optimization plan will emerge that is probably not unique. The goal is to obtain a computationally efficient set of functional equations to be used for the optimization.

First, it was necessary to deal with the recycle stream in the process involving the water flow rates from the economizer to the boilers. The decision variables, d_4, d_6, and d_8, were allowed to be independent initially. An interim cost was assigned to each of these streams to account for their values in the return functions at stages 4, 6, and 8. In the final results the sum of the flow rates to the boilers must be essentially equal to that for the economizer. At the optimum a check was made to ensure that the sum of the inputs to the boilers was essentially equal to the output from the economizer.

Additional simplifications were made, as shown in Figure 7-23. Decisionless stages were combined with adjacent stages according to the rules previously discussed. The burner was decisionless, and it was combined with waste-heat boiler 1. Converter A was decisionless, and it was combined with waste heat boiler 1 also. Converter B was decisionless, and it was combined with waste heat boiler 2. The absorber was decisionless, and it was combined with the acid cooler. There are five stages in the functional diagram, each one having one input and one decision, as shown in Figure 7-23. The recycle loop between the burner and the dryer makes the system cyclic.

The loop was eliminated by cutting the state between the dryer and the burner, and the system became a serial one, as shown in Figure 7-24. By cutting the state, the output from the dryer was fixed, and decision inversion was required. The dryer was combined with the acid cooler-absorber stage. However, a closer analysis revealed that cutting the state on the loop required specifying two state variables, the dry air temperature and flow rate. Consequently, the two decisions d_1 and d_2, the atmospheric air flow rate and the cooling water flow rate, were converted to computed outputs. Thus, the dryer-acid cooler-absorber stage had to be combined with the economizer stage.

The functional diagram shown in Figure 7-24 is the final form. It is a three-stage, initial-value, serial problem. A two-variable search was required

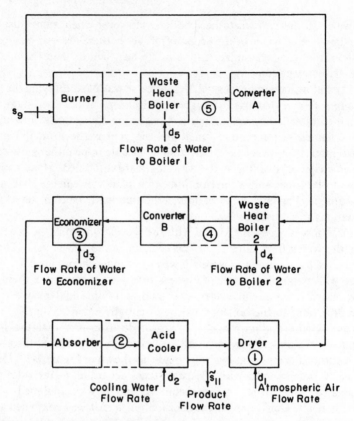

Figure 7-23. Intermediate, five-stage functional diagram for the contact process.

on the cut state values of the dry air temperature and flow rate for the optimization. As shown in the figure, the inputs to stage 3 are the cut state values of the dry air temperature and flow rate and the sulfur flow rate. The decision variable, d_3, is the flow rate of saturated water to waste heat boiler 1, which controls the temperature of the gas to converter A. This temperature determines the conversion of SO_2 to SO_3 in the converter, and the output state variable at stage 3, s_3, is the conversion. The return at this stage includes the cost of sulfur, the cost of the saturated water to the boiler, and the profit from the steam produced. The dynamic programming algorithm at this stage is:

$$f_3(s_{12},\ s_{13}) = \max_{d3}[R_3(s_{12},\ s_{13},\ d_3) + f_2(s_2)] \qquad (7\text{–}41)$$

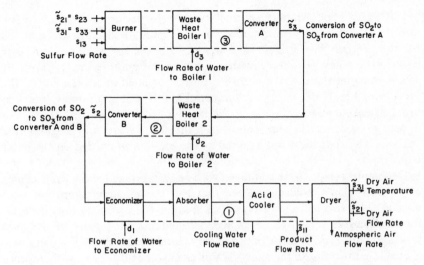

Figure 7-24. Final, three-stage functional diagram for the contact process.

At stage 2 the input state variable s_2 ($=\tilde{s}_3$) is the conversion of SO_2 to SO_3 in converter A; and the decision d_2, the flow rate of saturated water to waste heat boiler 2, controls the temperature of the gas to converter B. This temperature determines the final conversion of SO_2 to SO_3, and the output state variable s_2 is this conversion. The return at stage 2 includes the cost of the saturated water to the boiler and the profit from the steam produced. The dynamic programming algorithm for stage 2 is:

$$f_2(s_2) = \max_{d2} [R_2(s_2,\, d_2) + f_1(s_1)] \qquad (7\text{--}42)$$

At stage 1, the input state variable $\tilde{s}_1$ ($=\tilde{s}_2$) is the final conversion of SO_2 to SO_3, and the decision variable d_1 is the flow rate of water to the economizer. This flow rate determines the temperature of the gas entering the absorber, which controls the conversion of SO_3 to sulfuric acid. Also, the material and energy balance equations at this stage determine the product acid flow rate, the cooling water flow rate, and the dry air temperature and flow rate, as previously discussed. The return at this stage includes the sale of acid product, the cost of cooling and economizer water, and the other related operating and equipment costs. The dynamic programming algorithm at stage 1 is:

$$f_1(s_1) = \max_{d1} [R_1(s_1, d_1)] \qquad (7\text{--}43)$$

The partial optimizations at each stage were performed by Lowry (9), and detailed results were obtained for the optimum operating conditions for the process. The strategy just described is the one that resulted after considering many possible ways to formulate the optimization problem. It was found that there was no substitute for a detailed understanding of the process to be able to obtain a successful solution. For example, the first problem encountered was that of the interior loop. The procedure used to allow each stream to be independent gave an effective dynamic programming analysis. The constraint was satisfied as the solution proceeded on the outer loop.

Decisionless stages were combined with adjacent stages, and when a choice of adjacent stages existed, the one that had the smallest number of state variables was selected. However, in this study it was necessary to make arbitrary choices at times. These choices affected the complexity of the final functional diagram, and the only way to determine the effect of a particular choice was to complete the analysis. For example, in this process there were several combinations for each decisionless stage. This required a number of plans to be devised and rejected before the final plan emerged.

Results: A detailed discussion of the dynamic programming optimization results was given by Lowry (9). A summary of these results is given in Table 7-2. The maximum return was found to be $230.57 per hour and was obtained for a dry air flow rate of 135,000 pounds per hour and temperature of 430°K. The optimal operating conditions necessary to achieve this return are shown in the table also.

The highest value of the gas temperature, 1000°K, was specified from converter A to maximize steam production. The lowest value of the gas temperature was specified from converter B to maximize the conversion of SO_2 to SO_3. The gas temperatures entering both converters were at constraints. The inlet gas temperature to the first converter was at the ignition temperature of the catalyst, and the exit temperature of the second converter had to be equal to or less than 1000°K. Above this temperature the catalyst degrades rapidly.

The tabular information for the partial optimizations at stages 1 through 3 is given in Table 7-3. As indicated in the table, the overall optimum required an output from stage 3 of $\bar{s}_3 = 0.36226$. Linear interpolation was used at stage 2 to obtain the optimal decision d_2^* of 22,472 pounds per hour for the flow rate of water to boiler 2. Linear interpolation was used at stage 1 to obtain the optimal decision d_1^* of 45,214 pounds per hour for the flow rate of water to the enconomizer.

Optimal operating policies for selected cut state values of the dry air flow rate are given in Table 7-4. Total conversion $\bar{s}_2^*$ increased as the dry air

Table 7-2. Overall Optimum Operating Policy for the Contact Process.

Sulfur Flow Rate	Dry Air Flow Rate and Temperature		Optimal Return
s_{13}	s_{23}^*	s_{33}^*	f_3
10,000 lb/hr	135,000 lb/hr	430°K	$230.57/hr

STAGE 3

Conversion of SO_2 to SO_3 from Converter A	Flow Rate of Water to Boiler 1	Gas Temperature from Converter A
$\tilde{s}_3^*$	d_3^*	T_3^*
0.36226	25,513 lb/hr	1,000.0°K

STAGE 2

Conversion of SO_2 to SO_3 from Converters A and B	Flow Rate of Water to Boiler 2	Gas Temperature from Converter B
$\tilde{s}_2^*$	d_2^*	T_2^*
0.9859	22,472 lb/hr	700°K

STAGE 1

Production Rate of H_2SO_4	Flow Rate of Water to the Economizer	Absorber Gas Temperature	Water Flow Rate to Acid Cooler
$\tilde{s}_{11}$	d_1^*	T_1^*	
30,768 lb/hr	45,214 lb/hr	325°K	207,501 lb/hr

flow rate increased, but the total return f_3 reached a peak and then decreased. The optimal policy occurred at a dry air flow rate of 135,000 pounds per hour. An additional benefit of dynamic programming is the generation of related near-optimal solutions. As shown in Table 7-4, the optimal return is not sensitive to dry air flow rate. These results are typical of dynamic programming optimization studies.

OPTIMAL EQUIPMENT REPLACEMENT—TIME AS A STAGE

An important optimization problem is the planning required to obtain the maximum profit from a plant over its life. A new plant must recover the construction costs and provide a competitive return on investment through

Table 7-3.   Tabular Information for Partial Optimization at Stages 1 through 3 for the Contact Process.

STAGE 3

Decision, d_3^*	T_3^*	Return, f_3	Output, $\bar{s}_3^*$
25,513 lb/hr	1000°K	$230.57/hr	0.36226

STAGE 2

Input, s_2	Decision, d_2 (lb/hr)	T_2^* (°K)	Return, f_2 ($/hr)	Output, s_2
0.30	24,523	700	353.83	0.9859
0.35	22,828	700	353.49	0.9859
0.40	21,215	700	353.16	0.9859
0.45	19,657	700	352.85	0.9859
0.50	18,136	700	352.54	0.9859
0.55	16,637	700	352.23	0.9859
0.60	15,147	700	351.93	0.9859
0.65	13,653	700	351.63	0.9859
0.70	12,141	700	351.33	0.9859
0.75	10,593	700	351.01	0.9859
0.80	8,983	700	350.68	0.9859
0.85	7,264	700	350.34	0.9859
0.90	5,342	700	349.95	0.9859
0.95	2,931	700	349.46	0.9859

STAGE 1

Input, s_1	Decision, d_1 (lb/hr)	T_1^* (°K)	Cooling water (lb/hr)	Return, R_1 ($/hr)	Output, s_{11} (lb/hr)
0.80	81,512	325	152,736	284.54	24,967
0.82	80,167	325	158,630	291.57	25,591
0.84	78,733	325	164,523	298.59	26,215
0.86	77,183	325	170,416	305.61	26,840
0.88	75,481	325	176,309	312.62	27,464
0.90	73,551	325	182,201	319.63	28,088
0.92	71,364	325	188,093	326.62	28,712
0.94	68,695	325	193,986	333.59	29,336
0.96	65,208	325	199,877	340.53	29,960
0.98	59,827	325	205,769	347.39	30,585
1.00	10,135	325	211,660	352.41	31,209

the years that it operates. As the plant ages, maintenance costs increase, new technology brings on obsolescence, tax structure changes, and the costs of raw materials and the sales prices of product change. These and other related factors affect the decision about investing in a new plant or continuing to operate an existing one.

Table 7-4. Optimal Operating Conditions for a Range of Dry Air Flow Rates at the Optimal Dry Air Temperature of 430°K.

	Dry Air Flow Rate (lb/hr)	
A	85,000	
B	105,000	
C	115,000	
D	135,000*	* Overall optimum
E	155,000	
F	175,000	
G	195,000	
H	215,000	

STAGE 1

	Economizer Water Flow Rate d_1 (lb/hr)	Product Flow Rate s_{11} (lb/hr)	Absorber Gas Temperature T_1 (°K)	Acid Cooler Water Flow Rate (lb/hr)
A	30,497	34,445	350	251,983
B	37,314	30,697	350	239,593
C	38,383	30,738	350	232,830
D	45,214*	30,768*	325*	207,501*
E	49,582	30,795	325	191,815
F	54,241	30,813	325	176,033
G	59,061	30,825	325	160,196
H	63,979	30,832	325	159,134

STAGE 2

	Converter A & B Conversion s_2	Boiler 2 Water Flow Rate d_2 (lb/hr)	Gas Temperature from Converter B T_2 (°K)
A	0.9766	17,960	700
B	0.9830	20,003	700
C	0.9844	20,959	700
D	0.9859*	22,472*	700*
E	0.9867	22,945	700
F	0.9873	24,657	700
G	0.9877	26,360	700
H	0.9880	28,056	700

STAGE 3

	Return f_3 ($/hr)	Converter A Conversion s_3	Boiler 1 Water Flow Rate d_3 (lb/hr)	Gas Temperature from Converter A T_3 (°K)
A	228.51	0.3070	32,342	1,000
B	230.29	0.3379	29,727	1,000
C	230.49	0.3479	28,347	1,000
D	230.57*	0.3623*	25,513*	1,000*
E	230.46	0.3721	22,618	1,000
F	230.25	0.3792	19,688	1,000
G	230.00	0.3847	16,734	1,000
H	229.49	0.3890	13,223	1,000

Dynamic programming provides an excellent framework to structure the decisions about a plant to maximize the total profit over time. The concepts required to use this method are the same regardless of the time span or the complexity of the economic model used to predict the profitability of the plant through time. Also, if uncertainties about future prices, costs, interest rates, etc., can be estimated, then a stochastic version of the optimization algorithm can be used, as described by Roberts (3).

The following example illustrates using a span of time as a dynamic programming stage. Decisions about whether to continue to operate the plant or replace it with a new plant will be based on an annual evaluation of a simple linear economic model, and a 5-year period will be used as the total time to determine the maximum profit. With this simple model and annual evaluation, the concepts can be emphasized. The economic model can be evaluated readily, and the time span does not require excessive computations and is not restrictive. Depending on need and available information, the economic model can contain all the factors mentioned in the previous paragraph and others as well. Also, the time between evaluations, the dynamic programming stage, can be selected to be appropriate for the analysis, as can the total time for the evaluation. In addition, once the optimization analysis has been formulated, it could be updated as new information becomes available to provide a better set of future decisions. Finally, the procedure is not limited to a plant; it applies equally well to a process or equipment used in a plant.

EXAMPLE 7–6

Information about the annual net profit from the operation of a process over a 12-year period is shown in Figure 7-25, where the process operates at breakeven in year 10 and the following years. For convenience, the cost to replace the process with a new one using modern technology is taken to be equal to the net profit made in the first year of operation of the new process, i.e., $10,000. At the beginning of each year an annual review is held, and a decision is made to either continue to operate the process or replace it with a new modern one to have a maximum profit over a 5-year period. The process is currently 4 years old, and it is necessary to determine the best decision now and for each of the following 4 years to maximize the profit, i.e., determine the optimal replacement policy.

The procedure begins by considering the possible decisions to be made at the start of year 5 (end of year 4) i.e., either to keep or replace the process. Stage 1 is the time from the beginning to the end of year 5. The dynamic programming algorithm at stage 1 can be written as:

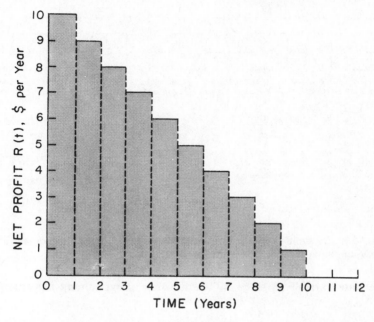

Figure 7-25. Annual net profit from the operation of the process over a 12-year period.

$$f_1(s_1) = \max_{d_1} [R_1(s_1, d_1)] = \max_{\substack{\text{keep} \\ \text{or} \\ \text{replace}}} \begin{cases} R_1(t) \\ -10 + R(0) = 0 \end{cases}$$

where the decision, d_1, is to keep or replace the process to maximize the profit, $R_1(s_1, d_1)$. Also the profit depends on the age of the process, the state variable s_1. The optimum decisions are listed in Figure 7-26 for stage 1 as a function of the state variable, and they are to keep the process operating. The range of state variables goes from a process 1 year old to having a process 10 years old at the start of the 5th year. In the case of a 10-year-old process, there is a tie between keeping the process and replacing it with a new one, and the decision made here is the one that is easier, i.e., keep the process operating. The values shown in Figure 7-26 were obtained from Figure 7-25. The output state variable from stage 1 s_0 is the age of the process at the end of the year.

At stage 2 the optimal decisions are made that maximize the sum of the return at stage 2 and the optimal return from stage 1 for a range of values

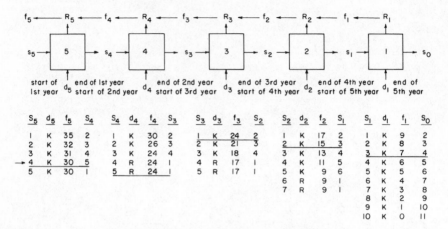

S_5	d_5	f_5	S_4		S_4	d_4	f_4	S_3		S_3	d_3	f_3	S_2		S_2	d_2	f_2	S_1		S_1	d_1	f_1	S_0
1	K	35	2		1	K	30	2		1	K	24	2		1	K	17	2		1	K	9	2
2	K	32	3		2	K	26	3		2	K	21	3		2	K	15	3		2	K	8	3
3	K	31	4		3	K	24	4		3	K	18	4		3	K	13	4		3	K	7	4
→ 4	K	30	5		4	R	24	1		4	R	17	1		4	K	11	5		4	K	6	5
5	K	30	1		5	R	24	1		5	R	17	1		5	K	9	6		5	K	5	6
															6	R	9	1		6	K	4	7
															7	R	9	1		7	K	3	8
																				8	K	2	9
																				9	K	1	10
																				10	K	0	11

Figure 7-26. Dynamic programming functional diagram and partial optimization results in the optimal replacement policy.

of the state variable at stage 2. The dynamic programming algorithm at stage 2 is:

$$f_2(s_2) = \max_{d_2} \left[R_2(s_2, d_2) + f_1(s_1) \right] = f_2(t) = \max_{\substack{\text{keep} \\ \text{or} \\ \text{replace}}} \begin{cases} R_2(t) + f_1(t+1) \\ -10 + R(0) + f_1(1) = 9 \end{cases}$$

If the decision is to keep the process, the optimal return, $f_2(t)$, is the sum of $R_2(t)$, the return during the year 4th for a process t years old, and $f_1(t+1)$, the optimal return from stage 1 for a process whose age is $t+1$. If the decision is to replace the process, the optimal return $f_2(t)$ is the sum of the cost of a new process, -10, the profit from operating a new process for a year, $R(0) = 10$, and the optimal return from stage 1 for a process 1 year old, $f_1(1)$. The optimal decisions are shown in Figure 7-26 at stage 2 for a process whose age can be from 1 to 7 years, s_2. As seen in the figure, the optimal decisions are to continue to operate the process if its age is from 1 to 5 years. However, if the process is 6 years old or older, the profit will be larger for years 4th and 5th if the process is replaced.

The same procedure is used at stage 3 to determine the maximum profit for years 3rd, 4th, and 5th. The dynamic programming algorithm is:

$$f_3(s_3) = f_3(t) = \max_{\substack{\text{keep} \\ \text{or} \\ \text{replace}}} \begin{cases} R_3(t) + f_2(t+1) \\ -10 + R(0) + f_2(1) = 17 \end{cases}$$

The optimal decisions for stage 3 are shown in Figure 7-26. At this stage the optimal decisions are to continue to operate the process if its age is from 1 to 3 years; and if it is older, the maximum profit over the 3-year period will be obtained by replacing the process with a new one.

Continuing to stage 4, the procedure is repeated to determine the maximum profit for the 4-year period. The dynamic programming algorithm to determine the optimal decisions for various age processes (the state variable) is:

$$f_4(t) = \max_{\substack{\text{keep} \\ \text{or} \\ \text{replace}}} \begin{cases} R_4(t) + f_3(t+1) \\ -10 + R(0) + f_3(1) = 24 \end{cases}$$

Based on Figure 7-26 the optimal decisions are to continue to operate the process if it is from 1 to 3 years old and to replace it with a new one if it is older.

The results for the final, 5th stage are obtained the same way as previously. However, it is necessary to consider only one value of the state variable, the existing 4-year old process. The dynamic programming algorithm is as follows:

$$f_5(t) = \max_{\substack{\text{keep} \\ \text{or} \\ \text{replace}}} \begin{cases} R_5(t) + f_4(t+1) \\ -10 + R(0) + f_4(1) = 30 \end{cases}$$

As shown in Figure 7-26, the maximum profit for the 5-year period is $30,000 for a 4-year old process and the optimal decisions are to keep the process for year 1st, to replace it with a new one at the start of year 2nd, and to operate this new process for the remaining 3 years. Also shown in the figure are other cases that were obtained using the dynamic programming algorithm for processes that are 1, 2, 3, and 5 years old. For example, for a 1-year old process, the maximum profit would be $35,000, and the optimal decisions would be to continue to operate it for the 5-year period. However, had the process been 5 years old, the maximum profit would be $30,000, and the optimal decisions would be to replace the existing process with a new one and operate it for the 5-year period. Consequently, the dynamic programming algorithm generated other possibly useful information without significant additional computational effort.

In summary, a time span can be used as a stage for the dynamic programming algorithm to establish an optimal set of decisions that maximize the profit over a specified length of time. The previous example illustrated the computational algorithm, and the methodology is the same for more elaborate economic models and different time spans for a stage and number of stages. Also, having once been performed, the optimization is readily modified as additional information becomes available. The discussion will continue for a related type of dynamic programming optimization, the optimum allocation problem.

OPTIMAL ALLOCATION BY DYNAMIC PROGRAMMING

A problem frequently encountered is to determine the best way to distribute a limited amount of resources among competing, profitable processes. These resources are frequently raw materials or money to purchase raw materials used to manufacture products. Also, at the process level, the problem may take the form of the best way to distribute raw material among processes to produce the range of products manufactured at the plant. Linear programming provided one method of making these distributions to maximize the profit when all the equations were linear. This is not a restriction for dynamic programming.

The optimal allocation problem requires specifying the total amount of the resource to be distributed and an expression that gives the profit (or cost) at each stage. A stage might be a plant, a process, or a part of a process. A diagram is given in Figure 7-27 to describe the procedure, and the key to the solution of optimal allocation problems is the definition of the state variables. At stage 1 the state variable is the amount of the resource allocated to this stage, and it has to range from using all the resource in the stage to using none of it here. The decision variable is the same as the state variable at stage 1. However, from stage 2 through stage N, the state and decision variables are different. The decision variable d_i is the amount of the resource allocated to stage i, but the state variable is the amount allocated to stage i plus the amount remaining to be optimally distributed over the previous stages from $i - 1$ to 1. The state variable s_i varies from allocating all the resource to the i stages to allocating none to these stages. At stage N the state variable is equal to the total amount of the resource to be allocated to the N stage, and the decision variable is the amount of the resource allocated to state N to maximize the profit from all N stages. It is necessary to perform only the partial optimization with the dynamic programming algorithm, using the value of the state variable s_N equal to the total amount of the resource available for the N stages (an initial-value problem).

Optimum resource allocation by dynamic programming optimization is illustrated in the following example where a limited amount of feed is to

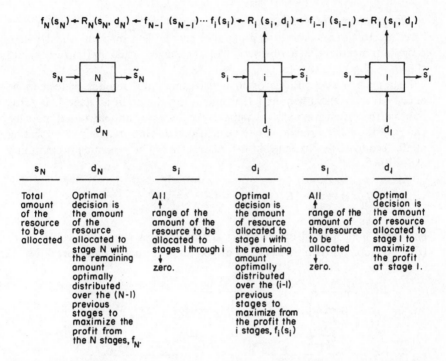

$$f_N(s_N) \leftarrow R_N(s_N, d_N) \leftarrow f_{N-1}(s_{N-1}) \cdots f_i(s_i) \leftarrow R_i(s_i, d_i) \leftarrow f_{i-1}(s_{i-1}) \leftarrow R_1(s_1, d_1)$$

s_N	d_N	s_i	d_i	s_1	d_1
Total amount of the resource to be allocated	Optimal decision is the amount of the resource allocated to stage N with the remaining amount optimally distributed over the (N-1) previous stages to maximize the profit from the N stages, f_N.	All range of the amount of the resource to be allocated to stages 1 through i ↓ zero.	Optimal decision is the amount of resource allocated to stage i with the remaining amount optimally distributed over the (i-1) previous stages to maximize from the profit the i stages, $f_i(s_i)$	All range of the amount of the resource to be allocated ↓ zero.	Optimal decision is the amount of resource allocated to stage 1 to maximize the profit at stage 1.

Figure 7-27. Functional diagram for optimal allocation by dynamic programming.

be distributed among three chemical reactors. Also, a more detailed discussion is given by Roberts (3), and Problem 7-9 is a mathematical form of the optimal allocation problem.

EXAMPLE 7-7

The total feed to be distributed among three chemical reactors operating in parallel is 700 pounds per hour. Each reactor has a different catalyst, and the operating conditions of temperature and pressure vary to be able to produced a required set of products. The profit for each reactor is determined by the feed rate, and the parameters in the return function for each reactor are determined by the catalyst and operating conditions, as shown below:

$$R_1 = 0.08F_1 - (F_1/100)^2$$

$$R_2 = 0.08F_2 - 2(F_2/100)^2$$

$$R_3 = 0.08F_3 - 3(F_3/100)^2$$

The problem is one of determining the best distribution of the feed among three reactors to maximize the profit. The process flow diagram, the dynamic programming functional diagram, and the stage partial optimizations are shown in Figure 7-28.

Beginning at stage 1, the optimal decision is the amount of feed to be allocated to chemical reactor 1 that maximizes the profit at stage 1. It turns out that the state variable is the same as the decision variable, but all possible values of the state variable have to be considered. These range from allocating all the feed to stage 1 to none of the feed to stage 1. The dynamic programming algorithm is:

$$f_1(s_1) = \max_{d_1} [R_1(s_1, d_1)] = f_1(F_1) = 0.08F_1 - (F_1/100)^2$$

and there is no partial optimization at this stage as such. The values of f_1 (F_1) were computed in increments of 100 and are shown in Figure 7-28.

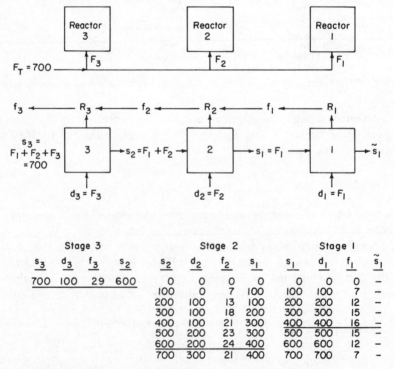

Figure 7-28. Process flow diagram, dynamic programming functional diagram, and the stage partial optimizations for Example 7-7.

There is a partial optimization at stage 2, and the dynamic programming algorithm is:

$$f_2(s_2) = \max_{d_2} [R_2(s_2, d_2) + f_1(s_1)]$$

or

$$f_2(F_1 + F_2) = \max_{F_2} [R_2(F_2) + f_1(F_1)]$$

At stage 2 the state variable is the sum of the feed to be distributed optimally between reactors 1 and 2. All possible values have to be considered from allocating all the feed to these two stages to none of the feed to these two stages. The decision variable is the feed to stage 2, and it is selected to maximize the profit from chemical reactors 1 and 2 for a specified value of the sum of feed to the two reactors. The amount of feed to reactor 1, F_1, is the difference between the state variable $s_2 = F_1 + F_2$ and the decision variable $d_2 = F_2$. The values of $f_2(F_1 + F_2)$ were computed in increments of 100, and the results are shown in Figure 7-28, along with optimal values of F_2.

The key to using dynamic programming for optimal allocation is recognizing that the state variable represents the amount of the resource, feed in this case, to be optimally distributed over the remaining stages. Also for stages other than the last stage, the range of possible values must be considered from distributing all to distributing none to the remaining stages. However, at the final stage it is necessary to consider only one value, the total amount to be distributed. This is shown in Figure 7-28 for the total feed rate of 700 pounds per hour, and the dynamic programming algorithm at stage 3 is:

$$f_3(s_3) = \max_{d_3} [R_3(s_3, d_3) + f_2(s_2)]$$

or

$$f_3(F_T = 700) = \max_{F_3} [R_3(F_3) + f_2(F_1 + F_2)]$$

The results of the partial optimizations at stage 3, as shown in Figure 7-28, have an optimal return of 29 and an optimal feed rate, F_3, of 100 pounds per hour to reactor 3. This means that 600 pounds per hour is to be optimally distributed to the other two reactors. From the partial optimizations at stages 2 and 1, the optimal value of F_2 is 200, and F_1 is 400. The optimal policy is underlined in Figure 7-28.

Optimal allocation problems are solved using the same approach as illustrated in Example 7–7. The state variable at each stage is the sum of the amount of the resource to be allocated to that stage and the previous ones. The decision variable is the amount of the resource allocated at that stage. The optimal values of the decision are determined for the range of values on the state variable to maximize the sum of the return at that state and the optimal returns from the previous stages, having the remaining resource distributed optimally. At each stage except the last stage, the possible values of the state variable must range from considering all the resources to be allocated to that and previous stages. At the last stage it is necessary to consider only the one value of the state variable, the total amount of the resource. At the last stage the bounds on the decision variable for the amount allocated to the stage range from having all to having none of the resource used at the stage. This is a no-state, one-decision partial optimization. From stage $(N - 1)$ to stage 2, there were one-state, one-decision partial optimizations. Frequently, at stage 1 the state and decision variables are the same, and in this case, as in the example, partial optimization is not required.

In summary, optimal allocation problems can now be solved using either linear or dynamic programming. Dynamic programming offers the advantage of not being limited to linear equations. Usually, the most difficult part of the dynamic programming analysis is formulating the problem and assembling the economic model and constraint equations. The partial optimizations at each stage require some computational effort that is frequently done using a computer. Selecting the optimal policy may require interpolation of information developed at each stage.

CLOSURE

In this chapter the objective has been to develop an understanding of the dynamic programming algorithm and illustrate its application to a number of types of optimization problems. The key is to be able to convert the process flow diagram to a dynamic programming functional diagram. This procedure was illustrated for network problems, serial and branched problems, equipment replacement problems, and allocation problems.

The theory of dynamic programming was given for large problems with loops and branches, along with rules for applying this theory to large processes to obtain the functional equations and diagram for the information flow for the dynamic programming optimization. A case study of the contact process for sulfuric acid manufacture illustrated the capabilities and limitations of the methodology for an industrial process.

The main advantage of dynamic programming is to convert a large optimization problem to a series of partial optimization problems. The techniques of the previous chapter on multivariable search methods were applicable to the partial optimizations. At this point there is methodology to solve large, constrained optimization problems. If the problem is too large for multivariable search methods, then the techniques of dynamic programming can be applied to give a series of smaller partial optimization problems. The texts by Cooper and Cooper (11) and Denardo (12) are recommended for further reading on the subject of deterministic dynamic programming, and the text by Ross (14) is recommended for stochastic dynamic programming.

REFERENCES

1. Bellman, R. E., *Dynamic Programming,* Princeton University Press, Princeton, N. J. (1957).
2. Bellman, R. E., and S. Dreyfus, *Applied Dynamic Programming,* Princeton University Press, Princeton, N. J. (1962).
3. Roberts, S. M., *Dynamic Programming in Chemical Engineering and Process Control,* Academic Press, New York (1964).
4. Aris, R., *The Optimal Design of Chemical Reactors,* Academic Press, New York (1961).
5. Mitten, L. G., and G. L. Nemhauser, "Multistage Optimization," *Chemical Engineering Progress,* 54(1):53 (January 1963).
6. Wilde, D. J., private communication, 1964.
7. Aris, R., G. L. Nemhauser, and D. J. Wilde, "Optimization of Multistage Cyclic and Branching Systems by Serial Procedures," *A.I.Ch.E. Journal,* 10(3):913 (November 1964).
8. Wilde, D. J. "Strategies for Optimization Macrosystems," *Chemical Engineering Progress,* 61(3):86 (March 1965).
9. Lowry, I., "A Dynamic Programming Study of the Contact Process," M.S. thesis, Louisiana State University, Baton Rouge, Louisiana, (1965).
10. Wilde, D. J., and C. S. Beightler, *Foundations of Optimizations,* Prentice-Hall, Inc., Englewood Cliffs, N. J. (1967).
11. Cooper, L., and M. W. Cooper, *Introduction to Dynamic Programming,* Pergamon Press, New York (1981).
12. Denardo, E. V., *Dynamic Programming: Models and Applications,* Prentice-Hall, Inc., Englewood Cliffs, N. J. (1982).
13. Anonymous, *Manual of 124 Process Flowsheets,* McGraw-Hill Publishing Co., New York (1964).
14. Ross, S., *Introduction to Stochastic Dynamic Programming,* Academic Press, New York (1983).

PROBLEMS

7-1. For Example 7–1, determine the shortest distance between the East and West Coasts.
7-2. Solve Example 7–5 as a network problem.
7-3. In Figure 7-29 a partially completed functional diagram of a process is given that involves a diverging branch and a feed-back loop. Complete the functional diagram by labeling it with the appropriate subscripts on the state and decision variables. Then give the dynamic

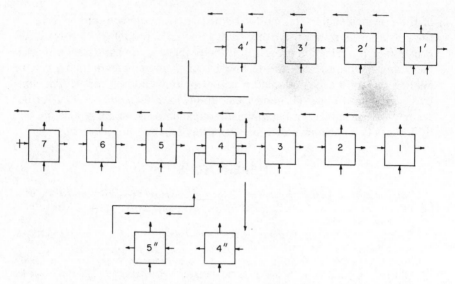

Figure 7-29. Functional diagram to be completed for Problem 7-3.

programming algorithm, transitions functions, and incident identities for each stage. Also, give the type of partial optimization at each stage, and describe how the feed-back loop and diverging branch are evaluated and included in the main branch.

7–4. In Figure 7-30 a partially completed functional diagram of a process is given that involves a converging branch and a feed-forward loop. Complete the functional diagram by labeling it with the appropriate subscripts on the state and decision variables. Then give the dynamic programming algorithm, transitions functions, and incident identities for each stage. Also, give the type of partial optimization at each stage, and describe how the feed-forward loop and converging branch are evaluated and included in the main branch.

7–5. The flow diagram shown in Figure 7-31 is a simplified version of a catalytic cracking unit and associated separation facilities. Develop the dynamic programming functional equations and diagram for this process flow diagram. Define each state and decision variable, transition function, and incident identity. Describe how to calculate the return at each stage. Simplify the functional diagram where required by applying Wilde's rules, and indicate the steps to obtain the optional return and policy.

7–6. The optimum equipment replacement policy for a 12-year period is to be determined for a process with the following annual net profit

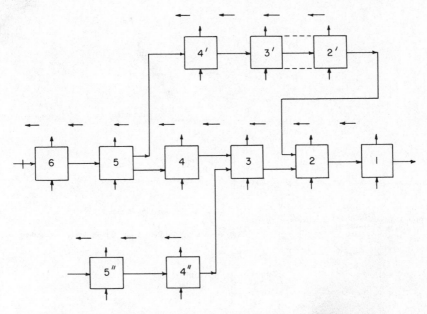

Figure 7-30. Functional diagram to be completed for Problem 7-4.

listed below. Also given is the effect of inflation on the construction of a new process and the salvage value:

TIME (YRS)	NET PROFIT ($M/YR)	NEW PROCESS CONSTRUCTION COST ($M)	SALVAGE VALUE ($M)
0	15	12	5
1	14	12	4
2	13	13	3
3	12	13	2
4	11	14	1
5	9	14	0
6	7	15	0
7	5	15	0
8	3	15	0
9	1	16	0
10	0	16	0
11	0	16	0
12	0	16	0

7-7. The refinery process for alkylation employs identical stirred reactors in series. A feed of isobutane and butene is catalytically reacted to

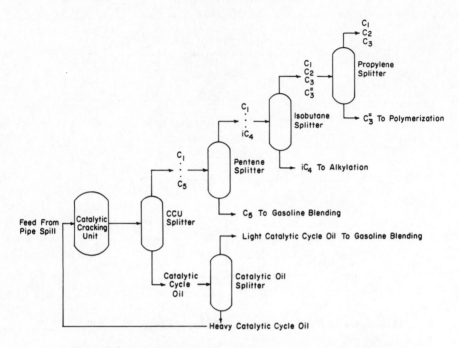

Figure 7-31. Process flow diagram for a catalytic cracking unit.

produce a main product of iso-octane. The fresh catalyst, 98% sulfuric acid, enters the first reactor and flows through the other reactors. As it passes through each reactor, it is degraded, and the concentration decreases. The concentration in the last reactor in the series must be at least 88% to prevent polymerization rather than alkylation. A refinery has three stirred alkylation reactors, as shown in Figure 7-32. The optimal feed rates to each reactor are needed that maximize the profit from the alkylation process. Because the reactors are identical, the profit (return) function for each reactor is the same. This profit function is shown in the figure, along with the catalyst degradation function, which gives the decrease in catalyst concentration across each reactor as a function of reactor feed rate.

Apply the dynamic programming algorithm at each stage, and with this information determine the optimal reactor feed rates, sulfuric acid catalyst concentrations, and the maximum profit.

7-8.[10] Solve the following initial-value problem by dynamic programming:

$$\text{Maximize: } \sum_{i=1}^{5} R(s_i, d_i)$$

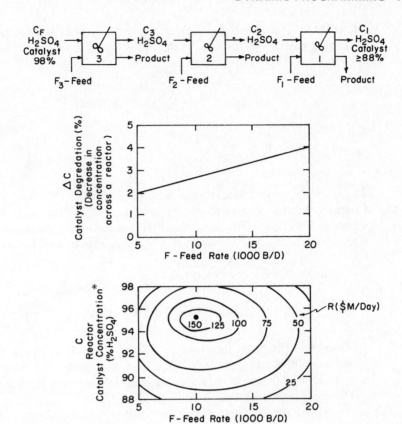

Figure 7-32. Process flow diagram, economic model, and catalyst transition functions for three alkylation reactors in series.

where

$$R_i(s_i, d_i) = s_i + 3d_i \qquad \text{for } i = 1, 2, \cdots, 5$$

$$s_{i-1} = s_i = 2s_i - 0.2d_i$$

$$0 \le d_i \le s_i$$

and the initial state variable $s_5 = 100$

7-9.[10] It is desired to optimally allocate a total of 7.0 units of a resource to four stages of a dynamic programming serial system. The return function at each stage is given by the following equations, and the problem can be stated as:

$$\text{Maximize: } P = \sum_{i=1}^{4} (8x_i - ix_i^2)$$

$$\text{Subject to: } \sum_{i-1}^{4} x_i = 7$$

$R_i(x_i) = 8x_i - ix_i^2$, and x_i has integer values of 0, 1, 2, 3.

7-10. Consider the three-stage, dynamic programming functional diagram shown in Figure 7-4. The functional diagram represents the transition functions, incident identities, and dynamic programming algorithm.

The total profit from the process is:

$$P = R_1(s_1, d_1) + R_2(s_2, d_2) + R_3(s_3, d_3)$$

a. Formulate the profit function, P, as a function of the decision variables illustrating the technique of direct substitution from the classical theory of maxima and minima, and state how the optimum is to be found.

b. Formulate the Lagrangian function illustrating the technique of Lagrange multipliers, and state how the optimum is to be found.

c. Give the dynamic programming algorithm at each stage, and discuss how the optimum policy is found.

d. Discuss the merits and difficulties in implementing each of the above three methods as applied to an industrial problem.

7-11[10] Find the shortest and longest path from 0 to P in Figure 7-33. No backward movement (toward 0) is allowed.

7-12 Solve problem 7-7, but have four stirred reactors in series instead of three. Use the same upper limit on the catalyst concentration of 98% entering but have $\geq 87\%$ leaving.

7-13 a. Extend the optimal equipment replacement problem 7-6, to determine the optimal equipment replacement policy over a ten year period starting with a process that is now two years old.

b. Extend the optimal equipment replacement illustration, Example 7-6, to determine the optimal equipment replacement policy over a ten year period start with a process that is now two years old.

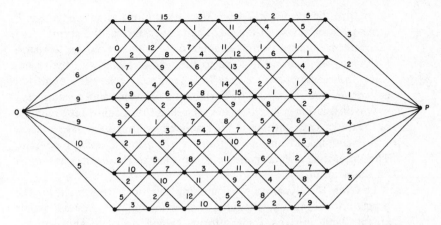

Figure 7-33. Network diagram for Problem 7-10, after Wilde et al. (10).

7-14. In Figure 7-34, the process flow diagram is given for a simplified pentane isomerization plant. This was taken from a description (13) of Phillips Petroleum Company's plant that produces 16,000 barrels per day of 95% isopentane from a reactor feed of 26,000 barrels per day of 85% normal pentane. The reactor uses a platinum catalyst and can operate in a temperature range between 700 and 900°F and with a pressure above 200 psig. The feed preparation facility is a distillation column, and the reflux ratio controls the purity of the

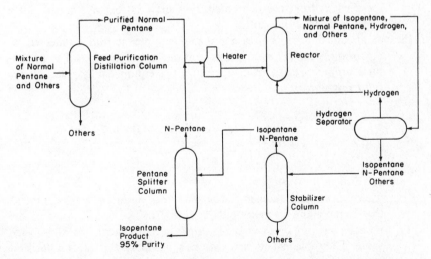

Figure 7-34. Process flow diagram for simplified pentane isomerization process.

normal pentane separated from the mixture of normal pentane and other hydrocarbons in the feed. The temperature of the normal pentane stream is increased in the heater to the optimum reactor temperature and pressure, and it is fed to the reactor along with hydrogen. Then the reactor product goes to a separator, where the hydrogen is removed and recycled. The purification of the product is completed in two distillation columns where the reflux ratios control the removal of the other hydrocarbons in the stabilizer column and the separation of isopentane and normal pentane in the pentane splitter column. The unreacted normal pentane is recycled to the heater, as shown on the diagram.

Develop the dynamic programming functionl diagram from the process flow diagram, assuming that economic and process models are available in a convenient form. Define the state and decision variables, and explain how the dynamic programming optimization will be performed. To perform this analysis, consider that the flow rate and composition to the feed purification distillation column are fixed and that the separation in the column is controlled by the reflux ratio. The conversion of normal pentane to iospentane is controlled by the reactor temperature and pressure, as is the amount of other hydrocarbons produced by side reactions. Also the separation in the stabilizer and pentane splitter distillation columns are controlled by the reflux ratio on each column. The isopentane produced must have a purity of at least 95%. The heater and the hydrogen separator can be treated as decisionless stages, and the flow rate of recycled hydrogen is computed by a material balance and is not a state or decision variable.

7–15. A chemical process uses a piece of equipment that is affected by corrosion, which causes a deterioration in performance. The net annual profit obtained from operating the equipment is given by the following equation:

$$P(t) = \begin{cases} 26 - 2t - \tfrac{1}{2}t^2 & \text{for } 0 \le t \le 4 \\ 0 & \text{for } t > 4 \end{cases}$$

where t can have integer values of 0, 1, 2, 3, and 4. For equipment that is more than 4 years old, the performance has declined to the point where no profit is made, and the equipment has no salvage value. The replacement cost with new equipment is 22. If a decision is to be made annually to keep the current unit or to replace it, determine the optimal policy for equipment replacement for the next 5 years, with the equipment being 1 year old at the start.

7-16. Solve the following four-stage, final-value, serial dynamic programming problems using decision inversion:

$$\text{Maximize: } \sum_{i=1}^{4} R_i(s_i, d_i)$$

where

$R_i = s_i + 3d_i$	return function
$\tilde{s}_i = 2s_i - 0.2d_i$	transition function
$\tilde{s}_i = s_i - 1$	incident identity
$\tilde{s}_1 = 2400$	specified final value, $\tilde{s}_1$
$0 \le d_i \le s_i$	bounds on decision variable, d_i
$0 \le s_4 \le 200$	bounds on initial value, s_4

for $i = 1, 2, 3, 4$

7-17. Solve the following cyclic optimization problem by dynamic programming:

$$\text{Maximize: } \sum_{i=1}^{4} R_i(s_i, d_i)$$

where

$R_i = s_i + 3d_i$	for $i = 1, 2, 3, 4$
$\tilde{s}_i = 2s_i - 0.2d_i$	
$s_{i-1} = \tilde{s}_i$	
$s_4 = \tilde{s}_i$	cyclic optimization
$s_4 \le 100$	

7–18. For a process, the following table gives the net profit for a 10-year period. Also, the sum of the cost of construction of a new process and the salvage value of the old process are given, with approximations for the effects of inflation, taxes, etc. Determine the maximum profit and the optimal equipment replacement policy for a 5-year period for the two cases of starting with a new plant and starting with a 5-year-old plant.

TIME (YR)	NET PROFIT ($M/YR)	NET COSTS* ($M)
0	23	–
1	22	5
2	21	5
3	20	6
4	18	6
5	16	7
6	10	7
7	7	8
8	4	8
9	2	9
10	0	10

* Sum of the cost of construction of a new process and salvage value of the old process.

8
CALCULUS OF VARIATIONS

INTRODUCTION

The calculus of variations and its extensions are devoted to finding the optimum function that gives the best value of the economic model and constraints of a system. The need for an optimum function, rather than an optimal point, arises in numerous problems from a wide range of fields in engineering and physics, which include optimal control, transport phenomena, optics, elasticity, vibrations, statics and dynamics of solid bodies, and navigation. Two examples are determining the optimal temperatures profile in a catalytic reactor to maximize the conversion and the optimal trajectory for a missile to maximize the satellite payload placed in orbit. The first calculus of variations problem, the Brachistochrone problem, was posed and solved by Johannes Bernoulli in 1696 (1). In this problem the optimum curve was determined to minimize the time traveled by a particle sliding without friction between two points.

This chapter is devoted to a relatively brief discussion of some of the key concepts of this topic. These include the Euler equation and the Euler-Poisson equations for the case of several functions and several independent variables with and without constraints. It begins with a derivation of the Euler equation and extends these concepts to more detailed cases. Examples are given to illustrate this theory.

The purpose of this chapter is to develop an appreciation for what is required to determine the optimum function for a variational problem. The extensions and applications to optimal control, Pontryagin's maximum principle, and continuous dynamic programming are left to books devoted to those topics.

FUNCTIONS, FUNCTIONALS, AND NEIGHBORHOODS

It will be necessary to discuss briefly functionals and neighborhoods before developing the Euler equation for the solution of the simplest problem in the calculus of variations. In mathematical programming the maximum or minimum of a function was determined to be an optimal point or set of points. In the calculus of variations, the maximum or minimum value of a functional is determined to be an optimal function. A functional is a function of a function and depends on the entire path of one or more functions, rather than a number of discrete variables.

For the calculus of variations the functional is an integral, and the function that appears in the integrand of the integral is to be selected to maximize or minimize the value of the integral. The texts by Forray (1), Ewing (2), Weinstock (3), Schechter (4), and Sagan (6) elaborate on this concept. However, at this point let us examine an example of the functional given by equation (8–1). The minimum of this functional is a function $y(x)$ that gives the shortest distance between two points $[x_0, y(x_0)]$ and $[x_1, y(x_1)]$.

$$I[y(x)] = \int_{x_0}^{x_1} [1 + (y')^2]^{1/2} \, dx \qquad (8\text{–}1)$$

In this equation y' is the first derivative of y with respect to x. The function that minimizes this integral, a straight line, will be obtained as an illustration of the use of the Euler equation in the next section.

The concept of a neighborhood is used in the derivation of the Euler equation to convert the problem into one of finding the stationary point of a function of a single variable. A function $\bar{y}$ is said to be in the neighborhood of a function y if $|\bar{y} - y| \leq h$ (5). This is illustrated in Figure 8-1(a). The concept can be extended for more restrictive conditions, such as that shown in Figure 8-1(b), when $|\bar{y} - y| \leq h$ and $|\bar{y}' - y'| \leq h$. For this case $\bar{y}$ is said to be in the neighborhood of first order to y. Consequently, the higher the order of the neighborhood, the more nearly the functions will coincide. Extensions of these definitions will lead to what are referred to as *strong* and *weak variations* (6).

EULER EQUATION

The simplest form of the integral to be optimized by the calculus of variations is the following one:

$$I[y(x)] = \int_{x_0}^{x_1} F(x, y, y') \, dx \qquad (8\text{–}2)$$

In addition, the values of $y(x_0)$ and $y(x_1)$ are known, and an example of the function $F(x, y, y')$ was given in equation (8–1) as:

$$F(x, y, y') = [1 + (y')^2]^{1/2} \qquad (8\text{–}3)$$

To obtain the optimal function that minimizes the equation (8–2), it is

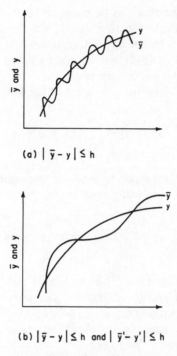

(a) $|\bar{y} - y| \leq h$

(b) $|\bar{y} - y| \leq h$ and $|\bar{y}' - y'| \leq h$

Figure 8-1. Illustration of the concept of a neighborhood.

necessary to solve the Euler equation, which is the following second-order ordinary differential equation.

$$\frac{d}{dx}\left(\frac{\partial F}{\partial y'}\right) - \frac{\partial F}{\partial y} = 0 \qquad (8\text{–}4)$$

It is not obvious that equation (8–4) is a second-order ordinary differential equation. Also, it probably appears unusual to be partially differentiating the function F with respect to y and y'. In addition, although the term *minimize* will be used, stationary points are being located, and their character will have to be determined using sufficient conditions. Consequently, it should be beneficial to outline the derivation of the Euler equation.

First, $y(x)$ is specified as the function that minimizes the functional $I[y(x)]$, equation (8–2). (However, the form of $y(x)$ has to be determined.) Then a function $\bar{y}(x)$ is constructed to be in the neighborhood of $y(x)$ as follows:

$$\bar{y}(x) = y(x) + \alpha n(x) \qquad (8\text{–}5)$$

where α is a parameter that can be made arbitrarily small. Also $n(x)$ is a continuously differentiable function defined on the interval $x_0 \leq x \leq x_1$ with $n(x_0) = n(x_1) = 0$, but is arbitrary elsewhere. The results from the derivation using equation (8–5) are described mathematically as weak variations (1), for $\alpha n(x)$ and $\alpha n'(x)$ are small.

Now equation (8–2) is written in terms of the function $\bar{y}(x)$ as:

$$I[\bar{y}(x)] = \int_{x_0}^{x_1} F(x, \bar{y}, \bar{y}') \, dx \qquad (8\text{--}6)$$

The above equation can be put in terms of the optimal function $y(x)$ and the arbitrary function $n(x)$ using equation (8–5).

$$I[\bar{y}(x)] = \int_{x_0}^{x_1} F(x, y + \alpha n, y' + \alpha n') \, dx \qquad (8\text{--}7)$$

The mathematical argument (3) is made that all the possible functions $\bar{y}$ lie in an arbitrarily small neighborhood of y, because α can be made arbitrarily small. As such, the integral of equation (8–7) may be regarded as an ordinary function of α, $\Phi(\alpha)$, because α would specify the value of the integral knowing $\Phi(\alpha = 0)$ at the minimum from $y(x)$.

$$I[\bar{y}(x)] = \Phi(\alpha) = \int_{x_0}^{x_1} F(x, y + \alpha n, y' + \alpha n') \, dx \qquad (8\text{--}8)$$

The minimum of $\Phi(\alpha)$ is obtained by sitting the first derivative of Φ with respect to α equal to zero. The differentiation is indicated as:

$$\frac{d\Phi(\alpha)}{d\alpha} = \frac{d}{d\alpha} \int_{x_0}^{x_1} F(x, \bar{y}, \bar{y}') \, dx \qquad (8\text{--}9)$$

Leibnitz' rule, equation (8–10), is required to differentiate the integral given in equation (8–9):

$$\frac{d}{dt} \int_{a_1}^{a_2} f(x, t) \, dx = \int_{a_1}^{a_2} \frac{df}{dt} \, dx + f(a_2, t) \frac{da_2}{dt} - f(a_1, t) \frac{da_1}{dt} \qquad (8\text{--}10)$$

where x_0 and x_1 correspond to a_1 and a_2, and α corresponds to t.

The upper and lower limits, x_1 and x_2, are constants; and the following derivatives in the second and third terms on the right-hand side of equation (8–10) are zero for this case:

$$\frac{dx_0}{d\alpha} = \frac{dx_1}{d\alpha} = 0 \tag{8–11}$$

Consequently, the order of integration and differentiation is interchanged, and equation (8–9) can be written as:

$$\frac{d\Phi(\alpha)}{d\alpha} = \int_{x_0}^{x_1} \frac{d}{d\alpha} F(x, \bar{y}, \bar{y}') \, dx \tag{8–12}$$

The integrand can be expanded as follows:

$$\frac{dF}{d\alpha} = \frac{\partial F}{\partial \bar{y}} \frac{d\bar{y}}{d\alpha} + \frac{\partial F}{\partial \bar{y}'} \frac{d\bar{y}'}{d\alpha} + \frac{\partial F}{\partial x} \frac{dx}{d\alpha} \tag{8–13}$$

where $dx/d\alpha = 0$, because x is treated as a constant in the mathematical argument of considering changes from curve to curve at constant x.

Substituting equation (8–13) into equation (8–12) gives:

$$\frac{d\Phi}{d\alpha} = \int_{x_0}^{x_1} \left[\frac{\partial F}{\partial \bar{y}} \frac{d\bar{y}}{d\alpha} + \frac{\partial F}{\partial \bar{y}'} \frac{d\bar{y}'}{d\alpha} \right] dx \tag{8–14}$$

The following results are needed:

$$\frac{d\bar{y}}{d\alpha} = \frac{d}{d\alpha} [y + \alpha n] = n \qquad \frac{d\bar{y}'}{d\alpha} = \frac{d}{d\alpha} [y' + \alpha n'] = n' \tag{8–15}$$

Using equation (8–15), we can write equation (8–14) as:

$$\frac{d\Phi}{d\alpha} = \int_{x_0}^{x_1} \left[\frac{\partial F}{\partial \bar{y}} n + \frac{\partial F}{\partial \bar{y}'} n' \right] dx \tag{8–16}$$

An integration-by-parts will give a more convenient form for the term involving n', i.e.:

$$\int_{x_0}^{x_1} \frac{\partial F}{\partial \bar{y}'} n' \, dx = \frac{\partial F}{\partial \bar{y}'} n \bigg|_{x_0}^{x_1} - \int_{x_0}^{x_1} n \frac{d}{dx} \left(\frac{\partial F}{\partial \bar{y}'} \right) dx \tag{8–17}$$

The first term on the right-hand side is zero, for $n(x_0) = n(x_1) = 0$. Combining the results from equation (8–17) with equation (8–16) gives:

$$\frac{d\Phi}{d\alpha} = \int_{x_0}^{x_1} n(x) \left[\frac{\partial F}{d\bar{y}} - \frac{d}{dx} \left(\frac{\partial F}{d\bar{y}'} \right) \right] dx$$

At the optimum $d\Phi/d\alpha = 0$, and letting $\alpha \to 0$ has $\bar{y} \to y$ and $\bar{y}' \to y'$. Therefore, the above equation becomes:

$$\int_{x_0}^{x_1} n(x) \left[\frac{\partial F}{\partial y} - \frac{d}{dx} \left(\frac{\partial F}{\partial y'} \right) \right] dx = 0 \qquad (8\text{–}18)$$

To obtain the Euler equation, the fundamental lemma of the calculus of variation is used. This lemma can be stated, after Weinstock (3), as:

If x_0 and x_1 ($>x_0$) are fixed constants and $G(x)$ is a particular continuous function in the interval $x_0 \leq x \leq x_1$ and if:

$$\int_{x_0}^{x_1} n(x) \, G(x) \, dx = 0$$

for every choice of the continously differentiable function $n(x)$ for which $n(x_0) = n(x_1) = 0$, then $G(x) = 0$ identically in the interval $x_0 \leq x \leq x_1$.

The proof of this lemma is by contradiction and is given by Weinstock (3). Applying this lemma to equation (8–18) gives the Euler equation:

$$\frac{\partial F}{\partial y} - \frac{d}{dx} \left(\frac{\partial F}{\partial y'} \right) = 0 \qquad (8\text{–}4)$$

This equation is a second-order ordinary differential equation and has boundary conditions $y(x_0)$ and $y(x_1)$. The solution of this differential equation $y(x)$ optimizes the integral $I[y(x)]$.

A more convenient form of the Euler equation can be obtained by applying the chain rule to $\partial F(x, y, y')/\partial y'$:

$$d\left(\frac{\partial F}{\partial y'} \right) = \frac{\partial}{\partial y'} \left(\frac{\partial F}{\partial y'} \right) dy' + \frac{\partial}{\partial y} \left(\frac{\partial F}{\partial y'} \right) dy + \frac{\partial}{\partial x} \left(\frac{\partial F}{\partial y'} \right) dx \qquad (8\text{–}19)$$

or

$$\frac{d}{dx}\left(\frac{\partial F}{\partial y'}\right) = \frac{\partial^2 F}{\partial y'^2}\frac{d^2 y}{dx^2} + \frac{\partial^2 F}{\partial y \partial y'}\frac{dy}{dx} + \frac{\partial^2 F}{\partial x \partial y'} \qquad (8\text{--}20)$$

Substituting equation (8–20) into equation (8–4) and rearranging gives a more familiar form for a second-order ordinary differential equation:

$$\frac{\partial^2 F}{\partial y'^2}\frac{d^2 y}{dx^2} + \frac{\partial^2 F}{\partial y \partial y'}\frac{dy}{dx} + \frac{\partial^2 F}{\partial x \partial y'} - \frac{\partial F}{\partial y} = 0 \qquad (8\text{--}21)$$

A more convenient way to write this equation is:

$$F_{y'y'}\frac{d^2 y}{dx^2} + F_{y'y}\frac{dy}{dx} + F_{y'x} - F_y = 0 \qquad (8\text{--}22)$$

The coefficients for the differential equation come from partially differentiating F.

A special case that sometimes occurs is to have $F(y, y')$, i.e., F is not a function of x. For this situation it can be shown that:

$$\frac{d}{dx}\left(F - y'\frac{\partial F}{\partial y'}\right) = 0 \qquad (8\text{--}23)$$

This equation may be integrated once to obtain a form of the Euler equation given below, which can be a more convenient starting point for problem solving:

$$F - y'\frac{\partial F}{\partial y'} = \text{constant} \qquad (8\text{--}24)$$

where the constant is evaluated using one of the boundary conditions.

At this point it should be noted that the necessary conditions of the classical theory of maxima and minima have been used to locate a stationary point. This point may be a minimum, maximum, or saddle point. To determine its character, sufficient conditions must be used, and these will be discussed subsequently. However, before that the following example is used to illustrate an application of the Euler equation.

EXAMPLE 8–1

Determine the function that gives the shortest distance between two given points. Referring to Figure 8-2, we can state the problem as:

$$\text{Minimize: } L = \int_{x_0}^{x_1} ds$$

and from the figure it follows that:

$$ds = [(dx)^2 + (dy)^2]^{1/2} = [1 + (y')^2]^{1/2}\, dx$$

Substituting for ds in the integral gives:

$$L = \int_{x_0}^{x_1} [1 + (y')^2]^{1/2}\, dx$$

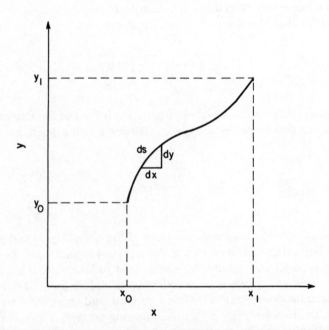

Figure 8-2.   Diagram to illustrate the shortest distance between two points for Example 8-1.

Evaluating the partial derivatives for the Euler equation:

$$F_y = 0 \qquad F_{y'x} = 0 \qquad F_{y'y} = 0 \qquad F_{y'y'} = 1/[1 + (y')^2]^{3/2}$$

Substituting, equation 8–22 becomes:

$$(1/[1 + (y')^2]^{3/2})\frac{d^2y}{dx^2} + (0)\frac{dy}{dx} + (0) - (0) = 0$$

Simplifying gives

$$\frac{d^2y}{dx^2} = 0$$

Integrating the above equation twice gives:

$$y = c_1 x + c_2$$

This is the equation of a straight line, and the constants, c_1 and c_2 are evaluated from the boundary conditions.

Another classic problem of the calculus of variation, as mentioned earlier, is the Brachistochrone problem (10). The shape of the curve between two points is to be determined to minimize the time of a particle sliding along a wire without frictional resistance. The particle is acted upon only by gravitational forces as it travels between the two points. The approach to the solution is the same as for Example 8–1, and the integral for the time of travel, T, is given by Weinstock (3) as:

$$T = \int_{x_0}^{x_1} \{[1 + (y')^2]^{1/2}/[2g(y - y_0)]^{1/2}\}\, dx \qquad (8\text{–}25)$$

and the solution is in terms of the following parametric equations:

$$x = x_0 + a[\theta - \sin(\theta)] \qquad y = y_0 + a[1 - \cos(\theta)] \qquad (8\text{–}26)$$

The details of the solution are given by Weinstock (3). The solution is the equations for a cycloid.

The method of obtaining the Euler equation is used almost directly to obtain the results for more detailed forms of the integrand of equation (8–2). The next section extends the results for more complex problems.

MORE COMPLEX PROBLEMS

In the procedure used to obtain the Euler equation, first a function was constructed to have the integral be a function of a single independent variable, α_i, and then the classical theory of maxima and minima was applied to locate the stationary point. This same method is used for more complex problems that include more functions, e.g., $y_1, y_2, \cdots, y_n$; in higher order derivatives, e.g., $y, y', \cdots, y^{(n)}$; and more than one independent variable, e.g., $y(x_1, x_2)$. It is instructive to take these additional complications in steps. First, the case will be considered for one function y with higher order derivatives, and then this will be followed by the case of several functions with first derivatives, all for one independent variable. These results can then be combined for the case of several functions with higher order derivatives. The results will be a set of ordinary differential equations to be solved. Then further elaboration on the same ideas for the case of more than one independent variable will give a partial differential equation to be solved for the optimal function. Finally, any number of functions of varying order of derivatives with several independent variables will require that a set of partial differential equations be solved for the optimal functions.

Functional with Higher Derivatives in the Integrand: For the case of the integrand containing higher order derivatives, the integral has the following form:

$$I[y(x)] = \int_{x_0}^{x_1} F[x, y, y', \cdots, y^{(m)}] \, dx \qquad (8\text{--}26)$$

In this case, boundary conditions will be required for $y(x_0)$, $y'(x_0)$, $\cdots$, $y^{(m)}(x_0)$, and $y(x_1)$, $y'(x_1)$, $\cdots$, $y^{(m)}(x_1)$.

The function constructed in equation (8–5) is used, and the integral of equation (8–26) becomes:

$$I[\bar{y}(x)] = \Phi(\alpha) = \int_{x_0}^{x_1} F[x, \bar{y}, \bar{y}', \bar{y}'', \cdots, \bar{y}^{(m)}] \, dx \qquad (8\text{--}27)$$

The mathematical argument is used that the integral is a function of α only, and differentiation with respect to α gives:

$$\frac{d\Phi}{d\alpha} = \int_{x_0}^{x_1} \frac{d}{d\alpha} F(x, \bar{y}, \bar{y}', \bar{y}'', \cdots, \bar{y}^{(m)}] \, dx \qquad (8\text{--}28)$$

and using the chain rule, we can write the integrand as:

$$\frac{dF}{d\alpha} = \frac{\partial F}{\partial \bar{y}} \frac{d\bar{y}}{d\alpha} + \frac{\partial F}{\partial \bar{y}'} \frac{d\bar{y}'}{d\alpha} + \frac{\partial F}{\partial \bar{y}''} \frac{d\bar{y}''}{d\alpha} + \cdots + \frac{\partial F}{\partial \bar{y}^{(m)}} \frac{d\bar{y}^{(m)}}{d\alpha} \qquad (8\text{--}29)$$

Using the function $\bar{y} = y + \alpha n$ and its derivatives gives:

$$\frac{dF}{d\alpha} = \frac{\partial F}{\partial \bar{y}} n + \frac{\partial F}{\partial \bar{y}} n' + \frac{\partial F}{\partial \bar{y}''} n'' + \cdots + \frac{\partial F}{\partial \bar{u}^{(m)}} n^{(m)} \qquad (8\text{--}30)$$

and equation (8–28) can be written as the following:

$$\frac{d\Phi}{d\alpha} = \int_{x_0}^{x_1} [F_{\bar{y}} \, n + F_{\bar{y}}' \, n' + F_{\bar{y}''} \, n'' + \cdots + F_{\bar{y}(m)} \, n^{(m)}] \, dx \qquad (8\text{--}31)$$

A series of integration-by-parts converts the terms in equation (8–31) as follows:

$$\int_{x_0}^{x_1} F_{\bar{y}'} \, n' \, dx = - \int_{x_0}^{x_1} n \frac{d}{dx} F_{\bar{y}'} \, dx \qquad (8\text{--}32)$$

$$\int_{x_0}^{x_1} F_{\bar{y}''} \, n'' \, dx = - \int_{x_0}^{x_1} n' \frac{d}{dx} F_{\bar{y}''} \, dx = \int_{x_0}^{x_1} n \frac{d^2}{dx^2} F_{\bar{y}''} \, dx$$

$$\vdots \qquad\qquad\qquad (8\text{--}33)$$

$$\int_{x_0}^{x_1} F_{\bar{y}^{(m)}} \, n^{(m)} \, dx = (-1)^m \int_{x_0}^{x_1} n \frac{d^{(m)}}{dx^{(m)}} F_{\bar{y}^{(m)}} \, dx$$

where equation (8–32) is the same as equation (8–17).

Equation (8–31) can be written as:

$$\frac{d\Phi}{d\alpha} = \int_{x_0}^{x_1} n \left[F_{\bar{y}} - \frac{dF_{\bar{y}}'}{dx} + \cdots + (-1)^m \frac{d^{(m)}}{dx^{(m)}} F_{\bar{y}^{(m)}} \right] dx \qquad (8\text{--}34)$$

At the optimum $\alpha \to 0$ to have $\bar{y} \to y, \cdots, \bar{y}^{(m)} \to y^{(m)}$; and $d\Phi/d\alpha = 0$ to give:

$$F_y - \frac{dF_y}{dx} + \cdots + (-1)^m \frac{d^{(m)}}{dx^{(m)}} F_y{}^{(m)} = 0 \qquad (8\text{--}35)$$

by employing the fundamental lemma of the calculus of variations.

This equation is normally written as follows and is called the *Euler-Poisson equation:*

$$\frac{d^{(m)}}{dx^{(m)}} F_y{}^{(m)} - \frac{d^{(m-1)}}{dx^{(m-1)}} F_y{}^{(m-1)} + \cdots + (-1)^m F_y = 0 \qquad (8\text{--}36)$$

This equation is an ordinary differential equation of order $2m$ and requires $2m$ boundary conditions. The following example illustrates its use in finding the optimal function.

EXAMPLE 8–2(1)

Determine the optimum function that minimizes the integral in the following equation:

$$I[y(x)] = \int_{x_0}^{x_1} [16y^2 - (y'')^2] \, dx$$

The Euler-Poisson equation for $m = 2$ is:

$$\frac{d^2}{dx^2} F_y{}'' - \frac{d}{dx} F_y{}' + F_y = 0$$

Evaluating the partial derivatives gives:

$$F = 16y^2 - (y'')^2$$

$$\frac{\partial F}{\partial y''} = F_y{}'' = -2y'' \qquad \frac{\partial F}{\partial y'} = F_y{}' = 0 \qquad \frac{\partial F}{\partial y} = F_y = 32y$$

Substituting into the Euler-Poisson equation gives a fourth-order ordinary differential equation:

$$\frac{d^4y}{dx^4} - 16y = 0$$

The solution of this differential equation is:

$$y = c_1 e^{2x} + c_2 e^{-2x} + c_3 \cos 2x + c_4 \sin 2x$$

where the constants of integration are evaluated using the boundary conditions.

Functional with Several Functions in the Integrand: For the case of the integrand containing several functions, y_1, y_2, $\cdots$, y_p, the integral has the following form:

$$I[y_1(x), y_2(x), \cdots, y_p(x)]$$
$$= \int_{x_0}^{x_1} F(x, y_1, y_2, \cdots, y_p, y_1', y_2', \cdots, y_p'] \, dx \qquad (8\text{-}37)$$

and boundary conditions on each of the functions are required, i.e., $y_1(x_0)$, $y_1(x_1)$, $y_2(x_0)$, $y_2(x_1)$, $\cdots$, $y_p(x_0)$, $y_p(x_1)$.

The function constructed in equation (8–5) is used, except in this case p functions are required:

$$\bar{y}_1 = y_1 + \alpha_1 n_1$$
$$\vdots \qquad\qquad (8\text{-}38)$$
$$\bar{y}_p = y_p + \alpha_p n_p$$

with p parameters α_1, α_2, $\cdots$, α_p, which can be made arbitrarily small. These equations are substituted into equation (8–37), and then the mathematical argument is used that the integral is a function of α_1, α_2, $\cdots$, α_p:

$$\Phi(\alpha_1, \alpha_2, \cdots \alpha_p) = \int_{x_0}^{x_1} F[x, y_1 + \alpha n_1, \cdots, y_p \qquad (8\text{-}39)$$
$$+ \alpha n_p, y_1' + \alpha n_1', \cdots, y_p' + \alpha n_p'] \, dx$$

To locate the stationary point(s) of the integral, the first partial derivatives of Φ with respect to α_1, α_2, $\cdots$, α_p are set equal to zero. This gives the following set of p equations:

$$\frac{\partial \Phi}{\partial \alpha_i} = \int_{x_0}^{x_1} \frac{\partial F}{\partial \alpha_i} \, dx \qquad \text{for } i = 1, 2, \cdots, p \qquad (8\text{-}40)$$

The chain rule is used with the function F, as previously to give:

$$\frac{\partial F}{\partial \alpha_i} = \frac{\partial F}{\partial \bar{y}_i} \frac{\partial \bar{y}_i}{\partial \alpha_i} + \frac{\partial F}{\partial \bar{y}_i'} \frac{\partial \bar{y}_i'}{\partial \alpha_i} = \frac{\partial F}{\partial \bar{y}_i} n_i + \frac{\partial F}{\partial \bar{y}_i'} n_i' \qquad (8\text{-}41)$$

Substituting into equation (8–40), we obtain an equation comparable to equation (8–16):

$$\frac{\partial \Phi}{\partial \alpha_i} = \int_{x_0}^{x_1} \left[\frac{\partial F}{\partial \bar{y}_i} n_i + \frac{\partial F}{\partial \bar{y}_i'} n_i' \right] dx \qquad \text{for } i = 1, 2, \cdots, p \qquad (8\text{-}42)$$

Integration by parts, letting $\alpha_i \rightarrow 0$ to have $\bar{y}_i \rightarrow y_i$ and $\bar{y}_i' \rightarrow y_i'$, and to have $\partial\Phi/\partial\alpha_i = 0$ gives the equation comparable to equation (8–18), i.e.:

$$\int_{x_0}^{x_1} n_i \left[\frac{\partial F}{\partial y_i} - \frac{d}{dx} \left(\frac{\partial F}{\partial y_i'} \right) \right] dx = 0 \qquad \text{for } i = 1, 2, \cdots, p \qquad (8\text{–}43)$$

Applying the fundamental lemma of the calculus of variations gives the following set of equations comparable to equation (8–4):

$$\frac{\partial F}{\partial y_i} - \frac{d}{dx} \left[\frac{\partial F}{\partial y_i'} \right] = 0 \qquad \text{for } i = 1, 2, \cdots, p \qquad (8\text{–}44)$$

This is a set of Euler equations, and the following example illustrates the use of these equations to find the optimum set of functions.

EXAMPLE 8–3(1)

Determine the optimum functions that determine the stationary points for the following integral:

$$I[y_1, y_2] = \int_{x_0}^{x_1} [2y_1 y_2 - 2y_1^2 + (y_1')^2 - (y_2')^2] \, dx$$

The two Euler equations are:

$$\frac{d}{dx} \left[\frac{\partial F}{\partial y_1'} \right] - \frac{\partial F}{\partial y_1} = 0 \qquad \frac{d}{dx} \left[\frac{\partial F}{\partial y_2'} \right] - \frac{\partial F}{\partial y_2} = 0$$

The function F and the partial derivatives needed for these Euler equations are:

$$F = 2y_1 y_2 - 2y_1^2 + (y_1')^2 - (y_2')^2$$

$$\frac{\partial F}{\partial y_1} = 2y_2 - 4y_1 \qquad \frac{\partial F}{\partial y_2} = 2y_1$$

$$\frac{\partial F}{\partial y_1'} = 2y_1' \qquad \frac{\partial F}{\partial y_2'} = -2y_2'$$

The two Euler equations become:

$$-y_1'' + y_2 - 2y_1 = 0 \qquad y_2'' + y_1 = 0$$

This set of two linear ordinary differential equations has been solved by Forray (1), using standard techniques, and the solution is:

$$y_1 = (c_1 x + c_2) \cos(x) + (c_3 x + c_4) \sin(x)$$

$$y_2 = c_1(x \cos(x) - 2 \sin(x)) + c_2 \cos(x) + c_3(2 \cos(x) + x \sin(x)) + c_4 \sin(x)$$

Functional with Several Functions and Higher Derivatives: We can now consider the case that combines the two previous ones, i.e., the integrand contains several functions with higher order derivatives:

$$I[y_1, \cdots, y_p] = \int_{x_0}^{x_1} F[x, y_1, y_1', \cdots, y_1^{(m)}, \cdots, y_p, y_p', \cdots, y_p^{(k)}] \, dx \qquad (8\text{–}45)$$

The procedure to obtain the set of ordinary differential equations to determine the stationary points is a combination of the derivations for the two previous cases. The integral is converted to a function of parameters α_1, $\alpha_2, \cdots, \alpha_p$, and the first partial derivatives with respect to these parameters are set equal to zero to give the following set of Euler-Poisson equations:

$$\frac{d}{dx^{(m)}} F_{y_1}{}^{(m)} - \frac{d}{dx^{(m-1)}} F_{y_1}{}^{(m-1)} + \cdots + (-1)^m F_{y_1} = 0$$

$$\vdots \qquad\qquad (8\text{–}46)$$

$$\frac{d^{(k)}}{dx^{(k)}} F_{y_p}{}^{(k)} - \frac{d^{(k-1)}}{dx^{(k-1)}} F_{y_p}{}^{(k-1)} + \cdots + (-1)^k F_{y_p} = 0$$

This is a set of p ordinary differential equations, and the order of each one is determined by the highest order derivative appearing in the integrand. The following example illustrates the use of these equations.

EXAMPLE 8–4

Determine the optimal functions that determine the stationary points for the following integral:

$$I[y_1, y_2] = \int_{x_0}^{x_1} \{[1 + (y_1')^2]^{1/2} + 16y_2^2 - (y_2'')^2\} \, dx$$

The Euler-Poisson equations for $y_1 (m = 1)$ and $y_2 (k = 2)$

$$\frac{d}{dx} F_{y_1'} - F_{y_1} = 0 \qquad \frac{d^2}{dx^2} F_{y_2'} - \frac{dF_{y_2'}}{dx} + F_{y_2} = 0$$

Computing the partial derivatives gives:

$$F'_{y_1} = y_1/[1 + (y_1)^2]^{3/2} \qquad F_{y'_2} = -2y''_2$$

$$F_{y_1} = 0 \qquad\qquad F_{y'_2} = 0$$

$$F_{y_2} = 32y$$

substituting gives

$$\frac{d}{dx}\left[\frac{y'_1}{[1+(y'_1)^2]^{3/2}}\right] = 0 \qquad \frac{d}{dx^2}(-2y''_2) + 32y_2 = 0$$

These are two ordinary differential equations in y_1 and y_2. The solution to each differential equation is given in Examples 8–1 and 8–2. In fact, the example was constructed from these two problems for a simple illustration of the application of a set of Euler-Poisson equations. However, it does not illustrate the coupling that would normally occur, which requires the set of equations to be solved simultaneously.

An example of this coupling is given in the outline of the optimal rocket trajectory problem by Wylie and Barrett (8), which requires a solution of two Euler-Poisson equations. The equation for the conservation of momentum is applied to the rocket, and the initial conditions on the position of the rocket and the rate of fuel use are required information to determine a family of optimal trajectories.

Functional with More than One Independent Variable: For this case the integrand contains more than one independent variable. The analogous form to equation (8–2) for two independent variables is:

$$I[y(x_1, x_2)] = \int_R \int F(x_1, x_2, y, y_{x_1}, y_{x_2})\, dx_1\, dx_2 \qquad (8\text{–}47)$$

where the integral is integrated over the region R, and y_{x_1} and y_{x_2} indicate partial differentiation of y with respect to x_1 and x_2.

The procedure to obtain the differential equation to be solved for the optimal solution of equation (8–47) follows the mathematical arguments used for the case of one independent variable. However, Green's theorem is required for the integration by parts, and the function $n(x_1, x_2)$ is zero on the surface of the region R. The function $\bar{y}(x_1, x_2)$ is constructed from the optimal function $y(x_1, x_2)$ and the arbitrary function $n(x_1, x_2)$ as:

$$\bar{y}(x_1, x_2) = y(x_1, x_2) + an(x_1, x_2) \tag{8-48}$$

where α is the parameter that can be made arbitrarily small.

Now the integral in equation (8–47) can be considered to be a function of α only, as was done in the previous mathematical arguments, i.e.;

$$I[\bar{y}(x_1, x_2)] = I[y(x_1, x_2) + an(x_1, x_2)] = \Phi(\alpha) \tag{8-49}$$

Then differentiating with respect to α gives an equation comparable to equation (8–12). The surface of the region R is a constant allowing the interchange of the order of differentiation and integration:

$$\frac{d\Phi}{d\alpha} = \int_R \int \frac{d}{d\alpha} F(x_1, x_2, \bar{y}, \bar{y}_{x_1}, \bar{y}_{x_2})\, dx_1\, dx_2 \tag{8-50}$$

Applying the chain rule, as was done previously where F is not considered a function of x_1 and x_2 for changes from surface to surface, the integrand becomes:

$$\frac{dF}{d\alpha} = \frac{\partial F}{\partial \bar{y}}\frac{\partial \bar{y}}{\partial \alpha} + \frac{\partial F}{\partial \bar{y}_{x_1}}\frac{\partial \bar{y}_{x_1}}{\partial \alpha} + \frac{\partial F}{\partial \bar{y}_{x_2}}\frac{\partial \bar{y}_{x_2}}{\partial \alpha} \tag{8-51}$$

and

$$\frac{\partial \bar{y}}{\partial \alpha} = n \qquad \frac{\partial \bar{y}_{x_1}}{\partial \alpha} = \frac{\partial n}{\partial x_1} \qquad \frac{\partial \bar{y}_{x_2}}{\partial \alpha} = \frac{\partial n}{\partial x_2}$$

The integral in equation (8–50) can be written in the following form, using equation (8–51):

$$\frac{d\Phi}{d\alpha} = \int_R \int \left[\frac{\partial F}{\partial y}\, n + \frac{\partial F}{\partial y_{x_1}}\frac{\partial n}{\partial x_1} + \frac{\partial F}{\partial y_{x_2}}\frac{\partial n}{\partial x_2} \right] dx_1\, dx_2 \tag{8-52}$$

which is comparable to equation (8–16).

In this case the integration-by-parts is performed using Green's theorem in the plane, which is:

$$\int_D \int \left[G\frac{\partial f}{\partial x_1} + H\frac{\partial f}{\partial x_2} \right] dx_1\, dx_2 \tag{8-53}$$

$$= -\int_D \int f \left[\frac{\partial G}{\partial x_1} + \frac{\partial H}{\partial x_2} \right] dx_1\, dx_2 + \int_C f(G\, dx\, - H\, dx_2)$$

This theorem is applied to the second two terms of equation (8–52), where $f = n$, $G = \partial F/\partial y_{x_1}$ and $H = \partial F/\partial y_{x_2}$. An equation comparable to equation (8–18) is obtained by allowing $\alpha \to 0$, such that $\bar{y} \to y$, $\bar{y}_{x_1} \to y_{x_1}$ and $\bar{y}_{x_2} \to y_{x_2}$; and $d\Phi/d\alpha = 0$ to have:

$$\int_R \int n \left[\frac{\partial F}{\partial y} - \frac{\partial}{\partial x_1} \left(\frac{\partial F}{\partial y_{x_1}} \right) - \frac{\partial}{\partial x_2} \left(\frac{\partial F}{\partial y_{x_2}} \right) \right] dx_1\, dx_2 = 0 \qquad (8\text{--}54)$$

Again, it is argued, using an extension of the fundamental lemma of the calculus of variations, that if the integral is equal to zero, then the term in the brackets is equal to zero, because $n(x_1, x_2)$ is arbitrary everywhere except on the boundaries where it is zero. The result is the equation that corresponds to the Euler equation, equation (8–4):

$$\frac{\partial F}{\partial y} - \frac{\partial}{\partial x_1} \left(\frac{\partial F}{\partial y_{x_1}} \right) - \frac{\partial}{\partial x_2} \left(\frac{\partial F}{\partial y_{x_2}} \right) = 0 \qquad (8\text{--}55)$$

Also, this equation can be expanded using the chain rule to give an equation that corresponds to equation (8–21), which is:

$$F_{y_{x_1} y_{x_1}} \frac{\partial^2 y}{\partial x_1^2} + 2 F_{y_{x_1} y_{x_2}} \frac{\partial^2 y}{\partial x_1 \partial x_2} + F_{y_{x_2} y_{x_2}} \frac{\partial^2 y}{\partial x_2^2} + F_{y_{x_1} y} \frac{\partial y}{\partial x_1}$$

$$+ F_{y_{x_2} y} \frac{\partial y}{\partial x_2} + F_{y_{x_1} x_1} + F_{y_{x_2} x_2} - F_y = 0 \qquad (8\text{--}56)$$

It can be seen that this is a second-order partial differential equation in two independent variables. Appropriate boundary conditions at the surface in terms of y and the first partial derivatives of y are required for a solution.

Prior to illustrating the use of equation (8–55), a general form is given from Burley (9) by the following equation for n independent variables with only first partial derivatives in the integrand:

$$\sum_{i=1}^n \frac{\partial}{\partial x_i} \left(\frac{\partial F}{\partial y_{x_i}} \right) - \frac{\partial F}{\partial y} = 0 \qquad (8\text{--}57)$$

The derivation of this equation follows the one for two independent variables.

The following example illustrates an application of equation (8–55). Other applications are given by Forray (1) and Schechter (4).

EXAMPLE 8–5 (1)

The following equation describes the potential energy of a stretched membrane, which is a minimum for small deflections. If A is the tension per unit length and B is the external load, the optimum shape $y(x_1, x_2)$ is determined by minimizing the integral:

$$I = 1/2 \int_D \int \left\{ A \left(\frac{\partial y}{\partial x_1} \right)^2 + A \left(\frac{\partial y}{\partial x_2} \right)^2 - 2By \right\} dx_1 \, dx_2$$

Obtain the differential equation that is to be solved for the optimum shape.

The extension of the Euler equation for this case of two independent variables was given by equation (8–55):

$$\frac{\partial}{\partial x_1} \left(\frac{\partial F}{\partial y_{x_1}} \right) + \frac{\partial}{\partial x_2} \left(\frac{\partial F}{\partial y_{x_2}} \right) - \frac{\partial F}{\partial y} = 0$$

The integrand for F in the above equation is:

$$F = A \left(\frac{\partial y}{\partial x_1} \right)^2 + A \left(\frac{\partial y}{\partial x_2} \right)^2 - 2By$$

The following results are obtained from evaluating the partial derivatives:

$$\frac{\partial F}{\partial y_{x_1}} = 2A \frac{\partial y}{\partial x_1} \qquad \frac{\partial F}{\partial y_{x_2}} = 2A \frac{\partial y}{\partial x_2} \qquad \frac{\partial F}{\partial y} = -2B$$

Substituting into the equation and simplifying gives:

$$\frac{\partial^2 y}{\partial x_1^2} + \frac{\partial^2 y}{\partial x_2^2} + \frac{B}{A} = 0$$

This is a second-order, elliptic partial differential equation. The solution requires boundary conditions that give the shape of the sides of the membrane. The solution of the partial differential equation will be the shape of the membrane.

The text by Courant and Hilbert (5) gives the extension for higher order derivatives in the integrand. Also, that book gives solutions for a number of problems, including membrane shapes of rectangles and circles, and is an excellent reference book on free and forced vibrations of membranes.

In the next section, the results for unconstrained problems are extended to those with constraints. The constraints can be of three types for calculus of variations problems, and they are algebraic, integral, and differential equations.

CONSTRAINED VARIATIONAL PROBLEMS

Generally, there are two procedures used for solving variational problems that have constraints. These are the methods of direct substitution and Lagrange Multipliers. In the method of direct substitution, the constraint equation is substituted into the integrand; and the problem is converted into an unconstrained problem, as was done in Chapter 2. In the method of Lagrange Multipliers, the Lagrangian function is formed, and the unconstrained problem is solved using the appropriate forms of the Euler or Euler-Poisson equation. However, in some cases the Lagrange Multiplier is a function of the independent variables and is not a constant. This is an added complication that was not encountered in Chapter 2.

Algebraic Constraints: To illustrate the method of Lagrange Multipliers, the simplest case with one algebraic equation will be used. The extension to more complicated cases is the same as that for analytical methods:

$$\text{Optimize:} \quad I[y(x)] = \int_{x_0}^{x_1} F(x, y, y')dx \qquad (8\text{--}58)$$

$$\text{Subject to:} \ G(x, y) = 0$$

The Lagrangian function is formed, as shown below:

$$L(x, y, y', \lambda) = F(x, y, y') + \lambda(x) \, G(x, y) \qquad (8\text{--}59)$$

The Lagrange Multiplier λ is a function of the independent variable, x, and the unconstrained Euler equation is solved as given below:

$$\frac{d}{dx}\left(\frac{\partial L}{\partial y'}\right) - \frac{\partial L}{\partial y} = 0 \qquad (8\text{--}60)$$

along with the constraint equation $G(x, y) = 0$.

There is a Lagrange Multiplier for each constraint equation when the

Lagrangian function is formed. A derivation of the Lagrange Multiplier method is given by Forray (1), and the following example illustrates the technique.

EXAMPLE 8–6 (8)

The classic example to illustrate this procedure is the problem of finding the path of a unit mass particle on a sphere from point $(0, 0, 1)$ to point $(0, 0, -1)$ in time T, which minimizes the integral of the kinetic energy of the particle. The integral to be minimized and the constraint to be satisfied are:

$$\text{Minimize: } I[x, y, z] = \int_0^T \left[(x')^2 + (y')^2 + (z')^2\right]^{1/2} dt$$

$$\textit{Subject to: } x^2 + y^2 + z^2 = 1$$

The Lagrangian function is:

$$L[x(t), y(t), z(t), \lambda(t)] = \left[(x')^2 + (y')^2 + (z')^2\right]^{1/2} + \lambda(x^2 + y^2 + z^2 - 1)$$

There are three optimal functions to be determined, and the corresponding three Euler equations are:

$$\frac{d}{dt}\left(\frac{\partial L}{\partial x'}\right) - \frac{\partial L}{\partial x} = 0 \qquad \frac{d}{dt}\left(\frac{\partial L}{\partial y'}\right) - \frac{\partial L}{\partial y} = 0 \qquad \frac{d}{dt}\left(\frac{\partial L}{\partial z'}\right) - \frac{\partial L}{\partial z} = 0$$

Performing the partial differentiation of L, recognizing that $[(x')^2 + (y')^2 + (z')^2]^{1/2} = s'$ (an arc length that is a constant), and substituting into the Euler equations, we obtain three simple, second-order ordinary differential equations:

$$\frac{d^2x}{dt^2} + \lambda x = 0 \qquad \frac{d^2y}{dt^2} + \lambda y = 0 \qquad \frac{d^2z}{dt^2} + \lambda z = 0$$

These can be integrated after some manipulations to give:

$$x + c_1 y + c_2 z = 0$$

which is the equation of a plane through the center of the sphere. The intersection of this plane and the sphere is a great circle, which is the optimal path. It can be shown that the minimum kinetic energy is π^2/T.

Integral Constraints: Isoperimetric problems (1) are ones where an integral is to be optimized subject to a constraint, which is another integral having a specified value. This name came from the famous problem of Dido of finding the closed curve of given perimeter for which the area is a maximum. For the Euler equation the problem can be stated as:

$$\text{Optimize:} \quad I[y(x)] = \int_{x_0}^{x_1} F(x, y, y')\, dx$$

$$\text{Subject to:} \quad J = \int_{x_0}^{x_1} G(x, y, y')\, dx \tag{8-61}$$

where J is a known constant.

To solve this problem, the Lagrangian function $L(x, y, y')$ is formed as shown below:

$$L(x, y, y', \lambda) = F(x, y, y') + \lambda G(x, y, y') \tag{8-62}$$

and the following unconstrained Euler equation is solved along with the constraint equation:

$$\frac{d}{dx}\left(\frac{\partial L}{\partial y'}\right) - \frac{\partial L}{\partial y} = 0 \tag{8-60}$$

For integral equation constraints, the Lagrange multiplier λ is a constant, and each constraint has a Lagrange multiplier when forming the Lagrangian function. The following example illustrates the use of Lagrange multipliers with an integral constraint. It is the classic problem of Dido mentioned previously.

EXAMPLE 8–7 (1)

Determine the shape of the curve of length J that encloses the maximum area. The integral to be maximized and the integral constraint are as follows:

$$\text{Maximize:} \quad I[y(x)] = \tfrac{1}{2} \int_{x_0}^{x_1} [y_1 y_2' - y_2 y_1']\, dx$$

$$\text{Subject to:} \quad J = \int_{x_0}^{x_1} [y_1'^2 + y_2'^2]^{1/2}\, dx$$

The Lagrangian function is:

$$L = y_1 y_2' - y_2 y_1' + \lambda [y_1'^2 + y_2'^2]^{1/2}$$

The two Euler equations are:

$$\frac{d}{dx}\left(\frac{\partial L}{\partial y_1'}\right) - \frac{\partial L}{\partial y_1} = 0 \qquad \frac{d}{dx}\left(\frac{\partial L}{\partial y_2'}\right) - \frac{\partial L}{\partial y_2} = 0$$

Performing the differentiation and substituting into the Euler equations give:

$$\frac{d}{dx}\{-y_2 + y_1' \lambda [y_1'^2 + y_2'^2]^{-1/2}\} - y_2' = 0$$

$$\frac{d}{dx}\{y_1 + y_2' \lambda [y_1'^2 + y_2'^2]^{-1/2}\} - y_1' = 0$$

The two equations above can be integrated once to obtain the following results:

$$y_2 - c_2 = \frac{-y_1' \lambda}{2[y_1'^2 + y_2'^2]^{1/2}} \qquad y_1 - c_1 = \frac{-y_2' \lambda}{2[y_1'^2 + y_2'^2]^{1/2}}$$

Squaring both sides and adding the two equations gives the following:

$$(y_1 - c_1)^2 + (y_2 - c_2)^2 = \lambda^2/4 = \text{constant}$$

which is the equation of a circle. Thus a circle encloses the maximum area for a given length curve.

Differential Equation Constraints: To illustrate the method of Lagrange Multipliers for differential equation constraints, a simple case will be used. Extensions to more detailed cases are the same as for the two previous types of constraints. The problem is as follows:

$$\text{Optimize: } I[y(x)] = \int_{x_0}^{x_1} F(x, y, y')\, dx \tag{8-63}$$

Subject to: $G(x, y, y') = 0$

As was done previously, the Lagrangian function is formed as follows:

$$L(x, y, y', \lambda) = F(x, y, y') + \lambda(x)G(x, y, y') \qquad (8\text{-}64)$$

Then the Lagrangian function is used in the Euler equation:

$$\frac{d}{dx}\left(\frac{\partial L}{\partial y'}\right) - \frac{\partial L}{\partial y} = 0 \qquad (8\text{-}60)$$

In this case the Lagrange Multiplier $\lambda(x)$ is a function of the independent variable. This procedure is illustrated in the following example, which was given by Beveridge and Schechter (10). Also, they extend these results to obtain Pontryagin's maximum principle for constraints placed on the range of the dependent and independent variables.

EXAMPLE 8–8 (10)

The following problem to minimize $I[y_1, y_2]$ has a differential equation constraint:

$$I[y_1(x), y_2(x)] = \int_{x_0}^{x_1} (y_1^2 + y_2^2)\, dx$$

subject to:

$$\frac{dy_1}{dx} = y_2 - y_1$$

The Lagrangian function is:

$$L = y_1{}^2 + y_2{}^2 + \lambda(y_1' - y_2 + y_1)$$

Using equation (8–60) obtains the two Euler equations for y_1 and y_2. They are to be solved with the constraint equation, and this gives the following set of equations:

$$-2y_1 - \lambda + \lambda' = 0$$

$$2y_2 - \lambda = 0$$

$$y_1' + y_1 - y_2 = 0$$

The solutions for y_1 and y_2 are obtained by manipulating and integrating the equation set to give:

$$y_1 = c_1 e^{\sqrt{2}x} + c_2 e^{\sqrt{2}x}$$

$$y_2 = c_1(1 + \sqrt{2})e^{\sqrt{2}x} + c_2(1 - \sqrt{2})e^{-\sqrt{2}x}$$

where the constants of integration c_1 and c_2 are evaluated using the boundary conditions. A particular solution for $y_1(0) = 1$ and $y_2(x_1) = 0$ is given by Beveridge and Schechter (10).

The previous examples were designed to illustrate the particular extension of the calculus of variations and were essentially simple mathematics problems with no industrial application associated with them. However, the following example was designed to illustrate the application of the calculus of variations to a process, and it employs unsteady material and energy balance equations to determine the optimum way to control the flow rate to an agitated tank. Although the example is relatively simple, it illustrates economic model and process constraints for a dynamic system; and an optimal control function is developed.

EXAMPLE 8–9 (11)

An agitated tank contains W pounds of water at 32°F. It is desired to raise the temperature of the water in the tank to 104°F in $(2.0)^{1/2}$ hours by feeding water at a rate of W pounds per hour. The tank is completely filled with water, and the overflow water at $T_2(t)$ is equal to the input flow rate at $T_1(t)$. The average residence time of water in the tank is 1 hour, and the tank is perfectly mixed. The temperature of the inlet can be adjusted as a function of time by an electric heater in the feed pipe, which is connected to a variable voltage transformer. The sensible heat accompanying water flowing into and out of the tank during the process must be considered lost. Therefore, it is, desired to minimize the integral of the sum of squares of the difference between the temperatures, $T_1(t)$ and $T_2(t)$, and the reference temperature, 32°F. This economic model is given by the following equation:

$$I[T_1(t), T_2(t)] = \int_0^{\sqrt{2}} \{[T_1(t) - 32]^2 + [T_2(t) - 32]^2\}\, dt$$

An unsteady-state energy balance on the water in the tank at time t gives the following equation relating the temperatures $T_1(t)$, $T_2(t)$ and the system parameters:

$$C_p W \frac{d}{dt} T_2(t) = W C_p[T_1(t) - 32] - W C_p[T_2(t) - 32]$$

For water the heat capacity, C_p, is equal to 1.0 BTU/lb°F, and this equation simplifies to the following form:

$$\frac{d}{dt} T_2(t) = T_1(t) - T_2(t)$$

The calculus of variations problem can now be formulated as:

$$\text{Minimize: } I[T_1(t), T_2(t)] = \int_0^{\sqrt{2}} \{[T_1(t) - 32]^2 + [T_2(t) - 32]^2\} \, dt$$

$$\text{Subject to: } \frac{d}{dt} T_2(t) - T_1(t) + T_2(t) = 0$$

with $T_1(0) = T_2(0) = 32°F$, and $T_2(\sqrt{2}) = 104°$ as boundary conditions.

Two optimal functions are determined, and the solution of two Euler equations is required, using equation (8–60). The Lagrangian function is:

$$L[T_1(t), T_2(t), \lambda(t)] = (T_1 - 32)^2 + (T_2 - 32)^2 + \lambda(t)[T_2' - T_1 + T_2]$$

and the Euler equations are:

$$\frac{d}{dt}\left(\frac{\partial L}{\partial T_1'}\right) - \frac{\partial L}{\partial T_1} = 0 \qquad \frac{d}{dt}\left(\frac{\partial L}{\partial T_2'}\right) - \frac{\partial L}{\partial T_2} = 0$$

The results of performing the differentiation are:

$$\frac{\partial L}{\partial T_1} = 2(T_1 - 32) - \lambda \qquad \frac{\partial L}{\partial T_2} = 2(T_2 - 32) + \lambda$$

$$\frac{\partial L}{\partial T_1'} = 0 \qquad \frac{\partial L}{\partial T_2'} = \lambda(t) \qquad \frac{d}{dt}\left(\frac{\partial T}{\partial T_1'}\right) = 0 \qquad \frac{d}{dt}\left(\frac{\partial L}{\partial T_2'}\right) = \frac{d\lambda}{dt}$$

$$\frac{d}{dt}\left(\frac{\partial L}{\partial T_1'}\right) = 0 \qquad \frac{d}{dt}\left(\frac{\partial L}{\partial T_2'}\right) = \frac{d\lambda}{dt}$$

Substituting into the Euler equations gives the following set of equations:

$$2(T_1 - 32) - \lambda - 0$$

$$2(T_2 - 32) + \lambda - \frac{d\lambda}{dt} = 0$$

$$\frac{d}{dt}T_2 - T_1 + T_2 = 0$$

The third equation is the constraint, and these equations are solved for $T_1(t)$ and $T_2(t)$. The set has two ordinary differential equations and one algebraic equation. Manipulating and solving this set for one equation in terms of $T_2(t)$ gives:

$$T_2'' - 2T_2 = -64$$

With the boundary conditions of $T_2(0) = 32$ and $T_2(\sqrt{2}) = 104$, the solution to the differential equation is:

$$T_2(t) = 9.91\,[e^{\sqrt{2}t} - e^{-\sqrt{2}t}] + 32$$

where $9.91 = 72/(e^2 - e^{-2})$. The constraint is used to obtain the entering water temperature as a function of time, and substituting in the solution for $T_2(t)$ gives:

$$T_1(t) = 9.91\,[(2.4144(e^{\sqrt{2}t} + (0.4144)e^{-\sqrt{2}t}] + 32$$

The solutions for the optimal functions, $T_1(t)$ and $T_2(t)$ are tabulated and plotted in Figure 8-3. As shown in the figure, the warm water temperature increases to 209°F for the water temperature in the tank to reach 104°F in $\sqrt{2}$ hours.

CLOSURE

Some of the important results from the chapter are summarized in an abbreviated form in Table 8-1. First, a set of Euler equations is shown in the table to be solved when the integrand contains several optimal functions and their first derivatives. Corresponding boundary conditions are required on each of these Euler equations, which are second-order ordinary differential equations. Next in the table is the integral that has higher order derivatives in the integrand. For this case the Euler-Poisson equation has to be solved, and it is of order $2m$, where m is the order of the highest derivative in the integrand

Also appropriate boundary conditions on y and its derivatives at x_0 and

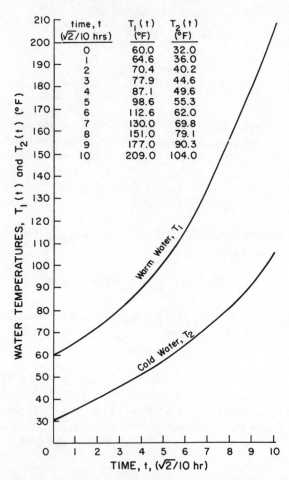

time, t ($\sqrt{2}/10$ hrs)	$T_1(t)$ (°F)	$T_2(t)$ (°F)
0	60.0	32.0
1	64.6	36.0
2	70.4	40.2
3	77.9	44.6
4	87.1	49.6
5	98.6	55.3
6	112.6	62.0
7	130.0	69.8
8	151.0	79.1
9	177.0	90.3
10	209.0	104.0

Figure 8-3. Optimal temperature functions for agitated tank application of Example 8-9 (11).

x_1 are required to obtain the particular solution of the differential equation. A combination of these two cases is given in the table where a set of Euler-Poisson equations is solved for the optimum functions.

When the optimal function involves more than one independent variable, a partial differential equation has to be solved, and the table shows the case for two independent variables, a second-order partial differential equation. Equation (8–57) gives the comparable equation for n independent variables. However, the results given in the table and the chapter are only for an optimal function with first partial derivatives in the integrand. Results compa-

Table 8-1.   Summary of Results for the Calculus of Variations.

1. Optimize:

$$I(y_1, y_2, \cdots, y_p) = \int_{x_0}^{x_1} F(x, y_1, \cdots, y_p, y'_1, y'_2, \cdots, y'_p)\, dx \tag{8-37}$$

Solve a set of p, second-order ordinary differential equations:

$$\frac{d}{dx_i}\left(\frac{\partial F}{\partial y'_i}\right) - \frac{\partial F}{\partial y_i} = 0 \qquad \text{for } i = 1, 2, \cdots, p \tag{8-44}$$

2. Optimize:

$$I[y(x)] = \int_{x_0}^{x_1} F(x, y, y', \cdots, y^{(m)})\, dx \tag{8-26}$$

Solve an ordinary differential equation of order $2m$:

$$\frac{d^{(m)}}{dx^{(m)}}\left(\frac{\partial F}{\partial y^{(m)}}\right) - \frac{d^{(m-1)}}{dx^{(m-1)}}\left(\frac{\partial F}{\partial y^{(m-1)}}\right) + \cdots + (-1)^m \frac{\partial F}{\partial y} = 0 \tag{8-36}$$

3. Optimize:

$$I[y_1, y_2, \cdots, y_p] = \int_{x_0}^{x_1} F(x, y_1, y'_1, \cdots, y_1^{(m)}, \cdots, y_p, y'_p, \cdots, y_p^{(k)})\, dx \tag{8-45}$$

Solve a set of p Euler-Poisson equations:

$$\frac{d^{(m)}}{dx^{(m)}}\left(\frac{\partial F}{\partial y_1^{(m)}}\right) - \frac{d^{(m-1)}}{dx^{(m-1)}}\left(\frac{\partial F}{\partial y_1^{(m-1)}}\right) + \cdots + (-1)^m \frac{\partial F}{\partial y_1} = 0$$

$$\vdots \tag{8-46}$$

$$\frac{d^{(k)}}{dx^{(k)}}\left(\frac{\partial F}{\partial y_p^{(k)}}\right) - \frac{d^{(k-1)}}{dx^{(k-1)}}\left(\frac{\partial F}{\partial y_p^{(k-1)}}\right) + \cdots + (-1)^k \frac{\partial F}{\partial y_p} = 0$$

4. Optimize:

$$I[y(x_1, x_2)] = \int_R \int F(x_1, x_2, y, y_{x_1}, y_{x_2})\, dx_1 dx_2 \tag{8-47}$$

Solve a second-order partial differential equation:

$$\frac{\partial}{\partial x_1}\left(\frac{\partial F}{\partial y_{x_1}}\right) + \frac{\partial}{\partial x_2}\left(\frac{\partial F}{\partial y_{x_2}}\right) - \frac{\partial F}{\partial y} = 0 \tag{8-55}$$

5. Optimize:

$$I[y(x)] = \int_{x_0}^{x_1} F(x, y, y')\, dx$$

Subject to:

$$G(x, y) = 0 \qquad J = \int_{x_0}^{x_1} G(x, y, y')\, dx \qquad G(x, y, y') = 0$$

constraints: algebraic   integral   differential equation

Form the Lagrangian function $L = F + \lambda G$ and solve the Euler equation with the constraint equation. The Lagrange Multiplier is a constant for integral constraints and is a function of the independent variable for algebraic and differential equation constraints.

rable to the Euler-Poisson equation with higher order derivatives are available in Weinstock (3).

When constraints are involved, the Lagrange function is formed, as shown in the table. This gives an unconstrained problem that can be solved by the Euler and/or Euler Poisson equation, along with the constraint equations.

The purpose of the chapter was to give some of the key results of the calculus of variations and to emphasize the similarities and differences between finding an optimal function and an optimal point. Consequently, it was necessary to select the methods given here from some equally important methods that were omitted. Two of these are the concept of a variation and the use of the second variation for the sufficient conditions to determine if the function was actually a maximum or minimum. These are discussed by Courant and Hilbert (5) along with the problem of the existence of a solution. Also, most texts discuss the moving (or natural) boundary problem where one or both of the limits on the integral to be optimized can be a function of the independent variable. This leads to extensions of the Brachistochrone problem, and Forray's discussion (1) is recommended. With the background of this chapter, extension to Hamilton's principle follows, and is typically the next topic presented on the subject. Also, this material leads to extensions that include Pontryagin's maximum principle; Sturm-Liouville problems; and application in optics, dynamics of particles, vibrations, elasticity, and quantum mechanics.

The calculus of variations can be used to solve transport phenomena problems, i.e., obtain solutions to the partial differential equations representing the conservation of mass, momentum, and energy of a system. In this approach the partial differential equations are converted to the corresponding integral to be optimized from the calculus of variations. Then approximate methods of integration are used to find the minimum of the integral, and this yields the concentration, temperature, and/or velocity profiles required for the solution of the original differential equations. This approach is described by Schechter (4) in some detail.

Again, the purpose of the chapter was to introduce the topic of finding the optimal function. The references at the end of the chapter are recommended for further information; they include the texts by Fan (12) and Fan and Wang (13) on the maximum principle and Kirk (14), among others, (7, 15, 16) on optimal control.

REFERENCES

1. Forray, M. J., *Variational Calculus in Science and Engineering,* McGraw-Hill Book Co., New York (1968).
2. Ewing, G. M., *Calculus of Variations with Applications,* W. W. Norton Co., Inc., New York (1969).
3. Weinstock, R., *Calculus of Variations,* McGraw-Hill Book Co., New York (1952).

4. Schechter, R. S., *The Variational Method in Engineering,* McGraw-Hill Book Co., New York (1967).
5. Courant, R., and D. Hilbert, *Methods of Mathematical Physics,* Vol. I, John Wiley & Sons, Inc., New York (1953).
6. Sagan, H., *Introduction to the Calculus of Variations,* McGraw-Hill Book Co., New York (1969).
7. M. M. Denn, *Optimization by Variational Methods,* McGraw-Hill Book Co., New York (1970).
8. Wylie, C. R., and L. C. Barrett, *Advanced Engineering Mathematics,* 5th Ed., McGraw-Hill Book Co., New York (1982).
9. Burley, D. M., *Studies in Optimization,* John Wiley & Sons, Inc., New York (1974).
10. Beveridge, G. S. G., and R. S. Schechter, *Optimization: Theory and Practice,* McGraw-Hill Book Co., New York (1970).
11. Fan, L. T., E. S. Lee, and L. E. Erickson, *Proc. of the Mid-Am. States Univ. Assoc. Conf. on Modern Optimization Techniques and their Application in Engineering Design,* Part I, Kansas State University, Manhattan, Kansas (Dec. 19–22, 1966).
12. L. T. Fan, *The Continuous Maximum Principle,* John Wiley & Sons Inc., New York (1966).
13. Fan, L. T. and C. S. Wang, *The Discrete Maximum Principal,* John Wiley & Sons, Inc., New York (1964).
14. Kirk, D. E. *Optimal Control Theory, An Introduction.* Prentice-Hall, Inc., Englewood Cliffs, N. J. (1970).
15. Miele, A., *Optimization Techniques with Applications to Aerospace Systems,* Ed., G. Leitman, Ch.4, Academic Press, New York (1962).
16. Connors, M. M., and D. Teichroew, *Optimal Control of Dynamic Operations Research Models,* International Textbook Co., Scranton, Pa. (1967).

PROBLEMS

8–1.[16] A product is being produced at a steady rate of P_0 pounds per hour. It is necessary to change the production rate to P_1 pounds per hour and minimize the cost resulting from raw material lost to off-specification product and overtime wages during the transition period. This is modeled by the following cost function:

$$C(t) = c_1 P'^2 + c_2 t P'$$

where c_1 and c_2 are cost coefficients and $P' = dP/dt$. The total cost for the change in the production schedule is given by:

$$C_T = \int_{t_0}^{t_1} [c_1 P'^2 + c_2 t P'] \, dt$$

where $P_0 = P(t_0)$ and $P_1 = P(t_1)$ are known.

Determine the optimum way the production rate $P(t)$ is to be changed to minimize the total cost.

8–2.[15] A classical problem in aerodynamics is to determine the optimum shape of a body of revolution that has the minimum drag. For a slender body of revolution at zero angle of attack in an inviscid hypersonic flow, the total drag is approximated by

$$D = 4\pi\rho v^2 \int_0^L y(y')^3 \, dx$$

where v and ρ are the free stream velocity and density, respectively.

a. Obtain the differential equation and boundary conditions that are to be solved to obtain the optimum body shape.

b. Show that the following is the solution to the differential equation obtained in (a):

$$y = (d/2)(x/L)^{3/4}$$

which, according to Miele (15), means that the contours of a body of revolution having minimum drag for a given diameter, d, and a given length L, is a parabola satisfying the 3/4-power law.

8–3. [1] Determine the minimum surface of revolution by finding the curve $y(x)$ with prescribed end points such that by revolving this curve around the x axis a surface of minimal area is obtained. The integral to be minimized is:

$$I = 2\pi \int_{x_0}^{x_1} y(1 + y'^2)^{1/2} \, dx$$

a. Show that the Euler equation for $F = F(y, y')$ gives only:

$$F - y' \frac{\partial F}{\partial y'} = \text{constant}$$

b. Apply this result to the problem to obtain:

$$y(1 + y'^2)^{-1/2} = c_1$$

c. Define the parametric variable $y' = \sinh t$ in order to obtain a more compact solution, and obtain the following result:

$$x = c_1 t + c_2$$

$$y = c_1 \cosh(t)$$

which is the parametric form of a family of catenaries, and c_1 and c_2 are boundary conditions for the end points of the curve.

8–4. [9] Find the shape at equilibrium of a chain of length that hangs from two points at the same level. The potential energy, E, of the chain is given by the following equation:

$$E[y(x)] = -\rho g \int_{x_0}^{x_1} y (1 + y'^2)^{1/2} \, dx$$

and is subject to the specified total length L by the following equation:

$$L = \int_{x_0}^{x_1} (1 + y'^2)^{1/2} \, dx$$

with boundary conditions of $y(x_0) = y(x_1) = 0$. To obtain the equilibrium shape of the chain, it is necessary to minimize the energy subject to the length restriction. Show that the following differential equation is obtained from the Euler equation.

$$y' = [k^2(y + \lambda)^2 - 1]^{1/2}$$

Make the substitution $k(y + \lambda) = \cosh\theta$, and obtain the solution given below:

$$\cosh k(x + a) = k(y + \lambda)$$

This curve is the catenary, and the constants k, a, λ can be obtained from the boundary conditions and the constraint on L.

8–5.[14] A simple optimal control problem related to an electromechanical system can be formulated as:

$$\text{Minimize: } I = \int_0^T [y_2^2(t) - y_3^2(t)] \, dt$$

$$\text{Subject to: } y_1' + y_1 = y_3$$

$$y_2' - y_1 = 0$$

a. Obtain the differential equations to be solved for the optimal functions. Show that there are sufficient equations to determine the dependent variables.

b. What boundary conditions are required?

8-6.[9] For steady flow of an incompressible fluid in a square duct, the equations of continuity and motion simplify to a partial differential equation that requires an elaborate analytical solution involving the sum of an infinite series. An approximate solution can be obtained using the calculus of variations, which gives a simple equation that predicts the volumetric flow rate within 1% of the exact solution. The equation that describes the flow at a point z along the axis of the duct is:

$$\frac{\partial^2 v}{\partial x^2} + \frac{\partial^2 v}{\partial y^2} = \frac{1}{\mu}\frac{dP}{dz}$$

where v is the axial velocity; μ is the viscosity of the fluid; dP/dz is the pressure gradient, a constant; and a is the length of one-half of the side of the duct. The boundary conditions are that there is no slip at the wall, i.e., $v = 0$ at $x = a$ for $0 < y < a$ and at $y = a$ for $0 < x < a$.

a. Show that the integral to be minimized corresponding to the differential equation is:

$$I[v(x,y)] = \int_0^a \int_0^a \left[\left(\frac{\partial v}{\partial x}\right)^2 + \left(\frac{\partial v}{\partial y}\right)^2 - \frac{2}{\mu}\frac{dP}{dz} v \right] dx\, dy$$

b. A simple approximation to v is given by the following equation, which satisfies the boundary conditions:

$$v = A(a^2 - x^2)(a^2 - y^2)$$

Using this equation, perform the integration of the equation in (a) to obtain the following result:

$$I[v] = (64/45)A^2 a^8 - (8/9\mu)(dP/dz)Aa^6$$

c. Find the value of A that minimizes I.
d. If the mass flow rate, w, through the duct is given by the following equation:

$$w = \rho \int_0^a \int_0^a v\, dx\, dy$$

show that the following result is obtained:

$$w = 0.556\, \rho(dP/dz)a^4/\mu$$

The analytical solution has the same form, but the coefficient is 0.560. Thus the approximate solution is within 1% of the exact solution.

8-7. In a production scheduling problem, the production rate is to be changed from 100 units per unit time to 300 units per unit time in 10 time units, i.e., $p(0) = 100$ and $p(10) = 300$. The costs as a function of time are associated with changes in machines, personnel, and raw materials. For this simple problem this cost is given as:

$$c(t) = 2(p') + 4tp'$$

where $p' = dp/dt$.

Determine the production rate as a function of time that minimizes the cost over the time.

8-8.[1] Determine the deflection in an uniformly loaded, cantilever beam, $y(x)$, where y is the deflection as a function of distance down the beam from the wall $(x = 0)$ to the end of the beam $(x = L)$. The total potential energy of the system to be minimized is given by:

$$I[y(x)] = \int_0^L [(E/2)(y'')^2 - qy]\, dx$$

where E is the bending rigidity and q is the load. The boundary conditions at the wall end are $y(0) = y'(0) = 0$, and at the supported end are $y'''(L) = y''(L) = 0$.

ANSWERS TO EXERCISES

CHAPTER 2

2–1. a. $x = 0$ (maximum), $x = 1/2^{1/2}$ (minimum), $x = -1/2^{1/2}$ (minimum)

  b. $x = 0$ (inflection point)

  c. $x_1 = x_2 = 0$ (minimum)

  d. $x_1 = 2$, $x_2 = 2$, $x_3 = 3$ (minimum)

2–2. Global maximum is on the boundary at (10,0), where $y = -55$.

2–3. $\dfrac{\partial y}{\partial x_1}\dfrac{\partial f}{\partial x_2} - \dfrac{\partial y}{\partial x_2}\dfrac{\partial f}{\partial x_1} = 0$ and $\dfrac{\partial y}{\partial x_1}\dfrac{\partial f}{\partial x_3} - \dfrac{\partial y}{\partial x_3}\dfrac{\partial f}{\partial x_1} = 0$

2–4. $x_1 = x_2 = \sqrt{2}/2$ $\lambda = -\sqrt{2}/2$

2–5. $x_1 = 5/52$, $x_2 = 53/130$, $\lambda = 8/325$ (minimum)

2–6. a. $(\lambda - 1)x_1 = 1$

  $(\lambda + 1)x_2 = 0$

  $\lambda x_3 = 0$

  $x_1^2 + x_2^2 + x_3^2 = 1$

  c. A (maximum), B (maximum), C (saddle point) and D (minimum)

2–7. a. $(c_{A0} - c_A)q - kc_A V = 0$

  $\qquad\quad 10 - kc_A V = 0$

  b. 5 equations and 5 variables

  c. $V = 3140$ ft³, $q = 1220$ ft³/hr, $c_A = 0.0318$ lb-moles/ft³

2–8. $x_1 = 17/7$, $x_2 = 6/7$, $y = -43.9$, minimum

2–9. $x_1 = 3/2$, $x_2 = 3/2$, $y = 2$, maximum

2–10. $F_1 = 600$, $F_2 = 300$, $F_3 = 200$, and the maximum profit is 88

2–11. Following the procedure of Cooper (7) and Walsh (8)

CASE	x_1	x_2	λ_1	λ_2	y	CHARACTER
1	0	0	0	0	0	minimum
2a	± 5	0	-3	0	75	maximum
2b	0	± 5	-2	0	50	maximum
3	-3	$3\sqrt{2}$	0	2	63	saddle point
4a	4	3	$-42/17$	$-8/17$	56	maximum
4b	4	-3	$-42/17$	$-8/17$	56	maximum
4c	-13	$\sqrt{-144}$	$-$	$-$	$-$	no solution

2–12. Following the procedure of Cooper (7) and Walsh (8)

CASE	x_1	x_2	λ_1	λ_2	$x_3{}^3$	$x_4{}^2$	y	CHARACTER
1	5/4	2	0	0	$-2\frac{1}{4}$	$3\frac{1}{2}$	$-1\,1/8$	minimum, but a constraint is not satisfied
2	17/7	6/7	$-1/49$	$-115/49$	0	0	$-3\,2/49$	maximum
3	43/38	49/38	9/19	0	0	115/38	-6.59	minimum
4	29/12	5/6	0	$-7/3$	1/12	0	$-3\,1/24$	maximum

2–13. $i = [(1 + i)^{n+1} - 1]/(1 + n)$
2–15. $a = 81/19$; and the point is a minimum

CHAPTER 3

3–1. $y = 7.61$, $x_1 = 1.06$, $x_2 = 0.747$
3–2. $y = 26.60$, $x_1 = 0.4765$, $x_2 = 0.9750$, $x_3 = 0.5310$
3–3. $y = 125.8$, $x_1 = 1.12$, $x_2 = 0.944$
3–4. a. $y = 8$, $x_1 = x_2 = \frac{1}{2}$
3–5. $y = \$17.41$, $x_1 = 0.6597$, $x_2 = 0.6597$, $x_3 = 1.320$
3–6. b. $y(\mathbf{w}_1) = 6.79$, $y(\mathbf{w}_2) = 6.86$
3–7. $D = 6.0$ inches, $Q = 1.20$ cubic feet per second, $C = \$1440$
3–8. $W = [3P_1V_1/e] [(P_4/P_1)^{e/3} - 1]$
$P_2 = P_1(P_4/P_1)^{1/3}$, $P_3 = P_4(P_1/P_4)^{1/3}$
3–9. $y = \$719.62$, $D = 4.0$ inches
3–10. $C = \$2.97 \times 10^6$/year, $L = 42.5$, $D = 24.8$, $F = 0.0292$,
$r = 1.140$
3–11. a. $L = 10$ feet, $T = 1000°$K, $C = \$25,000$
3–12. a. $w_1 = 12/11$, $w_2 = 6/11$, $w_3 = 4/11$, $w_4 = 6/11$
$w_5 = 3/11$ and $w_6 = 2/11$
b. $P = 92$
c. $x_1 = 502$, $x_2 = 251$, and $x_3 = 167$
3–13. a. $V = 0.2421$ feet^3, $t_1 = 0.5269$ hours, $t_2 = 0.4138$ hours
b.

Maximize: $y(w) = \prod\limits_{t=1}^{t=5} \left(\dfrac{C_t}{w_t}\right)^{w_t}$

Subject to:
$$w_1 + w_2 + w_4 + w_5 = 1$$
$$0.57w_1 - 0.22w_2 + 0.54w_3 - 0.72w_4 + 0.52w_5 = 0$$
$$-w_1 + w_2 = 0$$
$$-w_3 + w_4 = 0$$

One degree of difficulty and an optimization problem has to be solved.
c. $315(0.57) V^{-0.43}t_1{}^{-1} + 370(-0.22) V^{-1.22}t_1 +$
$460(0.54) V^{-0.46}t_2{}^{-1} + 450(-0.72) V^{-1.72}t_2 = 0$
$-315 V^{0.57}t_1{}^{-2} + 370 V^{-0.22} = 0$
$-460 V^{0.54}t_2{}^{-2} + 450 V^{-0.72} = 0$

A set of three nonlinear algebraic equations to be solved for the stationary point.

3–14. c. $100

d. $x_1^* = 2$ yards, $x_2^* = 1/2$ yard, $x_3^* = 1$ yard

CHAPTER 4

4–1. $47/27 \leq x_1 \leq 2, 0 \leq x_2 \leq 14/9, p = 12$

4–2. $x_1 = 5/2, x_2 = 5/2, x_3 = 5/2, p = 15$

4–3. a. $x_1 = 4, x_2 = 2, p = 10$

b.
$$
A^{-1} = \begin{bmatrix} 1/2 & 1/2 & 0 & 0 \\ 1/2 & -1/2 & 0 & 0 \\ -3/2 & 1/2 & 1 & 0 \\ 1/2 & -3/2 & 0 & 1 \end{bmatrix} \quad \Delta b = \begin{bmatrix} -6 \\ -2 \\ -10 \\ -1 \end{bmatrix}
$$

4–4. $x_1 = 2, x_2 = 6, p = 18$

4–5. a. $x_1 = 30, x_2 = 25, p = 80$

b. $\lambda_1 = -1/3, \lambda_2 = 0, \lambda_3 = -1/3, \lambda_4 = 0$

4–6. a. $x_1 = 0, x_2 = 15, p = 150$

b.
$$
A^{-1} = \begin{bmatrix} 0 & 1 \\ -1 & 1 \end{bmatrix} \quad \lambda = \begin{bmatrix} 0 \\ -10 \end{bmatrix}
$$

c. $\Delta b_1 = -5, \Delta b_2 = -15$

4–7. $x_1 = 0, x_2 = 0, x_3 = 1, c = 1$

4–8. a. $x_1 = 7\frac{1}{2}, x_2 = 2\frac{1}{2}, p = 17\frac{1}{2}$

b. c_3', new $= -1$, c_4', new $= -19/4$, c_5', new $= 3/4$, all coefficients remain negative, and the optimal solution remains optional.

c. $x_1 = 2\frac{1}{2}, x_2 = 1\frac{1}{2}, p = 8\frac{1}{2}$

4–9. a. $x_1^* = 33/7, x_2^* = 6/7, x_3^* = 25/7, x_6^* = 11/7, p^* = 10\ 2/7$

c. $\lambda_1 = 0, \lambda_2 = -0.143, \lambda_3 = -0.527, \lambda_4 = 0$

d. $\Delta b_1 = -10, \Delta b_2 = -12, \Delta b_3 = -15, \Delta b_4 = -4$

4–10. a. $x_1 = 1, x_2 = 4$

b.
$$
A^{-1} = \begin{bmatrix} 0 & -1/9 & 4/9 \\ 0 & 1/3 & -1/3 \\ -1 & 8/9 & -5/9 \end{bmatrix}
$$
$\lambda_1 = 0, \lambda_2 = -2\ 7/9, \lambda_3 = -13\ 8/9$

c. $x_{1,\ new} = 1\ 2/9, x_{2,\ new} = 4\ 1/3, x_{3,\ new} = 6\ 2/9$

$z_{new} = 169\ 4/9$

4–11. a. $x_1 = 0, x_2 = 4\frac{1}{2}, P = 40\frac{1}{2}$

b.
$$
A^{-1} = \begin{bmatrix} \frac{1}{2} & 0 \\ -1 & 1 \end{bmatrix} \quad \lambda_1 = -9/2, \lambda_2 = 0
$$

c. $\Delta b_1 = -9, \Delta b_2 = -15, \Delta c_1 = -1, \Delta c_2 = -9$

4–12. $x_1 = 2, x_2 = 4$, and $P = 10$

4–14. $x_1 = 12, x_2 = 8, p = 3.04$

4–15. 200 gallons of A, 600 gallons of B for a maximum profit of $260

4–16. $x_1 = 500$, $x_2 = 0$, $x_3 = 150$, $x_4 = 650$, $P = \$18.25$

4–17. a. $x_1 = 300$, $x_2 = 200$, $P = 1400$

b. $\mathbf{A}^{-1} = \begin{bmatrix} 5/7 & -4/7 \\ -2/7 & 3/7 \end{bmatrix}$ $\lambda_1 = -2/7$, $\lambda_2 = -4/7$

c. i. $x_1 = 300 \ 5/7$, $x_2 = 199 \ 5/7$, $P = 1400 \ 2/7$

  ii. $P = 1435 \ 5/7$, an increase in profit of $35 5/7 for an additional cost of $7   •

d. $3 1/21

4–18. $p = p_5x_5 + p_6x_6 + p_7x_7 + p_8x_8 - c_1x_1 - c_2x_2 - c_3x_3 - c_4x_4$

$x_1 - 2x_7 = 0$

$2x_2 - x_5 - 3x_7 - x_8 = 0$

$2x_3 - 3x_5 - x_6 - 9x_7 - 4x_8 = 0$

$2x_4 - x_6 - x_8 = 0$

$x_6 + x_8 \leq 1,500$

$x_5 + 3x_7 + x_8 \leq 2,000$

4–19. See page 556 of Reference 8

4–20. a. $8.046/barrel

b. $P^*_{new} = \$669,285$; and see Table 4-13, row 15

c. Add 10.00 RF to the objective function, add constraint RF $\geq$ 5000 barrels/day, and change constraint row SRFO to: SRFO $-$ SRFOCC $-$ SRFODF $-$ RF $= 0$

4–21.

VARIABLES	SULFUR	STB1	STB2	H$_2$SO$_4$	DRYAIR	WATER	
Objective Function:	−0.025	0.011	0.011	0.050	−0.005	−0.007	= Max
Products and Raw Materials:							
Sulfur	1						$\geq$ 10,000
Steam		1	1				$\geq$ 40,000
H$_2$SO$_4$				1			$\geq$ 30,000
Process Unit Capacities:							
Waste Heat Boiler 1		1					$\leq$ 40,000
Waste Heat Boiler 2			1				$\leq$ 40,000
Acid Cooler				1			$\leq$ 35,000
Dryer						1	$\leq$ 150,000
Economizer						1	$\leq$ 60,000
Stream Splits:							
Water		1	1		−1		= 0
Sulfuric Acid	3.06			−1			= 0

4–22. a. Maximize: $8x_1 + 4x_2$

Subject to: $x_1 + x_2 \leq 10$

$\qquad\qquad 5x_1 + x_2 \leq 15$

b. $v_1 = 3$ and $v_2 = 1$

c. $x_1 = 1\frac{1}{4}$, $x_2 = 8\frac{3}{4}$ $P = 45$

4-23. a.

$$
\begin{array}{llll}
- \quad v_2 & \qquad - \quad v_5 = P - 8 & \qquad P = 8 \\
4v_2 + v_3 & \qquad - \tfrac{1}{2}v_5 = 6 & \qquad v_3 = 6 \\
2v_2 & + v_4 - \tfrac{1}{2}v_5 = 2 & \qquad v_4 = 2 \\
v_1 + \quad v_2 & \qquad + \tfrac{1}{2}v_5 = 4 & \qquad v_1 = 4 \\
& & \qquad v_2 = 0 \\
& & \qquad v_5 = 0
\end{array}
$$

b. $x_1 = 0$, $x_2 = 0$, $x_3 = 1$, $\lambda_1 = -4$, $\lambda_2 = 0$

c. $A = \begin{bmatrix} 2 & 0 \\ 2 & -1 \end{bmatrix} \quad A^{-1} = \begin{bmatrix} \frac{1}{2} & 0 \\ 1 & -1 \end{bmatrix}$

d. $\lambda_1 = -4$, $\lambda_2 = 0$

e. $[c_6 + a_{16}\lambda_1 + a_{26}\lambda_2] = -18$, and the problem will have to be resolved

CHAPTER 5

5-1. $y_1(10.73) = 147$, $y_2(14.27) = 100$, $y_3(8.54) = 125$, $y_4(12.08) = 130$, $y_5(9.90) = 149$, $y_6(9.37) = 147$
$y_5 = y_{\max} = 149$ in $9.37 \leq x^* \leq 10.73$, $I_6 = 1.36$

5-4.

NUMBER OF EXPERIMENTS	FINAL INTERVAL		
	SIMULTANEOUS	FIBONACCI	GOLDEN SECTION
2	0.5	0.5	0.618
5	0.333	0.125	0.146
10	0.167	0.0122	0.0132

5-6. Bolzano: $I_5 = 1/32$, $I_{10} = 1/1024$;
Fibonacci: $I_{10} = 1/89$; Golden Section: $I_{10} = 1/76$

5-7. Possible final intervals: 2.2, 1.9, 2.3, 2.1, 2.3, 2.4, 1.7, and 2.5; maximum final interval: 2.5; interval that contains the maximum: 2.3

5-8. $I_5 = 0.144$ for Fibonacci search and $I_5 = 0.146$ for golden section search.

5-9. $y_{gs} = 17.987$, $x = 2.92$; $y_{ct} = 18$, $x = 3$

5-10. $N = 12$ years, $P = \$62,600$

5-11. Bounding: $y(1.0) = 1.5$, $y(1.618) = 1.927$, $y(2.618) = 1.809$ golden section search $y_3(1.0) = 1.5$, $y_4(2.0) = 2.0$, $y_5(2.236) = 1.972$, $y_6(1.854) = 1.989$, $y_7(2.090) = 1.996$, $y^*(2.0) = 2.0$

5-12. b. $P = \$120,023$ at $T_{out} = 231.6$ on the final interval from 220 to 234.4°F
c. $P = \$120,715$; $T_{out} = 227.6$°F

5-13. b. Nine
c. $y(x_1 = 0.3814) = 1.1734$, $y(x_2 = 0.6190) = 1.091$, $y(x_3 = 0.2376) = 1.155$, $y(x_4 = 0.4752) = 1.1567$, $y(x_5 = 0.3314) = 1.1733$

5-14. a. Yours—read assignment, professor–no quiz
b. Yours—read assignment, professor—no quiz

CHAPTER 6

6-1. a. x_1 (−1.25, −1, 1.125, 1.625), x_2(−2.75, −1, 1.875, 1.375)

b. 0.75

6-2. a. $x_1 = 2\alpha, x_2 = 1 - \alpha, x_3 = -1 + \alpha, x_4 = 3$

b. $2x_1 - x_2 + x_3 + 2 = 0$

6-3. (0, 0, 0)

6-4. b_1(4, 4), b_2(4½, 4½), b_3(5½, 5½), b_4(7, 7), b_5(9, 9)

6-8. x^* (0, 0, 0)

6-9. $x_j^* = x_{j0} - \left[\dfrac{\partial y}{\partial x_j}(\mathbf{x}_0)\right] / \left[\dfrac{\partial^2 y}{\partial x_j^2}(\mathbf{x}_0)\right]$ for $j = 1, 2, 3$

x^* (0, 0, 0)

6-10. a.

Maximize: $P = 450 - \sum\limits_{i=1}^{3} [6(F_i - 10)^2 + 24(C_i - 95)^2]$

Subject to:

$$
\begin{aligned}
C_1 - C_2 \quad\quad + 2F_1/15 \quad\quad\quad\quad + 4/3 &= 0 \\
C_2 - C_3 \quad\quad + 2F_2/15 + 4/3 &= 0 \\
C_3 \quad\quad + 2F_2/15 + 99\ 1/3 &= 0 \\
C_1 \quad\quad\quad\quad\quad\quad - 88 &\geq 0
\end{aligned}
$$

b. $P = 450 - \sum\limits_{i=1}^{3} [6(F_i - 10)^2 + 24(C_i - 95)^2]$

$\quad - \dfrac{1}{r^{1/2}}[(C_1 - C_2 + 2F_1/15 + 4/3)^2 + (C_2 - C_3$

$\quad + 2F_2/15 + 4/3)^2 + (C_3 + 2F_3/15 + 99\ 1/3)^2]$

$\quad - r/(C\text{-}88)$

6-11. x_0(0, ½), x_1(0.5, 0.75), x_2(0.75, 0.875), x_3(0.781, 0.891), x_4(0.781, 0.891), $y(\mathbf{x}_4)$ = 1.477. The optimal solution is x^*(0.792, 0.896) with $y^* = 1.471$

6-12. x_0(1, 1), x_1(2.0, 2.0), x_2(3.0, 2.0), x_3(3.5, 2.0). The optimal solution is x^*(3.5, 2.0) with $y^* = 16$

6-13. x_0(1, 1), x_1(2, 2), x_2(3, 3), x_3(3½, 3½), x_4(3, 3½), x_5(3¼, 3¾), x_6(3, 3¾), x_7(3⅛, 3⅞). x_8(3, 3⅞), x_9(3.063, 3.938), x_{10}(3, 3.938), x_{11}(3.031, 3.969), x_{12}(3, 3.969), x_{13}(3.016, 3.984). The optimal solution is x^*(3, 4) with $y^* = -57$

6-14. x_0(2, 1), x_1(2 1/2, 1 1/2), x_2(2 2/3, 1), x_3(3 1/6, 5/8), x_4(3 2/3, 1/4), x_5(3 11/12, 0), x_6(3 47/48, 0); and the optimum solution is x^*(4, 0) and $y^* = 32$

6-15. x_0(1, 1), x_1(3, 3), x_2(4.0, 3.167), $x_3$3.99, 3.01). The optimal solution is x^*(4, 3) with $y^* = 66$

6-16. a. Minimize: $(-2 + 2x_{1k})\Delta x_1^+ + (-4 + 2x_{2k})\Delta x_2^+$

$\quad\quad\quad\quad -(-2 + 2x_{1k})\Delta x_1^- - (-4 + 2x_{2k})\Delta x_2^- = y$

$\quad\quad\quad\quad -(-2x_{1k} - 4x_{2k} + x_{1k}^2 + x_{2k}^2 + 5)$

Subject to: $\quad -\Delta x_1^+ + 2\Delta x_2^+ + \Delta x_1^- - 2\Delta x_2^- \leq 2 - (-x_{1k} + 2x_{2k})$

$\quad\quad\quad\quad \Delta x_1^+ + \Delta x_2^+ - \Delta x_1^- - \Delta x_2^- \leq 4 - (x_{1k} + x_{2k})$

$\quad\quad\quad\quad \Delta x_1^+ \quad\quad - \Delta x_1^- \quad\quad\quad \leq 1$

$\quad\quad\quad\quad\quad\quad \Delta x_2^+ \quad\quad - \Delta x_2^- \leq 1$

b. x_1(1, 1)

c. x_2(1, 1.5), x_3(1.1, 1.6), x_4(1.2, 1.6) optimum

6–17. $x_1 = 1.2$, $x_2 = 1.6$, $y = 1/5$
6–18. $x_1 = 12/19$, $x_2 = 15/19$, $y = 111/19$
6–19. $x_1 = 1\ 1/3$, $x_2 = 2/3$, $y = 5\ 1/3$
6–20. $x_1 = 2\ 1/4$, $x_2 = 3\ 7/8$, $y = 8\ 15/16$
6–21. $x_1 = 17/7$, $x_2 = 6/7$, $y = -43.9$
6–22. Optimum value of parameter of reduced gradient line is 3/13
6–23. $x_0(2, 1, 3, 1)$, $x_1(1, 1, 2, 0)$, $x_2(1/3, 1/3, 0, 0)$, $x_3(1/2, 1/4, 0, 1/4)$, $= x^*$
6–24. $x^*(2\frac{1}{2}, \sqrt{55}/2, 4\frac{1}{2})$
6–25. $x_0(1, 1, 0)$, $x_1(-3, -11, 0)$, $x_2(3, 55, 0)$, $x_3(-1, -165, 0)$, $x_4(0, 330, 0)$, $x_5(0, -462, 0)$ $x_6(0, 462, 0)$, $x_7(0, -330, 0)$, $x_8(0, 236, 0)$, $x_9(0, -78.6, 0)$, $x_{10}(0, 15.7, 0)$ $x_{11}(0, -1.425, 0)$, $x_{12}(0, 0, 0)$, the optimum

CHAPTER 7

7–1. 16 in relative distance units
7–6. $f_{12} = 131$; optimal policy for 12 years starting with a new plant is k, k, k, k, k, k, r, k, k, k, k, k
7–7. $f_3 = 312$, $s_3 = 98$, $d_3 = 10$, $\tilde{s}_3 = s_2 = 95.4$, $d_2 = 10$, $\tilde{s}_2 = s_1 = 92.8$, $d_1 = 10$, $\tilde{s}_1 = 90.2$
7–8. $f_5 = 9964$, $s_5 = 100$, $d_5 = 0$, $s_4 = 200$, $d_4 = 0$, $s_3 = 400$, $d_3 = 400$, $s_2 = 720$, $d_2 = 720$, $s_1 = 1296$, $d_1 = 1296$
7–9. $P = 32$, $d_1 = x_1 = 3$, $d_2 = x_2 = 2$, $d_3 = x_3 = 1$, $d_4 = x_4 = 1$
7–11. shortest path: 29, longest path: 73
7–12. $f_4 = 310$, $s_4 = 98$, $d_4 = 10$, $\tilde{s}_4 = s_3 = 95.4$, $d_3 = 10$, $\tilde{s}_3 = s_2 = 92.8$, $d_2 = 10$, $\tilde{s}_2 = s_1 = 90.2$, $d_1 = 10$, $s_1 = 87.6$
7–13. a. $f_{10} = 104$; optimal policy for ten years starting with a two-year-old process is: k, k, k, k, r, k, k, k, k, k.
   b. $f_{10} = 63$; optimal policy for ten years starting with a two-year-old process is: k, k, k, r, k, k, r, k, k, k.
7–15. $f_5 = 91$; optimal policy for five years is: k, k, r, k, k.
7–16. $f_4 = 15,000$, $s_4 = 200$, $d_4 = 0$, $s_3 = 400$, $d_3 = 0$, $s_2 = 800$, $d_2 = 0$, $s_1 = 1,600$, $d_1 = 4,000$.
7–17. $f_4 = 24,000$, $s_4 = 100$, $d_4 = 0$, $s_3 = 200$, $d_3 = 0$, $s_2 = 400$, $d_2 = 0$, $s_1 = 800$, $d_1 = 7,500$
7–18. New Plant: Keep, keep, replace, keep, keep with a profit of \$106,000. Five-year-old plant: replace, keep, replace, keep, keep with a profit of \$101,000.

CHAPTER 8

8–1. $P = P_0 - c_2 t^2/4c_1 + [(P_1 - P_0)/(t_1 - t_0) + c_2(t_1 + t_0)/4c_1]t - [(P_1 - P_0)/(t_1 - t_0) + c_2 t_1/4c_1]t_0$; this is the equation of a parabola
8–2. a. $3yy'' + (y')^2 = 0$
8–5. a. $\lambda_1' - \lambda_1 + \lambda_2 = 0$, $\lambda_2' - 2y_2 = 0$, $2y_3 + \lambda_1 = 0$, $y_1' + y_1 - y_3 = 0$, $y_2' -$

$y_1 = 0$; five differential equations and five dependent variables: y_1, y_2, y_3, λ_1, and λ_2

b. $y_1(0)$, $y_1(T)$, $y_2(0)$, $y_2(T)$, $y_3(0)$, $y_3(T)$

8–6. c. $A = 5(dP/dz)/16\mu a^2$

8–7. $p = -t^2/2 + 25t + 100$

8–8. $y = \dfrac{q}{2E}\left(\dfrac{x^4}{12} - \dfrac{Lx^3}{3} + \dfrac{L^2x^2}{2}\right)$

AUTHOR INDEX

SUBJECT INDEX